MAINTAIN LIFE ON EARTH

Documentation of the Sixth World Congress of the IPPNW

D1258360

Maintain Life on Earth

Documentation of the Sixth World Congress of the International Physicians for the Prevention of Nuclear War in Cologne May 29 to June 1 1986

Edited by Karl Bonhoeffer and Dieter Gerecke on behalf of the International Physicians for the Prevention of Nuclear War (IPPNW). ✳ Editorial Staff: Nick Bramley-Steinemann and Stephen A. Schug. ✳ Publisher's Adviser: Joyce Mayer

Jungjohann Verlagsgesellschaft Neckarsulm und München

©1987 by authors and Jungjohann Verlagsgesellschaft m.b.H., Neckarsulm and Munich
All rights reserved
Cover: Celestino Piatti
Production and typesetting: Satz + Buch W. Hartmann, D-8035 Gauting
Printing: Druckhaus Schwaben, D-7100 Heilbronn

ISBN 3–88454–784–4
Printed in the Federal Republic of Germany

Contents

SCIENTIFIC PROGRAMME

PHYSICIANS SUPPORT AN ECUMENICAL CONVOCATION FOR PEACE

THE YEAR AHEAD

MESSAGES OF GREETING

DECISIONS OF THE IPPNW INTERNATIONAL COUNCIL

Foreword

F rom May 29 until June 1, 1986, the city of Cologne was host for the 6th World Congress of IPPNW (International Physicians for the Prevention of Nuclear War). Being dedicated to Olof Palme, the congress was conducted according to the motto "Gemeinsam leben – nicht gemeinsam sterben" "Maintain Life on Earth". 4,510 participants from 59 countries attended the meetings and the events were observed by 539 journalists, 303 coming from the Federal Republic of Germany.

For many foreigners the image of Germany is still determined by war and tyranny. By arranging this congress we wished to show that a different Germany also exists: a Germany expressing due reverence to life and to the dignity of man by striving for peace and justice. For the German people such efforts are based on the remembrance of those crimes which were committed in the name of our nation during the immediate past. In this context the lecture on "Medicine under National-Socialism" at the congress was of central significance, as was the "Act of Remembrance" at the graves of the victims of war and tyranny at the cemetery to the West of Cologne. Yet, the success of the congress ultimately was made possible only by the unprejudiced, confident attitude of our foreign guests.

The congress was in part separated for international delegates and for German-speaking participants. Correspondingly, an English and a German congress documentation will be edited. Events with simultaneous translation like the plenaries, lectures and core curricula are included in both editions.

It would have been impossible to publish this congress documentation without support by so many people devoting their effort to the goals of the IPPNW. We would like to express our gratitude to all those who worked in an altruistic way, in particular to the secretaries Ursula Kriese and Sabine Berg, for their untiring contribution.

Cologne, March 1987   Dieter Gerecke   Karl Bonhoeffer

The Opening Ceremony

THE OPENING CEREMONY

Urban Waldenström, Sweden

In memoriam Olof Palme

T he cold and dark grip of the Swedish winter was just about to give way to the glowing spark of spring, the time for hope and promises, when a glowing spark for peace was put out in the streets of Stockholm. The never ending flow of a man's energy and dedication to the cause of peace and justice was killed, and the next morning the people of Sweden and the rest of the world woke up shocked by the message that they had lost a friend. Renowned as a man of the highest personal integrity, enjoying great confidence among international politicians, Olof Palme became a central character in the movement for peace of the world, be it in the international policy-making circles, be it Stockholm or in the village of Bungalore in India. He was a never compromising enemy of nuclear weapons, which he considered weapons of genocide as he himself would put it. It has thus become possible for us humans not only to annihilate an enemy, but also all other living on this planet. We can kill animals and plants, we can destroy towns and villages, we can devastate all that has been built up over generations all around the whole of our earth. And above all we can destroy the future of our entire civilization, devastate the existence for our children and grandchildren, eradicate all that would have to come after us. That simply is the role of the nuclear weapons, if they are used.

Olof Palme had the courage and the intuition, coupled with a deep knowledge, the personal contacts and that indefinable extra to make a man able to break a new road when the old route has come to a desert end. One of several initiatives he took was the foundation of the Five Continents' Peace Initiative. The fundamental idea was, in his own words: "A nuclear war can hit all peoples and all states, even those who are farest away from the theatre of war. But this also means that all peoples and all nations have a right to have a say about these weapons of mass destruction." He was a peace-loving man, but he was not a man of peace. He was aggressive in his demands for nuclear disarmament and he would never accept or tolerate mere talking. He called for concrete steps and measures. He claimed that both sides admit that nuclear weapons are militarily useless. This ought to be understood as a common signal that the nuclear arms' race at last could be reversed into disarmament. We must not only hope that this shall happen. All of us in the non-nuclear states have the moral right to demand this.

From the very beginning Olof Palme was a solid supporter of IPPNW, and many of you met him at our congress in Amsterdam. He often mentioned us in the speeches he gave. Talking to the Swedish Institute of Foreign Affairs last year he said: "The scientists, who have worked with the effects of a nuclear war, have made extremely important contributions to the international debate on how peace should be secured. Especially I would call attention to the International Physicians for the Prevention of Nuclear War." We should be thankful for all the years he lived and worked for peace. We mourn his death and the loss of all he could have fulfilled had not the years to come been taken from him. His wife Lisbet, who is here with us today, lost a beloved husband and his sons lost a beloved father. And I wish to convey to you the grief that we all share with you. All of us lost a friend in the work for the prevention of a nuclear war. Humanity lost a fire for a good cause and the orchard of earth lost one of its most abundantly blooming fruit-trees. Hoping that this memorial speech could have been postponed at least some thirty years, I want all of you to feel that he was right here, reading his finishing words when he opened the "Conference on Nuclear War by Mistake" arranged by us a year ago.

"Ladies and Gentlemen, I think all of us present here would agree that nuclear war is preventable and must be prevented. But we also know that it will be difficult, it requires knowledge and the commitment and untiring efforts of all of us. You have the knowledge and the commitment and I know that you are also prepared to make the efforts. I wish you every success. I am confident that reason will prevail in the end and that the arms race can be stopped if only the proper measures are taken in time. Yet the question remains, will there be time for reason to prevail. Your conference is therefore addressing the most vital issue of the world today." This congress, dedicated to Olof Palme, is thus opened with his own words.

THE OPENING CEREMONY

Karl Bonhoeffer, Federal Republic of Germany

Address of the Congress President

Mrs. Palme, Ladies and Gentlemen, a great international congress taking place on German soil and concerning itself with the themes of war and peace is anything but self-evident for me when I recall the grief and misery the German people caused this world only fourty years ago.

Many of you, who have come here from abroad, may well share these feelings of mine, and many of you may have had to struggle against an inner resistance before deciding to make this journey. I extend my particular thanks to those of you who have had to overcome such a resistance. You can be assured: We will not and cannot forget! We want to remember!

And it is the memory of the dreadful consequences of war and tyranny, which is the foundation of this congress, both in the figurative as well as the material sense.

The Cologne Congress Halls where we meet today were an outstation of Buchenwald Concentration Camp during the last years of the war – a concentration camp today located in the German Democratic Republic where thousands of prisoners were tortured to death by the Nazi regime for their political convictions.

The memorial plaque, which will be presented to the mayor of Cologne at the end of the opening ceremony by one of the few remaining survivors of the concentration camp, will serve to uphold the memory of this reality.

The Act of Remembrance, which will take place tomorrow at the cemetery after the evening lecture, is to demonstrate that we ourselves will never forget the fate of sixty million people who fell victim to war and tyranny during the time of the Nazi regime.

As the president of this congress, I would like to ask all of you to participate in this memorial act. For very personal reasons I would be grateful to you, because I myself come from a family whose members had to pay with their very lives for their resistance to the Nazi regime. War and tyranny – people who have had to experience these evils would renounce them forever as a means of political confrontation and replace them by peace and freedom.

But how will peace come to be? How do we attain it? Every attempt to secure it has failed. Peace cannot be secured, one has to risk it. The risk lies in trusting each other. But trust is not only a risk, it is also strengthening.

We can no longer afford to place a greater emphasis on the risk rather than on the strength of trusting each other. We must recognize this strength as the only thing that makes a new way of living together possible and the only thing protecting us from a common death.

Hope for peace lies not in striving for physical strength, but rather in striving for moral strength. If human society is to value this moral strength above physical strength, each and everyone of us must contribute to the process. Each of us must seek out new ways to contribute, with his own personal qualities, experience, and knowledge, to create new directions in politics and enable us to rediscover the human dimension we all need in order to survive.

One very important way, in my opinion, is for politically mature citizens to come together in professional groups, to then step out of their professional ghettos and to publicly state their political opinions. Only in a world of specialists – in which an exaggerated division of labour is the rule and in which individuals care solely about their own professional success rather than engaging themselves in general political questions from a professional standpoint – only in such a world can politicians and the military be allowed to carry the sole responsibility for the survival of the planet. The IPPNW has recognized and accepted this challenge. Our task is clear:

We as physicians are obligated to preserve the life and health of our fellow human beings;

We see the arms race, and in particular the nuclear arms race, as an enormous catastrophe approaching us – in peace as well as in war;

We know that we and our medical efforts would be totally overwhelmed by the medical consequences of such a catastrophe, in peace as well as in war;

We must therefore regard it to be our medical obligation to confront the political causes of such a catastrophe with political means.

There are diseases which cannot be cured; we must prevent them, if we are to control them. The arms race with its consequences is such a disease. The so-called peaceful uses of nuclear energy – if I may add my personal opinion here – belongs to this category.

The sixth congress of IPNNW will give us the opportunity to deepen our knowledge of the causes and consequences of the arms race and our doubts about controlling technology. The congress will also give us the opportunity to broaden our experiences in working with the public at large.

It will also give us the opportunity – and this seems to me no less important – to approach each other in private discussions, to make new friendships and to confirm old ones.

Such discussions are of particularly great value when they are conducted among representatives of different social systems having incompatible opinions about the discussion topic. It is imperative to build trust on a small scale; in these discussions we can test our readiness to understand each other and to make compromises; from them we can possibly gain the most important experience of the congress: the experience of ourselves.

We have linked this congress with the name of Olof Palme, and we are deeply aware of the responsibility this decision bears upon us.

We have given this congress a motto which places high demands on our moral commitment.

May this congress endow us with the strength to intensify our work for peace – both in reverence for life and in reverence for the dignity of mankind.

THE OPENING CEREMONY

Bernard Lown, U.S.A. & Evgueni Chazov, U.S.S.R.

The Co-Presidents' Message

On behalf of Dr. Chazov and myself, I am honored to greet you. – This congress could not have taken place without the zeal and hard work of our German colleagues. They have maintained equanimity when challenged by divisive pressures. Their principles and their resolution evoke our admiration. We commend Professor Bonhoeffer, Dr. Gerecke, Dr. Schug, and their many co-workers, who have labored to make our gathering memorable and productive.

An IPPNW congress represents a culmination of activities for the year. From the very inception of our movement, a mere five and a half years ago, we pledged to meet anually until the scourge of nuclearism no longer threatened our fragile planet. We are here in Cologne because humankind continues to teeter perilously at the precipice of oblivion. We gather here to deepen understanding of issues, to celebrate achievements, to examine shortcomings, and above all to chart new directions. If we are to succeed, we must awaken world public opinion and reach the millions who as yet remain uninvolved in the momentous struggle confronting humankind.

Achievements

This past year marked a remarkable recognition of our activities. The Nobel Peace Prize is a pinnacle of distinction. The Chairman of the Nobel Committee, Egil Aarvik, stated: "Through this year's award of the Peace Price, the Norwegian Nobel Committee wishes . . . to direct attention to the way in which the problem of disarmament is a concern, not only of politicians, but also of the general public in all countries." He continued, ". . . in this way [the IPPNW] has made an important contribution to activating the general opposition to nuclear armaments and to mobilizing of opinion which is now taking place all over the world."

We can indeed point with pride to significant accomplishments. We have helped millions to penetrate the fog of denial and to confront for the first time the unthinkable reality of nuclear war. We have exposed to wide view the litany of horrors that would result from the use of these genocidal weapons. We have persuaded ever-growing numbers that medicine has nothing to offer – not even of token benefit, since most of the fatally injured would die in the solitude of their unrelieved agony. We have demonstrated the collossal deception of nuclear civil defense preparations, be they oriented to sheltering or to evacuating communities. We have researched the effects on children who live with gnawing uncertainty. We have communicated widely our conviction that no ideological, no political, no national differences can justify the scale of disease, suffering, death, and ecological catastrophe that nuclear war portends.

East-West Cooperation

IPPNW was the happy recipient of The Nobel Peace Prize for an additional reason. The award statement makes this clear: "The committee attaches particular importance to the fact that the organization was formed as a result of a joint initiative by Soviet and American physicians ..." In a world riven with confrontation, strife and terrorism, the IPPNW has become a model of cooperation among physicians from East and West, and from North and South. Dr. Chazov and I share the view that the unique quality of our movement is the potential for developing a broad-based, free-flowing dialogue between physicians of contending power blocs. Such a dialogue nurtures trust, promotes friendship, and thereby combats the stereotyping and demonizing of fellow human beings. This policy of IPPNW addresses the central pathology of our age, wherein mistrust and suspicion spawn paranoid fantasies which encourage ordinary people to fear an adversary more than they fear nuclear extinction of their own societies. We physicians have declared a truce. We refuse to be mobilized as cold warriors in crusades that demean our humanity and threaten the continuance of life on earth. That same principle resounded throughout The Enlightment, two centuries ago. Dr. Edward Jenner of smallpox fame put it aptly, "The scientists," he said, "are never at war. Peace must always preside in those bosoms whose object is the augmentation of human happiness."[1]

What is the basis for our success? How have we physicians been able to forge effective dialogue and cooperation when so many other well-intentioned groups have floundered? In part this is due to our medical tradition, which is pragmatic and unencumbered with ideology. It derives also from our medical ethic, which affirms the right to live as the highest human right preconditioning all others. But insuring the conditions of life requires preventing the conditions which promote death. Combatting the nuclear threat, which may extinguish all life, therefore has been and will continue to be our exclusive preoccupation. Steadfast adherence to this objective demands that we do not permit ourselves to be sidetracked to other issues no matter how morally significant.

A recent event conveys our philosophy more effectively than a tome of print. As you recall, during the tense press conference in Oslo preceding the Nobel award ceremonies, a Soviet correspondent, Lev Novikov, experienced cardiac arrest. We physicians plunged into instant action. It would have been unthinkable and unethical for us to digress even momentarily to inquire into the political affiliation, religious belief, or moral standards of the victim or the doctors. Little mattered save the rescue of an imperiled human life. The near death of Lev Novikov and the physicians' response was a powerful parable of our movement.

Can we act without the same single-minded resolution when sudden death threatens not a single individual but every inhabitant of the planet? Our sacred mission to preserve life on earth ist the categoric imperative of our time. We must summon all our knowledge – and yes, all our passion – to speak out for generations yet unborn. Posterity has no lobby with politicians. We must persuade our patients that the struggle is not for this or that national destiny, not for communism or capitalism, but for the prevention of unprecedented tragedy for human survival.

The Medical Prescription

IPPNW has not limited its agenda to decrying the horror of nuclear war or to indulging in dire prognostications. Physicians do not merely diagnose. They invariably prescribe. From the beginning we have searched for the weakest link in the chain of intransigence against accommodation. We have searched for a way to dismount the nuclear roller coaster and to work, in the words of Olof Palme, for "a world system of common security".[2]

At the Fourth IPPNW Congress in Helsinki, one of us called for a policy of reciprocating initiatives set in motion by an informed world public opinion.[3] Instead of stockpiling ever larger arsenals of overkill and heightening confrontation, a competition should be mounted to diminish peril. The function of IPPNW was to help mold a climate of understanding which would promote a unilateral initiative by a superpower and then compel its reciprocation by the other. Let propaganda advantage rightly accrue to the country which takes the biggest step away from the brink.

Cessation of Nuclear Explosions

As our first Medical Prescription, we selected a moratorium on nuclear explosions.[4] The reasons are numerous and cogent. In an age of distrust, a cessation of testing does not require trust. It is verifiable by national means down to explosions of less than one kiloton – a much lower yield than any of the weapons stockpiled in strategic arsenals. A moratorium is free of risk to either party; it is simple in concept yet substantive; it has wide public support and would serve as a strong restraint on proliferation by the many countries who now have the capacity to develop their own nuclear arms. Most important, a cessation of nuclear explosions would stop the development of ever more dangerous, ever more sophisticated and ever more destabilizing nuclear weapons. Testing is a major propellant in the upward spiral of the arms race.

There is an additional powerful argument for a moratorium: Nuclear testing is now the stimulus for a new direction in the arms race, the development of weapons in space. Such programs would pockmark the heavens with particle beams, geosynchronous relay space mirrors, laser battle stations, kinetic energy devices, directed microwave hypervelocity pellets, and a whole panoply of exotic weapons. The result would be quite predictable, namely the gluing of the accelerator pedal to the floor of the arms race. The frontier for weapons competition would be unlimited, and the outcome would be preordained.

For the IPPNW, a test ban has been the litmus test of political sincerity to put an end to a nuclear arms race, the outcome of which, if continued, cannot be in question. When racing toward a precipice, it is progress to stop. A halt to testing is symbolically the most important arms control measure that can now be undertaken. In effect, it represents a commitment to ending dependence on nuclear weapons at some future time. If enacted, it would promote confidence and nurture the trust essential to begin the long overdue task of reducing the swollen arsenals of annihilation.

The Soviet Moratorium

The IPPNW has been campaigning persistently for this singular and vital objective. We were therefore delighted when the Soviet Union stopped all nuclear explosions from August 6, 1985, through December 31, a moratorium that would be extended indefinitely if the United

States reciprocated. We had been fifty percent successful. But meaningful success requires a parallel commitment by the United States.

It was disconcerting to find that this important initiative was greeted in the West with indifference or skepticism. After all, there was an historic precedent in a much acclaimed act by a young American President twenty-two years earlier. On June 10, 1963, President Kennedy anounced that the United States would no longer conduct atmospheric testing. Three weeks later the U.S.S.R. followed suit, and within less than six weeks both sides agreed to sign a treaty.

As 1985 was ebbing and the Soviet moratorium was reaching its end, the IPPNW Executive Committee requested urgent meetings with both President Reagan and General Secretary Gorbachev. On December 18th Dr. Chazov and I had a long and fruitful meeting with Mr. Gorbachev. The aim of the meeting was to urge extension of the Soviet halt on testing for an additional three months. It was not an easy argument to pursue in light of the American government's stated opposition to a mutual moratorium. We were pleased that our words were heeded. A further unilateral Soviet extension was announced by General Secretary Gorbachev on January 15, 1986, and again just two weeks ago to last until next Hiroshima Day.

Arguments against a Testing Moratorium

Why has there not been a positive response to the Soviet initiative? During the past quarter century the prime reason given for the failure to stop testing was the uncertainty of verification. Advances in seismology makes this largely a non-issue. Furthermore, Mr. Gorbachev has indicated that the Soviets will agree to on-site inspections for monitoring compliance. It seemed therefore that the last obstacle had been surmounted for achieving a security objective central to the policies of six American Presidents. But as Tom Wicker, the distinguished columnist of *The New York Times*, bemoaned, ". . . the administration has not only refused to join in a moratorium on testing, it is unwilling even to enter negotiations for a test ban." [5]

A new argument often heard now is that the Soviets are "ahead" in testing, having recently completed a test series. What are the facts? According to *The New York Times* since 1945 the U.S.A. and its allies have conducted 979 tests compared to 604 by the Soviets. In the year of the moratorium the U.S. and its allies tested twenty-five times while the Soviets tested eight times.[6] An additional argument frequently heard is that without testing both sides would lose confidence in the reliability of their nuclear stockpiles. What is wrong with the loss of confidence in the operation of genocidal weapons? The less reliability, the less the likelihood of their use, and the safer the world would be. But this argument is untenable on factual grounds. Testing is not required to assure stockpile reliability. This has been categorically stated by Norris Bradbury, former Director of the Los Alamos Weapons Laboratory.[7] According to Glenn Seaborg, former Chairman of the United States Atomic Energy Commission, few such reliability tests have ever been conducted.[8]

The Task Ahead

A central fact long neglected is that the quality rather than the quantity of nuclear weapons determines the fragile stability of the nuclear balance. The race now is for new attack-support technologies that masquerade as defense system. We are about to cross a threshold into a far more dangerous world, where weapons are in hair-trigger readiness to launch – or counter –

a first strike. The time is short before high noon. It is proper to sound the alarm here in Germany, where a half century ago a criminal madness was unleashed on humanity.

The nuclear disasters at Chernobyl and Three Mile Island, the industrial catastrophe at Bhopal, and the tragedy of the space shuttle Challenger are sober reminders of the inevitable fallibility of all the works of man. Engineers had estimated that the odds for a meltdown at Chernobyl were one every ten thousand years. But the plant had been in operation for only three years.[9] World anxiety was roused by the Chernobyl accident. But there are 18,000 strategic nuclear weapons ready for instant use. The detonation of one of them would be many thousand times more devastating than what transpired in the Ukraine. Chernobyl is a warning. There is still time to reverse the course.

The Role of Physicians

We physicians have an urgent mission. We have not done enough to educate the public that nuclear testing is the engine of the arms race. The issue is clear-cut; it is readily understandable. Only by rousing multitudes can we hope that our policy of encouraging reciprocating initiatives in disarmament will become a vital process.

Inching toward catastrophe rouses the instinct for self preservation. Human beings must learn that we all reside in one global village. Borders and frontiers are but primitive tribal scars. Acid rain and atomic radiation do not require passports to traverse the world. Nuclear winter will respect no bounds. These truths are now being learned by millions. They are the seeds planted in the springtime of the atomic age. They will grow and ripen to create a new world culture that respects the fragile and indissoluble unity of the human family – a truth not foreign to us in the healing arts. A popular groundswell for peace is building worldwide.

Above all else, we physicians are teachers. We need to instruct that in a nuclear world security is either shared or it is non-existent. Only when people in East and West realize that their true enemy is not one another but the mushroom cloud; that their ultimate self-interest is the shared interest of survival – only then will survival be assured. May the vision, and the strength needed for its realization, emanate from this congress.

BIBLIOGRAPHY

1. Jenner W., cited by Commanger HS: Unexamined assumptions and inescapable consequences. In: *Long Darkness*. New Haven and London, Yale University Press, 1986, 147.
2. Palme O.: Common Security: A Programme for Disarmament. London and Sydney, Pan Books, 1982.
3. Lown B.: Physicians need to devise a prescription. IPPNW Report 2 (2), 1984.
4. Lown B. Pastore J. O.: A medical prescription for survival. Lancet 2:1285, 1985.
5. Wicker T.: Misleading the people, The New York Times, February 28, 1986.
6. New York Times, Section E, News of the Week In Review, Sunday, March 23, 1986; p. 3.
7. Letter from Norris Bradbury to President Carter, 1978, cited by Fred Kaplan, Boston Globe, February 3, 1986; p. 9.
8. Seaborg G., quoted by Dewitt, H. E., and Marsh, G. E.: An update on the test ban. Bulletin of Atomic Scientists 42 (5); p. 8, 1986.
9. Rylsky, M.: The nuclear power industry in the Ukraine. Soviet Life, February 1986, p. 8.

Maintaining Life on Earth –
The Political Challenge

MAINTAINING LIFE ON EARTH – THE POLITICAL CHALLENGE

David Lange, New Zealand

Reflections on the Ending of the Arms Race: New Zealand's Example

May I join you in tribute to the memory of Olof Palme. Our sorrow at his loss and the manner of his going gives fire to our determination to commemorate him in the continuation of his work for nuclear disarmament. I commend here the founders and members of International Physicians for the Prevention of Nuclear War. The citation made by the Nobel Committee when it announced its award of the Nobel Peace Prize for 1985 fairly describes your achievement. The committee wrote that your service to humanity arose from your dissemination of authoritative information and your creation of an awareness of the catastrophic consequences of nuclear war.

Your work and the work of your members throughout the world has brought home to us all the horror which is the reality of nuclear war. You have told us the extent of our common danger. You have in stark simplicity made clear that there is no medical response to nuclear war. All your skill could not restore us. You have made it impossible for the view to prevail that nuclear war could be a war like any other or that nuclear force can be an instrument of policy like any other. You have in that made medical reality a part of political reality.

I would like to talk about political reality in all its complexity. My point is this: It is the political process which began the arms race, the political process which sustains it and the political process which must end it.

The arms race began in the search for security. It began with an assessment of national interest which generated the compulsion to arm with nuclear weapons. That assessment is what sustains it.

The arms race will end with the understanding that nuclear weapons themselves are the greatest danger to us. It will end when we see nuclear arsenals not as a symbol of security but as a dreadful threat. It will end when the predominant element in the calculation of national interest is not to arm but to disarm, not to expand nuclear arsenals but to reduce them, not to encourage the proliferation of nulear weapons but to limit them.

There is no answer to nuclear weapons in the weapons themselves. They cannot be disinvented. The whole history of the nuclear arms race shows that there is no technical refinement which will once and for all eliminate nuclear weapons from political calculations by securing for one side or another an overwhelming advantage.

It is in fact the relentless search for technical advantage which drives the arms race. Technical improvement has been countered by technical improvement. Every advance in scientific capability and every refinement in military strategy has been met, or is being met, in a continuing process of escalation.

The result is an arsenal which could destroy us all not once but many times over. Every solution to the nuclear arms race, which has been attempted in terms of the weapons themselves, has succeeded only in worsening our predicament. The intentions of governments are subverted. Security is not enhanced but diminished by the proliferation of weapons so inherently dangerous.

If nuclear weapons cannot be disinvented, and there is no answer to them in technology, the answer to them must lie in the decision not to use them as an instrument of policy. That decision has not been taken, because other demands seem more important. The search for genuine measures of arms control has foundered in a world, in which the imperative is to prepare for war, albeit in the hope that it will never be fought, and to accumulate the weapons of war, albeit in the hope that they will never be used.

The measures of arms control which have been adopted have done little to limit the expansion of nuclear arsenals or to restrain the relentless search for technical advantage. Arms limitation talks between the nuclear powers have been given priority over disarmament measures which have emerged from multilateral forums. Those talks are couched in contradiction. They seek balance in armaments when it is the search for balance which feeds the urge to compete which drives the arms race. In the broad context of nuclear escalation these arsenals have been preserved for the existing participants.

Efforts to press for disarmament through the United Nations have succeeded only in so far as they are compatible with the imperatives of the arms race. I remind you of the events which led to the conclusion of the partial test ban treaty in 1963.

It seemed for a while that there was a real prospect that a comprehensive test ban was within reach; there seemed to be a genuine will to submit to the procedures of inspection and verification which are an essential part of such a treaty; then those procedures became the subject of dispute and the treaty was lost. There came in its place a treaty whose signatories agreed to defer from testing nuclear weapons in the atmosphere, above the atmosphere and in the sea. The treaty, welcome though it was, has hardly been a restraint at all on the testing and refinement of nuclear weapons. That has continued unabated.

The preamble to the treaty declared it to be first step towards a comprehensive test ban treaty but the next step was never taken.

Every year since 1972 Australia and New Zealand have put forward a resolution at the United Nations which calls for the urgent conclusion of a comprehensive test ban treaty. Each year we receive the overwhelming support of countries which are not nuclear powers. Each year our initiative founders because the nuclear powers do not see it as in their interest that it should succeed.

The Non-Proliferation Treaty of 1967 equally shows how measure of arms control which once gave many of us cause for hope has in fact been subordinated to the impulse to compete. There have been no new nuclear weapons states but those who have those weapons have continued to refine them, to develop new weapons and to station them in host countries. This is a form of proliferation which is not limited by the obligations set forth in the treaty.

That is not to say that the obligations the signatories undertook have not been observed. It is simply that the spirit of non-proliferation is not sustained by the letter of the treaty.

Clearly the vision of the framers of the treaty has yet to be achieved.

There is an example from the South Pacific which shows how the best intentions can be defeated. France used to test its nuclear weapons in the air above the Pacific ocean. There could be no real dispute about the pollution it was causing or the environmental damage it was doing. The case against the tests was overwhelming. When Australia and New Zealand took their case against France to international forums they had a sympathetic hearing. France was exposed to the pressure of international disapproval which was strongly expressed and genuinely felt. There were signs that an element of opinion in France itself was sympathetic to the South Pacific's case.

The result was that the tests went underground. There they continue. There they are tolerated by those elements of international opinion which support testing in any form and by the more squeamish element which could not stomach atmospheric testing. The objections of the countries of the South Pacific are no less strong because the environmental dangers of the testing are potential rather than actual. The difference now is that our objections meet no response.

It is a sense of the futility of existing restraints on the development and deployment of nuclear weapons which has entered so largely into our perspective in New Zealand. We too are exposed to the dangers posed by nuclear weapons.

Those who build nuclear weapons and those who devise nuclear strategies do far more than provide for their own defence. They can decide the fate of all. A nuclear conflict cannot be contained or limited. When it begins it will be our end.

The South Pacific is far removed from any likely or foreseeable cause of nuclear war. Yet if we watched the northern hemisphere destroy itself it would be in the certainty that there is no escape for us. The nuclear winter would not spare the South Pacific. We would be condemned to accept decisions we had not part in making and calculations which we could not influence. Our interest in the control and limitation of nuclear weapons is just as compelling as for those, whose involvement is more immediate.

If there is to be disarmament, if nuclear weapons themselves are to be limited and the doctrines which govern their threatened use are to be restrained, then the idea that there is an alternative to nuclear weapons must come to form part of the calculations of responsible governments. The alternative must be real. It must also be realizable. There can be no wishful thinking about security. If the alternative to the arms race is not founded in a reality as compelling as the calculations which have led to the proliferation of nuclear weapons, then responsible governments will not be moved by it.

In saying that I am conscious, as you must be, of the complexity of the political process and of the extraordinary demands of the assessments which go into the making of a decision to arm or not to arm with nuclear weapons.

What I say to you today is the product of a political process which has its own imperatives. New Zealand is a parliamentary democracy of a kind which is common in Europe and the South Pacific. In New Zealand, a combination of circumstances, which I shall describe to you shortly, has led the government to the view that it should exclude nuclear weapons from New Zealand and disengage itself from any nuclear strategy for the defence of New Zealand. In that, the government simply reflects political reality as it is in New Zealand now. If I were not its Prime Minister, nuclear weapons would still be excluded from New Zealand today and some other man or woman would be here to say what I say to you now.

That being so, I must acknowledge that other calculations have led other governments to make quite different choices. Responsible governments throughout the world have decided that the security of those they represent is best served by engagement in a nuclear strategy for their own defence. They do not rejoice in that decision. I have met heads of government who do not share the views of the New Zealand government and who have argued vigorously against the course of action taken by the New Zealand government. I do not say of any of them that they exult in the fact that their countries are girt around by nuclear weapons. The reality is that they see no alternative.

A large part of our reasoning is the product of circumstance. New Zealand is not targetted by nuclear weapons. We are not threatened by any military force. We are islands in the Pacific a thousand miles and more from our nearest neighbours, which are like-minded states. A nuclear defence is irrelevant to New Zealand. More than that, a nuclear strategy is an inappropriate response to the small-scale conflicts which have arisen in the region and might arise there in the future. Such conflict can and should be resolved by diplomacy or if need be, by conventional military force.

New Zealand adopted and will continue to adhere to a conventional military strategy. It seeks to express it in an alliance with Australia and the United States which is a military reflection of New Zealand's commitment to the traditions of our common heritage.

I do not need to emphasise how fortunate New Zealand is in its position. The alternative to a nuclear defence is real enough to be a sustainable element in the calculations of the New Zealand government.

I also point out to you that there is in New Zealand a large and genuinely popular disarmament movement. The creation of a nuclear free zone in the South Pacific has widespread public support.

Popular support for disarmament was undoubtedly given considerable impetus by New Zealand's unwilling involvement in the politics of nuclear weapons at their most unpleasant. Our isolation did not prevent an intrusion by a nuclear weapons state: That fact still echoes in New Zealand today.

France continues to test nuclear weapons under a coral atoll at Mururoa in spite of the objection of every independent South Pacific nation. Our objections have been raised through every channel open to us, yet France declines to move its test site out of the region. France sent agents of the state to New Zealand to carry out an act of terrorism in order to protect its nuclear weapons testing.

Two of the agents who helped to carry out that act of terrorism were found and arrested. In fulfilment of its obligations to counter terrorism, New Zealand duly tried the arrested agents and imprisoned them. France has not yet apologised for its action nor made reparation to New Zealand. If you wonder why a large element of public opinion in New Zealand has come to reject the politics of nuclear weapons there is part of the reason.

I do not want to suggest to you that public opinion in New Zealand is entirely at one on the question of New Zealand's disengagement from a nuclear strategy for its defence. There is a current of opinion in New Zealand which maintains that it is wise to prepare a nuclear defence in case some threat as yet unseen should one day arise. There is another current of opinion which notes that a military association with a nuclear power confers advantages, and reasons that those advantages are greater than the advantages which arise from New Zealand's disengagement from a nuclear strategy.

All of that opinion forms part of the political calculations which are made in New Zealand both by the government and by the opposition to the government. My point is that having made those calculations the government holds itself bound to exclude nuclear weapons from New Zealand. That is our political reality in New Zealand.

We in New Zealand *have* an alternative to nuclear weapons. That is why we can, and do, stand back from the process of nuclear escalation. And that adds another dimension to the conviction with which we call for genuine and urgent measures of arms control.

You will understand why it is impossible for me to advance any simple answer to the control of nuclear weapons and the limitation of the arms race. The answer for New Zealand will not be the answer elsewhere. Political reality is complex and the calculations which are made in pursuit of national interest are demanding in their variety and intensity. The calculations which have led the governments of the nuclear powers to engage in the arms race are the most compelling in history. Only compulsion at its most urgent could have allowed countries to divert resources sorely needed elsewhere into nuclear arsenals which have the capacity to destroy us many times over.

If the compulsion to arm is to be defeated, it will have to be replaced by a reality whose imperative is different. I said, when I began, that you had by informing us about the medical consequences of nuclear war made medical reality a part of political reality. You have in that way altered political reality and by altering the calculations of politicians have made nuclear war less likely. I think that we have the chance now to build on what you and many others have done. We must use the understanding of the horror of nuclear war and of the all-encompassing tragedy of nuclear war to secure arms control agreements which are genuine and lasting. They are not beyond us.

I said to you that New Zealand's diplomatic effort over many years has been directed towards the conclusion of a comprehensive test ban treaty. That is where our effort and that of many others will continue. We believe it to be the single most important step that can be taken in the immediate future to slow the nuclear arms race. If that treaty is one day concluded, it will come about, because governments throughout the world will have decided that enough is enough. They will have grown tired of adding to arsenals which can destroy the world many times over. The dangers of nuclear weapons will loom larger than the advantages to be had from their continued improvement. The need for alternative means of security will have been accepted. That is what in the end will oblige them to call a halt.

A comprehensive test ban treaty would blunt the quest for technical advantage which helps drive the arms race and would in time limit the growth of nuclear arsenals. An effective ban must incorporate a system of verification which is acceptable to all parties. The technology which can provide the means of verification is available. What is required is the political will to make the agreement.

The political calculations which have led the nuclear powers into their relentless competition must be replaced by a new assessment. It must be founded in the understanding that our common danger is greater than any possible competitive advantage. Unless we are brought by that understanding to seek genuine measures of disarmament and arms control and alternative means of security, the process of escalation and proliferation will continue.

* * *

May I tell you that in the South Island of New Zealand in the province of Nelson there is a place called Brightwater. It is a pleasant sunny district of farms and orchards. Over a hundred years ago Ernest Rutherford was born there. He was educated in Nelson and at the university in Christchurch. Then he went to England where he did the scientific work which split the atom and let the genie out of the bottle.

Rutherford was moved as scientists must be by the search for the truth. The scientific truth which he and others revealed did not it itself create the nuclear arms race. It became an instrument of politics and politics began the arms race. The medical and scientific truth which you and others have revealed will not in itself end the arms race. It will become an instrument of politics so that one day politics will end the arms race. Those who seek to advance our understanding of nuclear weapons and their dangers are engaged in the highest task there is.

MAINTAINING LIFE ON EARTH – THE POLITICAL CHALLENGE

Inga Thorsson, Sweden

The Great Peace Journey

B eing a citizen of a tiny, neutral European country, I feel in the best of company sitting in a committee composed of American and Soviet citizens. After 41 years of living in the nuclear age, and when taking the relations between the two largest nuclear powers, i.e. the superpowers into consideration, our starting point indicates that an urgent need for viable strategies to maintain life on earth does exist. It is our task to present the strategies that can be effectuated by political action.

My first question would be: By whom? Who are the key figures? I suggest that one should not count on the political leaders of the dominating military powers. The "tour guides" leading us into the twenty-first century in this fourty-first year of the nuclear age are just as shortsighted and unimaginative as their predecessors in the pre-nuclear age. In their view the task entrusted to them by their political constituents is to promote peace through military strength, and if need be, through military superiority. Born of this arrogance is the political manoeuvering conducted towards small and medium-sized nations. Policy is established based upon the conflict-ridden interrelations between these smaller nations. In other words: smaller nations are being held hostage.

This arrogance, coupled with the feeling of being at the centre of the universe, yes, even as a hybris, most certainly exists. I can remember a comment made by the President of the U.S.A. during the talks with Mr. Gorbachev six months ago in Geneva: "The world can stop holding its breath, because we have met and spoken to one another again."

Yes, they do believe it to be their prerogative to keep the rest of humanity at their mercy and act on their behalf, be it benevolently or not. Based upon many factors, I am convinced that they will not be able to pursue these arrogant policies for very long. They are like Ikarus in their hybris, i.e. flying too close to the sun, consequently, their wings will melt and they will fall into the sea.

What will happen then? Will the successors or those existing right-hand men be more modest in their actions towards the rest of the world and humanity? What about the small and medium-sized nations and their capacity to lead a movement towards a better world?

Let me refer briefly to a seminar in Stockholm organized by the Swedish Institute of International Affairs held a week ago "in memory of Olof Palme". Various courses of action by smaller nations were discussed at this time for obvious reasons; these possibilities were named "the powers of the powerless".

In my opinion, a logical consequence of the discussion on the abuse of power by the superpowers was, at least in part, a discussion on the imperative to get away from the increasing tendency to disguise the issues with international law, to organize public opinion, and to build up trust through the U.N. leading to true international cooperation.

Of interest are Olof Palme's views and his role in approaching and influencing decision-makers around the world, encouraging them to examine international problems from their own perspective. A participant at this conference referred to the importance not only of the decision-making role of a politician, but also of the therapeutic role in maintaining life in face of the adversities of our time.

The above more closely approaches the main topic of my presentation: the enlighted political leaders of the smaller nations must accede to worldwide public opinion in its irrevocable search for acceptance – by the existing political leaders – of the right of this generation of humanity to maintain life by dealing with the global and human problems of today in a totally different way.

But first, at least a few words on something I do not intend to elaborate on. Based upon what I have said so far, one could assume that I'm quite pessimistic as to the possibilities for much needed progress within the sector of the political action to be taken in the disarmament talks. There is an urgent need, also, to look for other approaches to stopping the arms' race.

Having studied the negative economic implications of the arms' race on the national and international level for about ten years in various positions, I maintain that one political consequence of these effects will be the gradual diminuation of the arms' race. No country, no economy, not even the richest one, can in the long run escape the consequences of economic malaise, social unrest and political instability caused by the present use of resources for military purposes. The present mode of setting priorities in resource utilization is a shameful insult to the desparate need for preserving the lives of human beings now living in dearth, poverty and hunger. We often hear that thirty children die every minute of hunger, poverty or disease, and at the same time two million dollars are spent every minute on military purposes. Sooner or later, hopefully sooner, there will be an outcry against the obscene policies of a handful of political leaders, who behind a façade of outdated phrases from a past era of supremacy claim their right to dictate the use of world resources to humanity as a whole.

Who are the actors, who could put the political strategies needed to maintain life into action? Most decidedly: public opinion and the collective will.

The facts are in, analyses completed, conclusions reached. The time has come for decisions and actions. If the governments fail to change their values, attitudes, priorities and direction, then the public must speak out and become the force behind the political action needed to guarantee the preservation of life.

What are the chances that this may come to pass? Are there any chances at all? Sometimes one feels desparate. I would like to quote a few lines from the "Talk of the Town" section from the April 7th, 1986, issue of the *New Yorker:*

"We have that old feeling, familiar to us from previous crises, that mankind has been transformed into a mass of spectators, watching passively but nervously, as everyone's life or death is being decided upon somewhere out of sight by a handful of people, some of whom may not even be in their right minds. The events themselves become the determinants of decisions made, without any human intervention."

This is certainly the way that a large number of affected citizens are feeling in this day and age. But this feeling should not prevail. Concerned citizens must not be transformed into passive spectators of what is happening as a result of decisions taken by a very few at the top. They are not, and they should not allow themselves to be, helpless hostages or victims.

About a month ago, a conference at U.N. headquarters with "eminent" personalities in attendance ended with the following unanimous declaration:

"Our small planet is being endangered by the arsenals of weapons that could blow it up, by the burden of military spending that could cause it to be destroyed, and by the unfulfilled basic needs of two thirds of its population which subsists on less than one third of its resources. We belong to a universal community, which believes that we have inherited this earth from our forefathers and, equally so that we are borrowing it from our children. Neither the carrying capacity of this earth nor its resources are infinite. The need for national security is a legitimate one, and must be met. However, must we stand by as helpless witnesses of a tendency towards less security with rising costs?"

The answer to this last rhetorical question is, of course, a definitive no. But how should we address this generation of mankind, and spark a reaction in them?

In the January 1986 issue of the *Bulletin of the Atomic Scientists* an article appeared written by two communications experts. It was titled: "Scared stiff or scared into action". With its emphasis on the appropriate mode of communication it proved most informative and educational. If one presents information about the horrors of an eventual nuclear war in a very factual way, without offering any viable countermeasures, it may lead to a "psychological numbing", as referred to by Robert Jay Lifton. It is the very state of mind that will not motivate people to be active in the prevention of nuclear war. Terror might only lead to apathy and paralysis. This is the exact opposite of what we hope to achieve.

The authors of the *Bulletin's* article put forward the alternative: Four antidotes to numbing, namely anger, love, hope, and action. These concepts, the authors' claim, are the keys to mobilizing a large popular movement against nuclear weapons.

While many negative emotions: depression, guilt and shame, are directed inwards and immobilizing, anger focusses the attention outside oneself and is therefore conducive to action. Anger and love are compatible. Something or someone to fight for is as indispensable to activism as something or someone to fight against. "The main obstacle to action," writes Jerome D. Frank, "is neither apathy nor terror, but simply a feeling of helplessness." On the other hand, hope is closely associated with willingness to act. People must be offered things to do that seem achievable and worthwhile, but this must be based on affirmation and credible vision, the construction of which the authors consider a top-priority task. And finally, while people are most likely to take action when they feel angry, loving and hopeful, rather than terrorized into numbness, it is also true that action tends to liberate people's anger, love and hope. In other words, the growth of commitment is circular.

I would like to conclude this presentation by referring to one recent popular initiative that fulfills the requirements of the *Bulletin* article: The Great Peace Journey. This project, which originated in Sweden, is now a worldwide undertaking, although still mainly organized and led by Sweden, and supported by all the big popular movements such as the churches, the trade unions, political parties, the Red Cross and Save the Children. Needless to say, Olof Palme was an enthusiastic supporter, as is the U.N. Secretary-General. It is based on the idea that the people had to confront the governments of U.N. member states with some basic questions concerning their duties and obligations as governments of member states of the U.N., having freely signed the charter of the United Nations, which opens with the words: "We, the peoples of the United Nations ...". This means that the governments act on behalf of their citizens when in the U.N., which – in turn – means that the governments are accountable to them for what they do or do not do to preserve peace, to implement genuine disarmament measures, to convert resources used for military purposes to constructive and meaningful civil use, and to solve conflicts among states in accordance with, and in obeyance of Article 33 of the U.N. Charter.

The first three of the five questions are formulated on one and the same pattern: "If all other members of the U.N. undertake to do the same ... are you willing to ...?" Answers are requested in written, signed and clear yes-or-no terms. Personally, I do have difficulty in accepting a no-answer from any government of a country having voluntarily signed the U.N. Charter. "If all other U.N. members undertake to do the same", which government would put itself in a position to be the only one to say no?

None of us involved in the Great Peace Journey is of course naive enough to imagine yes-answers to alter the course of history, to solve, as it were overnight, the problems of a world, which is over-armed and under-nourished. But such answers would, we believe, contribute to paving the way towards new security systems and creating a new basis for international negotiations. The first phase, visits to all European capitals, was undertaken one year ago. Twenty-seven out of twenty-eight governments received the delegations. Twenty of them, in neutral, NATO and Warsaw Treaty countries, answered "yes" to all five questions, four said "yes" to some of them, three reacted most dissatisfactorily. Those have now received letters explicitly demanding straight yes-or-no answers. This request is based on the fact that the people have the right to ask questions and the governments have the duty to answer them.

In the fall of this year, the U.N. International Year of Peace, other governments in Africa, Asia and Latin America will, in one way or another, be given the opportunity to answer the questions, and finally, the two super-power governments, in Washington and Moscow, will be confronted with the will of the people of the world. The power of the people will no longer have to manifest itself only by marching in the streets. They will begin a direct dialogue with the governments themselves, they will become a political force, intervening in the political process, based upon the opening words of the U.N. Charter: "We the peoples of the United Nations ...". In the final analysis, the governments are accountable to the people of the world for preserving life on this planet.

MAINTAINING LIFE ON EARTH – THE POLITICAL CHALLENGE

John Kenneth Galbraith, U.S.A.

Military Power: Tension as a Servant; Arms Control as an Illusion

T here comes a time in the troubled course of human affairs when we must step back and examine the fundamental concepts by which our public attitudes and policies are guided. This, I am persuaded, is now needed as regards the weapons race.
No one can look at the present position with satisfaction. The two great powers now deploy weapons of unimaginable destructive potential. They plan incontinently for yet more. And for weapons systems of ever more perilous computer control and hair-trigger tendency.

Meanwhile, the negotiators come together in Geneva; they talk and then adjourn for weeks or months. One of the world's most leisured occupations. Differences, when they assemble, are aired and emphasized, not compromised or resolved. The differences turn on deeply theological points, and this is more nearly appropriate than we realize. The negotiators are minor figures subordinate to a higher and controlling authority – to the overriding military power. In consequence, from the negotiatons we no longer, in our realistic moments, expect any genuine step back from the peril under which we, our children and the planet itself live in suspension of death.

The condition behind this disastrous charade is one which we must now accept. It is that the military power has become an independent force on both sides of the superpower relationship. The arms control negotiations are not meant even to limit and reduce the threat of nuclear devastation; they have become a cover for the larger expression of military power. They are now a design for quieting public fear of nuclear war.

There is now an interacting dynamic that serves the military in each of the two great powers – each takes action that produces responding action in the other country. This one country must do, because it is what the other does or intends to do. Thus each military power builds on the other. And so on to infinity and the eventual catastrophe. What is this military power: what are the sources of its strength?

The first source of the military power in the United States is the belief that any government instrument is subject to democratic process. This belief is strong in our rhetoric; it is what our children are still taught in school; but it is, in fact, what no fully informed citizen can believe. The modern military establishment, in the organization it controls, the money it deploys, the captive politicians it commands, the scientific community that it subsides, and under the cloak of patriotism that protects it, has become a polar force in its own right. The military services, the Defense Department civilians, the serving industries, employ 6.5 million and generate $ 46 billion in business to private enterprise. The military power embraces the civilian authority to which legally and constitutionally it is presumed to be subject.

Leaving office almost exactly a quarter of a century ago, President Dwight D. Eisenhower warned of the dangers of the acquisition of power, deliberately or because of neglect, by the military-industrial complex. "In the councils of governments," he said, "we must guard against the acquisition of unwarranted influence, whether sought or unsought, by the military-industrial complex. The potential for the disastrous rise of misplaced power exists and will persist." He could not, were he to return, think his fear unnecessary. Last January on the anniversary of that warning, there was a major assemblage of concerned individuals – businessmen, scholars, politicians, citizens-at-large. None of those so gathered thought it unmerited.

I do not speak with equal authority of the military power in the Soviet Union. There it will be said with no slight emphasis – just as we say it in the United States – that it is under full control, fully subject to the larger authority of the socialist state. Alas, no great organization is ever without power; it is not in the nature of great bureaucracy to submit passively to external control or fail to assert its claims on society. Certainly the interacting dynamic serves a military purpose in the U.S.S.R. as it does in the United States.

There are two further consequences of the rise and awesome triumph of this interacting military power that are also evident. To these I now turn.

The first is the need of any military power for an enemy – a plausible enemy. In the absence of such an enemy, both its influence and, more pertinently, its financial support are gravely at risk. The second is its need to contend with the main threat to its power in our time; that threat is the deep, even urgent, public fear that modern nuclear weaponry, by its nature, arouses. In all countries and not least in the United States, there is a strong resistance to the idea of nuclear euthanasia. So just as the military power must have a plausible enemy, so also it must have a plausible design for countering or containing this public fear. This is what arms control negotiations now principally accomplish. But first the need for an enemy.

The United States in the last century and again in the years between the World Wars had no plausible military adversary. In consequence, the American military establishment had negligible power and resources. Our army in that period was about on a par with that of Portugal. This condition has been remedied. In recent years enemies have been manifestly more available – or have been made so. China, until it was promoted to its role as an honorary bastion of free enterprise, for a time so served. The new atomic yellow peril, North Vietnam, Cuba and Nicaragua have also been enemies. We now have Colonel Khadafy and Libya. But overwhelmingly and durably the plausible enemy has been the Soviet Union.

The Soviet Union is indispensable to the military power in the United States. Tension in our relations with the Soviets directly and overtly serve that power; any relaxation of tension would be specifically damaging to the resources it commands. From this comes a further fact of our time. That is the cultivation of tension in order to support the military power. Military appropriations were once in response to external threat. But let us not now be in doubt. Action and response have been reversed. External threat is now in the service of military appropriations and weapons development.

Once again, I do not identify this grim development peculiarly with the United States. The charge that the United States poses a grave imperialist threat to the world comes regularly from the Soviet Union. There is recurrent mention of sinister capitalist intention. In both countries we live perilously in a world where tension and hostility serve military purpose and power.

They serve it, let us note, in a world where a basic presumption that underlies the very word *superpower* is now strongly in question. That presumption is of a relentless extension of power by the Soviet Union and the United States – in the Soviet view, of unfulfilled imperialist ambition by the United States; in the accepted American view, of a relentless move to world socialist domination by the U.S.S.R.

The highly evident reality, in contrast, is the powerful and successful desire on the part of all countries of the world, without exception, to assert and preserve their independence, to be free of superpower influence and control.

This, over the last twenty-five years, has been the Soviet experience in China, in Egypt, in Algeria and Ghana. Also in Indonesia and, in visible measure, in Eastern Europe – and in Afghanistan. Ethiopia, Mozambique and South Yemen are not masterpieces of socialist achievement; Marx would be appalled at the thought of socialism at their stage of development. Similarly, the thrust for independence is or has been the experience of the United States in Central and South America, in Iran, elsewhere in the Middle East, and notably and sadly in Vietnam.

Nonetheless in face of these massive retreats Soviet spokesmen still speak of the American imperialist design, we of the relentless Soviet Thrust to world domination. The purpose I cannot think in doubt. The imagery of socialist and imperialist expansion serves the military power in both countries. The hard fact of universal retreat must be kept subordinate to that need.

So I summarize. Our present situation is not military need in response to tension and hostility; it is tension and hostility in the service of military need. I come now to the role of arms control.

International tranquility is not the only threat to the military power. In the age of nuclear alarm and terror there is also the threat posed by massive popular concern and reaction. As I earlier noted, there is, and not surprisingly, a strong public concern for continued existence. This has made itself evident in recent times in the United States in the freeze movement, which alarmingly invaded the preserve of the nuclear arms control theologians. And in the pressure for a comprehensive test ban. And in the peace movement in general. This popular reaction was greatly encouraged in the early years of the present administration by compulsive talk in Washington of the strategy, tactics and survival in nuclear war – of the acceptability of nuclear war, of prevailing in nuclear war, of the strategy for protracted nuclear war. There were also some notably insane suggestions as to how individuals and communities might survive nuclear war. "With a thrown-down door and enough earth on top almost everyone will make it."

I have been sufficiently in the Soviet Union to know that the same sensitivity to the threat of nuclear war exists strongly in the Russian mind. Perhaps more so than it does in the United States. Twice in this century Russia has been massively the victim of war. We have not. Russians see themselves as victims in war; we think of ourselves as the people who escape.

Contemplating death, all people resort to psychological denial. This they do where nuclear war is concerned. We turn our minds to happier prospects. This the arms negotiations have allowed us to do. In further consequence, the nuclear theologians are maintained in their monopoly of the arms control issue. This monopoly, as we see it in the United States, is an extraordinary thing. We would not readily delegate power over taxes; we are rather relieved to delegate it over death. This delegation we must withdraw. The psychological denial we must reject. We must, East and West, see and emphasize the peril to which we are subject. We must see arms negotiation not as a way of quieting fear but as a step to eliminating the causes of fear.

What are the avenues of escape – escape to survival? The first need is for a full acceptance of the role of the military power in our time. The military power has invaded and escaped democratic process. And likewise, I venture, socialist authority. The answer in our case is not less democracy; it is full and effective democracy. While I do not advise the Soviet Union, I do suggest that no good socialist can ever be at the mercy of generals or subject to their power. Nothing so demonstrates and serves the military power as the tendency of people on all sides to avoid the subject and attribute all responsibility and blame to the other side of the interacting dynamic.

We must, as the next step, be fully and completely aware of how tension and hostility serve the military power. In the United States we must enlist both public opinion and democratic process in seeking to reduce that tension. We must have politicians who react powerfully against those who cultivate tension. We must vigorously expose the purpose it serves. We must ask the Soviet Union for similar restraint. I would hope as an American that we might set an example in this regard; there is no harm or weakness in that. Our public leaders have sufficiently indicated to the Soviets that they are less than approving of their economic and social system. Repetition is unneeded. But I appeal to the leaders of the U.S.S.R. also for the greatest restraint in speech and action.

Next, let us recognize one of the great facts of our time: it is that the nations of the world do not want to be ruled, or guided, by the great powers, as in courtesy they still are called. If we accept that, it will ensure that there will be no collision of American and Soviet policy in Nicaragua, Angola, the Middle East – or Ethiopia. In independence, the people of these countries will not all be well and democratically governed, all happy and free. But it is not for us – or the Soviet Union – to alter that fate.

Let us now also have the strongest possible effort by Canadians, Western Europeans, Latin Americans, the countries of Eastern Europe and China, to urge against and minimize the conflict and tension that so serve the military power. To reduce tension is not a task for the United States and the Soviet Union alone, it is for all governments and all people.

Finally, having reduced the tension that serves it, having come otherwise to terms with the military power, let us have effective action on arms control. The first step is to arrest the dynamic by which American arms action serves the Soviet Military power and their response serves ours. Accordingly, let us have the freeze on nuclear deployment and development and the comprehensive test ban. And go on from there.

In asking for effective, understandable progress on arms control, we must not hesitate to call the present charade a charade. And we must call those so engaged and their principals to full political account. In the West we must deliver ourselves of politicians, great and small, who accept the charade, who are reluctant or ineffective in the arms control effort.

On both sides let us move to reduce the military claim on the economy – and on government budgets. This acts directly to reduce the military power. It sacrifices nothing as to defense in an age of reciprocal overkill.

It will also – no slight matter – have a strongly beneficial effect on the economic life of both East and West. The German Federal Republic and Japan have been the two great economic success stories since World War II. Both have used resources in lesser measure for sterile military purpose, more for refreshing the capital of civilian industry. This is not a theoretical judgment; the hard practical evidence, especially in the case of Japan, is for all to see. Nor would the transition to a rational use of economic resources be difficult or traumatic. I am disturbed by the number of intelligent people who believe that the modern economy is somehow sustained by military spending and would collapse without it.

Once again, let us be aware of the role of the military power in our time. Let us not fear to speak of it; let us appreciate fully the interacting dynamic by which military initiative on each side serves the other side; let us not have a polemical battle as to which side is most to blame for the interaction. That only serves the military purpose.

The United States and the Soviet Union have now lived together peacefully, if not always amicably, for almost seventy years. We can conclude that capitalism and socialism can coexist. But they cannot and will not coexist if they yield to the military power and to the interacting dynamic that now dominates this relationship. And in the nuclear collision, premeditated or unpremeditated, that it assures neither capitalism nor socialism will survive. No one, not even the most talented ideologue, will be able to tell the ashes of capitalism from the ashes of socialism.

MAINTAINING LIFE ON EARTH – THE POLITICAL CHALLENGE

Valentin Falin, U.S.S.R.

The Rationale of Peaceful Coexistence

T he question discussed here today, ladies and gentlemen, is a very difficult one: politically, philosphically, and under human aspects. Why is that so? Why are we not able, with all the experience accumulated until today, to arrive at constructive conclusions? What hinders us? Where is, as Germans, Russians, and other nations say, "the dog burried"? A child is born, being neither good nor bad. During his or her development the child becomes good-natured or evil-hearted. An American scholar and author has written a book entitled "Mankind-Computer". Everything an adult person performs is in one way or the other put into his head, his heart, his soul, by his family, by his society, by friends and enemies. This external influence during the process of growing-up is reflected in certain actions and procedures later on, which do not always make our lives more comfortable or improve our living conditions. Why is that so? Your society and our society have different answers for that question. Your society and our society have their own, egotistic explanation for this phenomenon. The explanations are egotistic because we too often do not look into the future, but concentrate on experiences of the past and trust that history alone will provide an answer to the question how to proceed. Unfortunately, I must state here that the past has only one implication to be considered: It should prevent us from *repeating* mistakes, as the experiences of the past give no other answers for the future, because little was existing in former times of what rules and dictates our lives today. We are increasingly confronted with new facts and new insights, for which no preexisting answers and solutions are at hand.

That is why we want to propose a new thesis here and now: There is an urgent necessity for a new way of thinking, a necessity to reconsider everything with new understanding, and to abandon what does not correspond to the experience of today or tomorrow. Let us put aside what belongs to the past, without emotions. What does belong to the past? First of all those ways of thinking which brought about all former wars and conflicts, all our former problems. The political category of power and violence belongs to the past, because it has produced not one ton of oil, not one ton of coal, has provided nothing of benefit to mankind and the living conditions on our planet. The scientists continue to dispute today: How old actually is mankind? The corresponding question is seldom heard: What are the dimensions of time for the human future? One reason why the latter question is not frequently raised today lies in the fact that many people unconsciously feel that the resources we consume actually belong to subsequent generations. Is it acceptable that during this century mankind consumes more resources than during the 2.5 million years before? Is it acceptable that for the preparation of wars during this century more raw material and energy is wasted compared to the former history of mankind as a whole? And if that is true, then subsequent generations are from the beginning poorer than we are, since the resources of the earth are exhaustible. To reconstitute them is impossible today as well as tomorrow.

That is why some political terms and categories are obsolete, for example the term "superpower". What is the meaning of "superpower"? It is the attempt of a mighty nation to dominate other nations, to prescribe to other nations what they ought to do and what they are not permitted to do. We, that is the Soviet Union, have de facto reached the stage of a superpower, but are ready to give up this status.

We document our readiness by our proposal to abolish nuclear weapons, because the possession of nuclear weapons defines the separation line between powerful and less powerful nations, between authoritarian and non-authoritarian nations in the political sense. I would like to underline: nuclear weapons are, in many ways, immoral. Immoral, because nuclear weapons split the world into nations of different rank. Nuclear weapons after the Second World War have first split Europe and later on the rest of the world. If we do not abolish nuclear weapons, I mean all of us (it makes no sense that only one nation should abolish nuclear weapons), then mankind is sooner or later going to perish. Such a development is inherent to the properties and existing amount of these weapons. At this point, if you permit, I will raise an important, perhaps delicate question. Why does the Soviet Union put so much emphasis on a nuclear test ban? In nine years from now, the Nuclear Non-Proliferation Treaty will expire. In nine years from now all nations which do not possess nuclear weapons today, will have to consider whether they will in the future be able to defend their interests without theses weapons, which are in the hands of other nations and have been compiled, modernized and further developed during the time of validity of this treaty. This is not just a theoretical question, it is a realistic, practical question which will be topical within nine years. Please keep in mind that today we have only five nuclear nations, and yet no solution for the abolishment of nuclear weapons is found. Among these five nations there is up to now no agreement to prohibit and remove these weapons until the end of the century. This will become far more difficult when we are dealing with ten, fifteen, or twenty nuclear nations. During such a negative development the risk of a war, intentional or unintentional, will steadily increase. That is why a new way of thinking is necessary, a new thinking which realizes that not only nuclear weapons provide a fatal threat to mankind. Other weapons are being developed, which bear basic implications for the health and for the existence of mankind. In fact there are projects under construction, which according to all available data, are even more dangerous than nuclear armament and nuclear weapons. It is the duty of the politician to think about such perspectives and developments. However, politicians do not always keep up with this task. The development of mankind itself and the development of the economic conditions relevant for that development, bring up a number of most important questions.

The question, for example, whether a war today is permissible or not, is not a theoretical question, but an important practical one for the politics of all nations and governments. This question is not new. Probably not all of you in this hall remember the Kellog-Briand-Treaty signed in 1928. At that time the experience from the First World War was summarized in this treaty in the way that war as a method of solving political, economic, and other problems between nations was declared unuseful, immoral, and worthless. That treaty was violated by the aggression of the Italian nation against Abessinia. But the important fact remains to my opinion that so many years ago, far-going attempts were made to abandon war as a means of political competition, the necessity of which was accepted by nations and governments, in contrast to the situation today. If sixty years ago it was already clear that new ways were to be found, then it should be in even sharper perspective today that in the coming years and decades politics of power and violence will create new problems instead of solving or reducing forthcoming challenges. This insight must not merely be proclaimed, but must rule the politics of any single nation, regardless of the system that nation is allied to.

If we discuss a new way of thinking I want to emphasize: The idea is that today and in the future problems of security cannot be solved by military strategies and military weapons. The problems of security today can only be solved politically. A political solution implies the understanding and acceptance of legitimate interests of all nations. As Michael Gorbachev pointed out, today security can only be guaranteed on the basis of actions taken together by a number of nations. There is no necessity and no possibility to unilaterally improve the security of the Soviet Union without altering the security of the United States. If the United States feel threatened, that is a serious situation for the Soviet Union, and vice versa. Our point of view is that today, tomorrow, and the day after tomorrow, and for all surveyable future, we will share the problem of security in common, and for the Soviet Union and the United States this security must rest on mutual agreement. There is no other solution to this problem. I may emphasize here that our side is ready to accept and practice such principles. We are ready to respect all problems and interests of relevance to the United States and to try to understand their point of view when they get into trouble without taking unilateral advantage from such a situation. There is a saying, an aphorism, which goes as follows: "When a man does not feel pain when he hurts an adversary, this man is not healthy." This is even more significant for a society. When a society, a nation, has no ears and eyes for the problems of its neighbours, something is wrong with that nation, with that society.

Unfortunately, experience of the last years shows that we are pretty far away from such an insight. I must even admit that the situation became worse, compared to what we had achieved some years ago. Why is that so? This question is not easily answered, if you want to be unbiased. Of course, it is easy to say that one side is guilty and the other side is innocent and most observers do not have the right understanding for the situation. And yet I must say that with all the polemics during the last years, important positive experiences have been lost, which we built up in a period which was in the East and in the West termed the period of "Detente". Do you know, how many days were needed in 1972 to formulate a Soviet-American declaration on principles of our interrelations? Probably you don't: two days! Not months, not years. Only two days, because both sides readily accepted that peaceful cooperation and coexistence was the only healthy and rational alternative. Do you know how long it took in the Federal Republic of Germany, in Bonn, with the former American ambassador Kenneth Rush to find a concept for Berlin? Three days! And why? Because at that time both sides were willing to solve this problem for the people involved as well as for our two nations.

This points to the fact that today it is felt difficult to do the first step, be it in the public or in our minds, as you wish; to acknowledge that the other side may also be right, that the other side is not an imperium of the devil, but has its own traditions, its own ideas and ideals, worthwhile to be considered. Perhaps up to now this is not a serious point to everyone. But a new way of thinking is made impossible if we hold on to the thesis formulated by Charles Weak two months ago. Charles Weak is the director of the American Information Office. I don't want to say nasty things about him, I just cite him. He said: "We Americans carry out a war of ideologies with the Soviet Union, and this our Information Department, our Information Board belongs to the arsenals of this war."

I must emphasize here that for the interrelations between nations there are only two possibilities: The rationale of peaceful cooperation, of peaceful neighborhood or the rationale of war, whatever paraphrase is used for that term. Call it war of ideologies or war in a wider sense, when a nation sticks to the rationale of war and confrontation, it will always increase its arsenal of weapons. Under the rationale of confrontation there is always a deficit of weapons, and only the rationale of peaceful coexistence, of a peaceful cooperation among nations can, hopefully in time, convince both sides that disarmament is not only possible, but useful for both sides. I want to close my contribution by quoting the American philosopher Emerson, as President Roosevelt did in his last address to the American Congress. This philosopher said: "When you need a friend, be a friend." We, the Soviet Union, are ready to be a friend to all nations. We are ready to cooperate with all nations in a constructive and positive way in order to solve the problems, so that the time ahead will always exceed the period mankind has already spent on this planet.

Maintaining Life on Earth – The Medical Challenge

MAINTAINING LIFE ON EARTH – THE MEDICAL CHALLENGE

Horst-Eberhard Richter, Federal Republic of Germany

Changing Minds: The Peace Process and the Part Physicians Can Play in It

I n 1963 the physician and Nobel Peace Prize-winner Albert Schweitzer wrote the following: "For years now the governments of those countries which possess nuclear weapons have been trying to negotiate an agreement on how those nuclear weapons could be abolished. Yet they are meeting with no success. All the proposals which they put forward are quite incapable of creating the grand mutual trust required for a mutual renunciation of nuclears arms ...".

"The abolition of nuclear weapons" – he continues – "will become a possibility only when public opinion in the nations on this earth both demands and guarantees it. The attitude of mind required to give rise to such public opinion can be created only by respect for life".

When Albert Schweitzer wrote these words he had already witnessed vain attempts to achieve even a ban on nuclear testing. He himself had called for such a ban as early as 1958.

Since his time, however, the governments of the superpowers have continued to negotiate more or less without interruption. What they have achieved is not a ban on nuclear testing nor progress in disarmament but progressively more and more dangerous nuclear weapons, weapons which bring with them the mounting danger of catastrophe on a vast scale. In some nations there has been indignation and anger about this development from time to time. But never has the kind of public opinion Schweitzer called been strong enough to compel the politicians to change course.

Nevertheless, once there was only one physician – Albert Schweitzer – raising his voice in warning, now there are 150,000 physicians. We physicians are today in the vanguard of the international peace movement. With the strength of our numbers, which are still on the increase, we have a chance to inform the broad public and to create unrest. And we are making a great effort to do just that. We encounter much agreement and approval, but we are confronted also with scepticism and rejection. Again and again, therefore, we have cause to examine critically the message, through which we are trying to influence the public. A congress like this gives us an important oppotunity to carry out such an examination.

Our main concern up to now has been to destroy the illusion that a nuclear war can be survived. In particular we have tried to make clear how helpless medicine is in a nuclear emergency. The report from the World Health Organization and the research papers on a "nuclear winter" were convincing evidence in support of our case. From questionnaires we know that the vast majority of people have now digested the information we have given them. People know what the threat is. 69 percent of West German citizens consider the construction of protective shelters to be senseless and 79 percent would not want to go on living in an environment destroyed by nuclear war even if, in the first instance, they were personally to survive that war. And equally the majority is no longer in doubt that the continuing nuclear arms race makes the onset of an atomic Armageddon – the extent of which they correctly assess – even more probable.

The major fire in the nuclear reactor at Chernobyl must surely have made clear to even the most short-sighted of people that even a local nuclear disaster necessarily affects countries far, far away. Chernobyl is more convincing than a thousand and one speeches and lectures. It demonstrates to people that the nuclear threat has long since united us right across the frontiers of power blocs, and that therefore even a so-called limited nuclear war would contaminate the air, the water, the soil and milk for friend and foe alike over wide areas. Can anyone now fail to realize that military nuclear technology and its automatic, computerized early warning systems involve at least as many risks of a break-down as do the civilian nuclear reactors, which were once praised to the skies as being absolutely safe and secure?

The danger is, however, that there will soon be a similar process of psychological suppression to that which followed Hiroshima and Nagasaki – that the majority will suppress this grim knowlegde, instead of making a lasting protest against the vast threat to which they are exposed. We must tackle with these forces of inhibition, if we are to achieve our goal.

The awarding of the Nobel Peace Prize to our organization was an instructive test case because it made as plain as plain can be one of the psychological barriers we are facing. Many people remain receptive for propaganda which says something like the following: The risk of an atomic war is grave – but graver still is the risk of abandoning without a struggle the values for which we stand on our side of the world. Moral priority, therefore – the propaganda continues – must be given to our readiness to fight, and if need be to sacrifice our lives, in order to protect the achievements of our own society. To contest this is to show cowardice, moral corruption and a lack of self-respect or even to commit moral treason.

It is basically a simple matter to point out the flaw in this pseudo-moral line of argument. The threatened nuclear genocide – or suicide – would destroy culture in its entirety in East and West with all its various values and achievements: thus none of the things which allegedly justify the risk of war would be left when war is over. Equally, all the immorality and vileness, of which the other side can be accused, is exceeded a thousand times over by the immorality and brutality of the weapons of destruction which would have to be employed in the alleged protection of morality and goodness.

Nevertheless, militaristic propaganda continues to evoke a fateful echo in people's hearts – not least because it exploits the seductive power of an enduring myth, which continues to be attractive for a significant part of male society. It is the dream that one can heal the many wounds, inflicted by the disappointments and humiliations of everyday life, by taking a fighting stand against evil in the world – a stand which can be as indirect as one likes but can, if need be, take the form of war. In the imagination, the scenario of such a war is idealized into a magnified replica of ancient battle legends, or of High Noon or Rambo. The act of assenting to the politics of nuclear threat is re-interpreted as proof of one's high-mindedness and heroism. The fictitious moral satisfaction this gives and the narcissistic visions of grandeur and victory connected with it are together quite capable of switching off people's sense of reality. Henceforth such people see the missiles of their own side as symbols of morality and potency, thus stabilizing their self-images, which have taken more than a few knocks in the frustratingly humdrum life of mass society.

Then we physicians come along and demand of these people that they give up their seductive illusions and face up to grim reality. Many of them, however, resist such a message, believing that it is only negative and that it robs them of a psychological crutch which they need to maintain their balance. We must ask ourselves therefore how we can strengthen this large group of people, helping them to bear the necessary disillusionment. We must link the hard and heavy truth to a message of encouragement capable of reinforcing people's powers of resistance.

History teaches us that whenever the masses are persuaded successfully to rise up against oppressive circumstances, then it is an affirmative Utopia which persuades them. Our opponents say: "What are you upset about? Your peace is the non-occurrence of a nuclear war, but this is something you've already got in our industrial nations, and you've got it precisely because of the nuclear deterrent! How can you ask for more?"

But our vision is not the continuation of peace which is no peace, as long as the continually increasing nuclear risks hang over our heads like a sword of Damocles. Our affirmative Utopia is different. It is the extension of the ethics of our healing professions to the way nations live and deal with one another. What we want to make clear to people is that it is only in the struggle for such a new way of thinking that human beings can really find the sense of meaningfulness and personal value to which the myth of military heroism lays false claim.

For us physicians – as we all know – each individual is to be considered primarily as a fellow human being, potentially in need of help. Only in the second place is he or she a compatriot or a foreigner, an American or a Russian, a member of this or that alliance, white or black, bourgeois or socialist. Why should it not be possible to make this humanitarian principle common practice among all people? Why should only physicians be bound by the principle that the need for help and the duty to give help cut right across the dividing lines and boundaries between parties, races, nations and ideologies?

In the post-Hiroshima age we are all – all of us together on this earth – people in need of help, because we all bear the stigmata of imminent death. This should give us the strength to see ourselves as one great community, a community in which, the whole world over, we are all dependent on each other. Our vision is thus a form of politics, whose policy it would be to carry out preventive medicine all over the globe.

It is not that we physicians want to become politicians: but we insist that the world of politics becomes aware of its medical responsibility. Because with its political means it must undertake that prevention which alone can preserve the generations now on earth and the generations still to come from total and utter extinction. Our vision, therefore, is that we come together as nations in a kind of worldwide self-help community, using the occasion of our common threat of death to mobilize our forces of resistance in mutual support for as long as we still have time to do so. To this task we should devote precisely those virtues which the militarists try to misuse for their own purposes: the virtues of commitment, of courage, of steadfastness and of self-sacrifice.

It is certainly no coincidence that this affirmative Utopia, which should become a central plank in our message, has again and again been summoned up by important physicians – as for example by Albert Schweitzer in 1958 in the following very straightforward words:

"The consciousness that we are all human beings together is a consciousness we have lost through wars and politics. We have come to treat one another only as members of allied or hostile nations and have become imprisoned in the resulting attitudes and prejudices, sympathies and antipathies. Our task now is to rediscover the fact that we are all human beings together and that we must grant each other that moral capacity which is part and parcel of human nature. In this way we can summon up the belief that members of other nations too may feel the need for a new spirit, a new approach. And so we might begin again to be trustworthy partners for each other."

In this context it seems worthwile to recall two great but half-forgotten physicians of the Latin Middle Ages – the Muslim Averroës and the Jew Maimonides. At a time when religious conflict, pogroms and the wars of the crusaders were tearing society apart, they both proclaimed the reconciling belief of one common truth and one common ethic for all human beings.

Averroës and Maimonides were both born – the one shortly after the other, in 1126 and 1135 – in the town of Cordoba, which was at that time the cultural metropolis of Moorish Spain. Averroës later became the personal physician of the caliph Abu Ja'kub Jusuf in Marocco, and Maimonides the personal physician to the court of the sultan Saladin, who during his reign recaptured Jerusalem from the Christians. The lives of both physicians were marked by the crusades, by the struggles of Christians and Muslims for the control of Palestine and Spain, by memories of the first horrifying anti-Jewish pogroms in Central Europe during the Peasants' Crusades and by the persecution of Jews carried out by the Islamic Almohads in Spain.

Averroës completed a medical encyclopaedia, and Maimonides wrote treatises on various illnesses, one of them being the first large-scale study on asthma. In addition, both of them sought – quite independently of the other – for a common philosophical truth capable of bridging the hostile gulf between the three monotheistic religions. Each of them looked to the philosophy of Aristotle for support, creating a kind of personal variation on a philosophical universal religion. Each of them supported the idea of a holistic world and of one reason and one ethic common to all men. Averroës taught that the intellects of all human beings are numerically one single intellect. And Maimonides declared that the goal of all creation was the man of insight, the sage. Of the sage he wrote: "May he love peace, may he be zealous for peace". "May he be among the persecuted and not among the persecutors: may he be among the humiliated and not among the humiliators".

Both men had difficulty in making their philosophies and ethics, bridging as they did, the theological conflicts and strife of the time, plausible to their own contemporaries. And this despite the fact that Averroës fully saw himself as a valid interpreter of the Koran and that Maimonides equally had deeply-held Jewish beliefs. Despite this they were persecuted and humiliated. Averroës became a considerable nuisance to the orthodox Islamic theologians, because his philosophy of reconciliation did not exactly assist the morale – today they would say the "willingness to defend cultural values" – of those fighting against the Christian Reconquista. His caliph therefore dismissed him. A tribunal declared him to be heretic – and he was burned to death. Maimonides, it is true, emigrated to Egypt and remained in high esteem with a sector of the Jewish community there. But embittered opponents outlawed him as a renegade, inscribed the word "heretic" on his grave and burned his books.

Their persecution, however, did not prevent these two great philospher-doctors from exerting an ongoing influence through their ideas and writings. Jewish translations rescued a few texts of Averroës from the Islamic inquisition. And his work, which came to be called Averroism, was for generations a subject of study at Christian universities. Maimonides has always been – and still is – respected and discussed as one of the most important Jewish philosophers of all time.

It would be unbecoming and presumptuous to lay claim to the one Islamic and the other Jewish doctor-philosopher as precursors of our physicians' movement today. Nevertheless the two men did make an exemplary attempt to oppose the confessional conflict and the "bloc thinking" of their age with a philosophy and ethic of unanimity.

We of today can perhaps feel an affinity with the two of them in that we also want to further the development of a new consciousness which binds people together worldwide. We hope that this consciousness will be able to keep a potentially violent opposition between nations and groups of nations within the bounds of peaceful argument and debate. Our special problem today, admittedly, is that the greatest danger lies not in the area of hostility between the polarized nuclear powers but in the fateful area of unity between them.

Irreconcilable, though Eastern communism and Western capitalism may today be in their public powers, their rivalry is certainly not an adequate reason for the leaders in either camp to consciously and continually increase the risk of a nuclear war and, with it, of mutual destruction. If they, nevertheless, continue the nuclear arms race in spite of all the risks it involves then they are thereby paying their homage to a process of scientific, technological and industrial advance over which they no longer exercise adequate control. The hostile images of each other which the two sides sustain in their propaganda support the arms race and the acceptance of it among the public, but they are not the decisive driving force behind it. The actual driving force on both sides is a vast will for power delegated to technological progress – an underlying attitude of the leading industrial nations deriving not from a respect for life, but from a wish to take absolute control of it. The resulting, breathtaking techno- logical development produces with an uncanny automatism phantastic achievements, the responsible use and control of which is evidently beyond all of us – and beyond the experts, too. The so-called "modernization" of the horrible weapons of mass destruction, the risk- ridden games played with nuclear technology in general, and the revolutionary possibilities now emerging in the field of genetics are coming up against a human consciousness which is no longer able to cope with these challenges it has itself created. The poison disaster at Bhopal, the nuclear plant accidents on Three Mile Island and now the devastating catas- trophe at Chernobyl are only isolated early symptoms marking the destructive path, whose infernal end can now be foreseen.

In demanding as a first step a strict ban on further nuclear tests and a subsequent run- down of nuclear weapons, we physicians are aware that effective disarmament can take place only in conjunction with psychological disarmament, with a re-directing of human thinking. This new thinking would have to take effect in many other areas also, where life is threatened or harmed by the interests of power – however they may be disguised – instead of being protected and cherished. We physicians, therefore, wish to act, hundreds of thousands of times over, as disseminators of that attitude which Schweitzer described as "respect for life".

If the concept of "respect" has come to seem odd and anachronistic to many people, then this shows only how far the impoverishment of our emotional relationships with our social and natural environments has now gone. It has almost sunk below the level of common awareness that it was originally our feelings which told us how closely we are linked with all living creatures around us and how jointly responsible we are for them. It is as if it needed the radio- active clouds from Chernobyl to remind us that we are compelled – as creatures both actively and passively involved – to protect and to be mutually responsible for all life on our planet.

Finally, however, we find ourselves being asked the question: "Is it business of physicians to act as moral educators of their nations? Is it their task to go beyond informing on the medical aspects of the nuclear threat and to preach in addition something akin to a political ethic?"

In answering this question we German physicians are helped by recalling how our profession reacted during the Hitler régime. We still have before our mind's eye the spectacle of a part of the medical profession horribly entangled in the world of politics. Physicians from various fields were involved in the development and inhuman application of the racial theory and racial policies of National Socialism. There are many among us who see this as a warning of the tangled webs physicians can weave when they become involved in doctrines of social salvation instead of restricting themselves in self-abnegation to their own narrow professional fields.

If one looks at this issue more closely, however, one comes to the opposite conclusion. For it was not through carrying their medical ethic over into politics that the Nazi-physicians became morally corrupt. On the contrary, it was through abandoning their Hippocratic ethic and delivering their medicine instead to the philosophy of domination inherent in Hitler's power politics. Thus they ended up by seeing mankind as involved in a life-or-death struggle, a struggle between life which had alleged racial value and life which had allegedly no value. And they had no scruples in placing their science in service of a macabre strategy of elimination – with the horrific consequences known to all of us. The end result were the gas chambres in psychiatric clinics, gas chambres which were then re-employed in Auschwitz. The danger is not yet past that it is easier for the philosophy of domination inherent in power politics to make medicine inhumane than it is for medicine to make politics more humane through the spread of a medical ethic. We physicians have no better way of combatting this danger than by a militant policy of informing the peoples with the aim – if I may simplify matters a little – of a "medicinalization" of politics.

Yet are we not merely succumbing to naive megalomania, if we set out, at this late hour, to turn back the advanced process of social militarization and all the manifold constraints which come with it by means of just a moral campaign?

It is important here, first and foremost, that we unwaveringly hold fast to the conviction that only a radical change in our way of thinking – and nothing else – can help us now. Agreements between the superpowers, however useful they may be – and they are still a long way off – will not save us unless they are ratified by a robust public opinion among the nations on this earth. The moral sensibility required for such a change to peaceful ways of thinking is present in sufficient quantities. But we must tap and release those quantities of it which are still channelled by apt propaganda into the false ideals of heroism and into the uncritical worship of progress. The events in the Phillipines a short while back have shown us how a campaign which is conducted almost exclusively on a moral basis can mobilize on a grand scale the forces which are there called "People's Power". In the people of the industrialized nations also there is still enough "People's Power" potential which could be won round to the idea of a genuine peace ethic. Among the young people of many countries one can already find traces of an alternative intellectual and spiritual movement, which is calling for something like a new respect for life in Albert Schweitzer's sense of that phrase and is trying to put it into practice in different forms of living.

But together with like-minded social groupings we as physicians can achieve greater things only if we ourselves practice what we are preaching as the yard-stick of political morality in the nuclear age. We must not fight shy of the conflicts which arise above all from our rejection of the immorality of nuclear deterrence. On this issue we are all of us heretics, and will remain so for as long as nuclear deterrence is the official criterion of orthodoxy. It is only this readiness to be declared heretical that ensures us the social appeal which we need. In an age in which "peace", "morality", "human rights" and "freedom" are misused daily as party-political shibboleths, it is up to us and to the other forces within the peace movement to protect our goal of a non-partisan ethic against any misappropriation or one-sided mis-interpretation. In differing social contexts this is sometimes more difficult, sometimes easier. We must give each other mutual support here to maintain our steadfast position. There is, at any event, no other argument which has anything like as much importance for our purposes as the proof of our unconditional credibility. People are so sick to the teeth of vetted, half-true, partisan or in some way or other manipulated information that everywhere there is an enormous demand for truth, authenticity and moral integrity. Our great opportunity is to fulfil this demand as best we can. And if we do so, then, as 150,000 – and soon, let us hope, many, many more – catalysors, we shall justifiably have the prospect of developing that counter-force which can alone prevent a nuclear war between our nations: the counter-force of trust and trustworthiness based on mutual respect for life.

MAINTAINING LIFE ON EARTH – THE MEDICAL CHALLENGE

Graham Brown, Australia

On the Improvement of Health Care in the Less-Developed Countries

Mr. Chairman, Ladies and Gentlemen, it is a great honour to have been invited to address this international gathering of physicians for the prevention of nuclear war on the subject of international health. Last year Dr. Victor Sidel reminded us all of the enormous problems facing us as we strive for improvements in health throughout the developing world.

Dr. Sidel introduced the concept of the metronome beating in front of our eyes. Many will remember this. With each return of the metronome a child dies somewhere in the world, i. e. a child less than five years old dies every two seconds, or 1700 every hour, or 15 million every year. These figures are absolutely shocking and we must immediately consider the underlying causes of this constant epidemic. Now the causes of death are not exotic diseases of the tropics, but mainly diseases such as pneumonia, diarrhea, measles and other infectious diseases which are now quite uncommon as killers in the overdeveloped countries. In fact all these diseases may be described as diseases of poverty and all are excessivated by that sinister alliance of infection and malnutrition. Malnutrition leads to infection and infection inevitably leads to malnutrition. Fortunately we know the prescription with which to prevent or cure at least fifty per cent of these deaths, but unfortunately we have been less successful in the application of this technology. I am sure the later speakers will tell us of the progress towards preventing these diseases by immunization, provision of plain water and provision of cheap, effective oral re-hydration solutions for treatment of diarrheal disease. We have started our journey but still there is a long, long way to go.

Apart from these diseases there are large numbers of tropical ailments, for which we have no solution. I refer to malaria, filariasis, helminth infections, schistosomiasis, trypanosomiasis and leprosy, for which effective vaccines are not available. I would like to turn to malaria as an example of an uncontrolled disease that is being tackled internationally in collaborative efforts to develop a vaccine. Malaria ist still an enormous problem throughout the world. More than 2000 million people live in areas where anti-malarial measures are being applied to control the mosquitos that transmit the disease and a further 400 million people live in malarious areas where no specific anti-malarial measures have been carried out at all. In other words, some fifty-six per cent of the world's population are at risk from this malaise and a million children die from the disease each year in Africa alone. Apart from this horrific mortality epidemic malaria takes an enormous toll on health and welfare of whole populations. John Grazer, the former Director of Health in Papua, New Guinea, discussed the high mortality of the disease and also highlighted the crippling effect a non-lethal disease may have on morbidity. He coined the term "the eighty per cent man of the tropics', i. e. the person who is forced to live his whole life with only eighty per cent of the so-called normal haemoglobin. Wrapped with fever, chills and headaches, he has only eighty per cent of the potential work capacity and eighty per cent of the dietary intake that the western world considers to be normal. For this reason we in the overdeveloped world with its capacity for self-destruction, with its potential to change lives, have an obligation to redress this imbalance of the "eighty per cent men of the tropics". As physicians we are in the unique position of being able to do something about this global health problem. Main methods that are now available for malaria control are to reduce mosquito breeding sites, to kill resting mosquitoes with drugs, and to use drugs for individual protection against infection. The obstacles to control have been the enormous cost of the chemicals involved, the problems of mosquitos becoming resistent to insecticides, and parasites becoming resistent to all available chemotherapy.

Given that malaria is not declining and if anything it's on the increase, the need for new ways is more pressing than ever. The great hope is that a vaccine will be developed to help our struggle against this parasite. We know that, if children survive childhood, adults in epidemic areas eventually develop an immunity to protect them against the lethal consequences. So the aim of the vaccine will be to accelerate the process of the development of immunity. The malaria parasite is vulnerable to attack in three points of its life-cycle. The first, the form injected by the feeding mosquito, the second, the form that multiplies in the blood to cause fever potentially lethal with complications and finally the sexual forms that lead to transmission of the parasite in the mosquito. The aim of such a vaccine would be to prevent infection or at least to prevent the consequences of infection in the blood. To aim against the sexual transmission of the parasite is somewhat altruistic. With this type of vaccine we don't aim to protect the individual who has been vaccinated, but aim to stop transmission to others – an unusual vaccine, we ask others to help others rather than themselves.

Progress has been made with the vaccine against the sporozoite stages. This is the mosquito stage that is injected into humans and in fact vaccination trials are currently being conducted in the United States. It is likely that a vaccine will include products against all these stages.

Major breakthroughs in malaria research have occured in the last ten years. In 1976 a description of a method for cultivating the parasites in vitro, and the next major contribution has come from the application of genetic engineering techniques to the study of infectuous disease. Just today I was shown the newspaper indicating "Building a new vaccine – breaking ground with genetic engineering". And I feel if it's in the lay press and if these revolutionary techniques are so widely available, it is essential for us as physicians to understand this technology and in particular to be innovative in its applications to the benefit of the whole of mankind.

To clone genes, we make use of the bacterium E-Coli and in particular a DNA passenger within the bacterium. These passengers that are known as plasmids are better known through their ability to make proteins that lead to bacterial resistance to antibiotics. Every time the bacterium divides, the plasmid divides, an information flows from the nuclear acid message to direct protein synthesis. The first step to cloning malaria genes is to harvest the

DNA or RNA molecules from the parasite and cut them to size. Second step is to harvest the plasmid and cut the circular rings of DNA with enzymes. Next, the two sources of DNA, from the malaria parasite and from the plasmid are brought together or recombined (this is where the word recombinant DNA comes from) and then they are reinserted into bacteria. Every time the bacterium divides, so does the plasmid and each time it directs synthesis of the foreign malaria gene that has been introduced. This new technology can be rather frightening to those not familiar with it. But we must not be afraid of genetic engineering techniques, but attempt to understand them and learn to apply them in appropriate ways to solve these global health problems. For the first time large amounts of individual malaria proteins can be obtained for analysis and already they are being used in vaccination experiments. I have already mentioned the sporozoite antigen that is currently the focus of human studies in the United States, and another antigen that we have worked with is found on the surface of infected red cells. And right now international collaboration is continuing to decide whether this antigen could be important for protection of individuals in West Africa, South America and Papua New Guinea. In addition within international collaboration the antigen is being assessed a the Centre for Disease Control in Atlanta, Georgia, in a vaccination trial for protection of monkeys against human malaria.

We have come in the past five years to the point where human sporozoite vaccine trials have already commenced and trials against blood stage parasites may not be far away. I have referred already to the difficulty of delivering these vaccines. And fortunately genetic engineering strategies once again have come to our aid for the production of stable, reliable products. Once we know the genetic information in DNA and RNA of these cloned genes, we can predict the structure and therefore produce this product by direct chemical synthesis, the so-called synthetic peptides. In several laboratories another approach is being used, in which cloned genes have been put into viruses, so that an infection of cells with the virus also leads to introduction of the cloned vaccine antigen. In many cases vaccinia virus, or the smallpox vaccine virus, has been used as a vehicle for introducing these foreign proteins into cells. We are very fortunate that smallpox is dead, but possibly the vaccinia virus may live on as a useful way of delivering vaccines to millions of individuals.

Use of either of these strategies that I have described would enable us to produce cheap, effective and stable vaccines to worldwide delivery. It would be inappropriate to be over-optimistic about the potential for vaccines, but progress has been achieved and we hope that we may soon have another weapon in our fight. Humanitarian arguments for disease control would no doubt sway the majority of members of this audience but unfortunately that is not enough. We must convince politicians and health planners that there is no alternative viable strategy than an attempt to eliminate or at least to control these infectuous diseases. But fortunately we can find persuasive arguments in economic terms to support the humanitarian case that motivates all of us here. The eradication of smallpox is a case in point. All round the world countries are benefitting from eradication of smallpox. The United States alone save 120 million dollars per year in quarantine and surveillance costs compared with their contribution of some 28 million dollars to the programme for smallpox eradication. I imagine similar cost/benefit ratios could to be found throughout the world. I have said already that eradication of malaria is unlikely for a very long time. The diseases like measles and polio can certainly be controlled and possibly eradicated with long lasting economic benefit for years to come. We know the benefit to cost ratio would be extremely favourable.

Now to return to the theme of this congress: The cost of arms spending for one hour is equal to the total cost of smallpox eradication. Who knows what we could do with one day of arms spending in the fight against malaria. We know that one hour of arms spending costs 100 million dollars, the same amount of money as an immunization programme for some 20 million children in the developing world. We must present the options, weigh up the cost and present our arguments with persuasion.

In this presentation I have tried to highlight some of the major problems facing us in international health and to indicate some of the strategies now available that could be implemented to reduce childhood mortality by fifty per cent. I have also outlined the problems associated with control of malaria, an important disease for which we have inadequate control strategies today. Using malaria as an example, I have tried to demonstrate the enormous potential that genetic engineering techniques have provided for developing new weapons to control these major diseases. The same is true for leprosy, sleeping sickness, schistosomiasis, pneumococcal disease, filariasis or very many others. The progress towards this objective has been a remarkable example of international collaboration between medical scientists both as individuals and through agencies such as the World Health Organisation and its Tropical Disease Research Programme. It is only in a peaceful world with harmonious international collaboration that we have any chance of both implementing the strategies we know should be successful and devising new approaches to deal with global problems in international health. Maintaining life on earth demands that we work hard against the madness and waste of nuclear war, but that is not enough. We must also share a very positive commitment to attack with equal vigour the problems that retard the health, welfare and development of more than half the population of the world.

MAINTAINING LIFE ON EARTH – THE MEDICAL CHALLENGE

William Foege, U.S.A.

Child Immunization Programmes in the Developing World as a Contribution to Peace

W e have heard a number of medical challenges today, and certainly one of the medical challenges that we face as a group is how to quickly, efficiently and effectively close the gaps that exist between the rich people and the poor people in terms of premature mortality, unnecessary suffering and life quality. At present the gap is large, it's an embarrassment, but even more than that it is an indictment of how we in the medical community have used our talents, our influence and our resources. It is a form of violence that takes place, that takes its toll of the poor. The accident of birth can place a child at a risk of dying during the first year of life that is 20 times the standard in other countries. The place of birth can provide a child with a 15 year, a 20 year handicap in terms of life-expectancy at birth. 20 years after wide-spread use of measles vaccine in the developed countries, this week, according to the World Health Organization, 40,000 children will sacrifice their lives to the measles virus in a pagan rite that exists only because we allow it to.

According to WHO estimates, 6,000 children will be condemned to a lifetime of crippling because of our slowness in closing the application gap. Disease by disease, problem by problem, the challenge to the medical community is clear, and it frequently seems overwhelming. We heard earlier this afternoon of the need for hope, the perspective that is often missing as we talk about international health problems concerns how much has already happened, it is not hopeless. And we should take hope from the past successes. For example, if we look at what has happened simply since 1960. We are surprised that there has been a quiet, steady progress from the summation of one small effort after another. Let me give you a few figures. It would be nice if I had them in front of you but let me explain. For infant mortality, in 1960 there were 59 countries of the world with an infant mortality of more than 150 per thousand births. That figure has decreased from 59 countries to only 11 countries at the present time. The median infant mortality in the last quarter of the century has decreased from 139 to 66. If we look at life-expectancy, in 1960 35 countries of the world had a life-expectancy less than 40. That figure has decreased from 34 countries to only 2 countries today. The median life-expectancy has increased from 48 to 62. And even in the area of crude birth rates, in 1960 69 countries had crude birth rates of over 45 per thousand population. Today that figure has dropped from 69 to 39. And looking at the most recent UNICEF report we can clearly show that the countries with the lowest mortality rates for children now have the lowest net population increases.

So these gains are heartening. They lead us to the conclusion that it is possible for us to make a difference. In addition, a new interest has developed in child survival just in the past three years, primarily with immunization programmes, but also with diarrheal disease control programmes and nutrition programmes. We see the United Nation agencies, particularly UNICEF and WHO, increasing their efforts in child survival. Countries are increasing their contributions, and I should especially note that Italy has given 100 million dollars for immunization programmes in Africa. But not just countries, service organisations, the Rotary International pledged 120 million dollars over the next 20 years for polio control. They have now changed that they will provide 120 million dollars not in twenty years but in the next five years. Governments are increasing what they have done. Columbia, India, Bourkina Fasso, Nigeria, Senegal, Turkey, El Salvador and many others have in the last year increased their immunization programmes. Social mobilization for health is coming of age.

The Columbia example has been often cited, but it is worth citing. President Betoncourt of Columbia actually has immunized children on live television in order to open the clinics for immunization days. The church has become involved giving sermons on the duties of parents the week before immunization days. Priests in Columbia now ask whether children are immunized at the time they are brought for baptism. In Columbia the Red Cross, the military, the police, TV and radio, voluntary groups, all combine their efforts in order to increase the coverage of immunization for their children. It is an important moment and it is an important movement because it brings our social resources to bear on a vulnerable segment of society.

As we heard earlier, every day 40,000 children die, half of them from vaccine-preventable diseases and diarrheal diseases. Immunization programmes are a logical place to start because vaccine-preventable diseases account for a fourth of that toll. But in addition, immunization programmes are an area where we have a great deal of experience and experteis. They are an excellent springboard for other primary health activities. How is the immunization effort doing? One decade ago, except for smallpox and B.C.G., there was not another vaccine where we had even five per cent coverage in the developing world. At the present time 39 per cent of children in the developing world have received a third dose of DTP. Over twenty per cent have now received measles vaccine. These are figures that have doubled in essentially three or four years. And 60 per cent of children have received a first dose of something, meaning they have access to an immunization programme. Deaths from the vaccine-preventable diseases have decreased from 5 million a year to 3½ million a year. And the Panamerican Health Organisation has now set an objective of no more polio in the Americas by 1990. This is only the beginning. We can eradicate several other diseases in addition to smallpox in this century, and I believe that polio will be one of these.

Two of the major challenges that we face in immunization are: number one, how to quickly improve our effectiveness in delivering what we already have, particularly measles, polio and tetanus. But, number two, how to get the immunization infrastructure in place in order to capitalize on the new vaccines which are soon to be available, not just malaria, but leprosy vaccine, inexpensive hepatitis B vaccine, hepatitis A vaccine, Rota virus vaccine, herpes vaccine. Immunization programmes are not just band-aid programmes. They are an important step in the provision of full primary health services.

Last year I mentioned that all children of the world could be fully immunized each year for less than twelve hours of the arms race. That means that all children born in the world today could receive full immunization in their life time, if the world would today divert only two minutes of the arms race for children. And if two minutes diverted today could make that kind of an impact, think what would happen if the leaders of the world would divert two hours of the arms race each day. The people in this room can make immunization programmes acceptable, worthy of support, and indeed mandatory. IPPNW has demonstrated it can influence both governments and the public. Your efforts can accelerate what is becoming a significant global movement which makes child survival a norm, a sign of a caring society and a mark of progress. Will Durants once said that the countries of the world will successfully unite only if they fear an alien force. As we hear in this meeting, nuclear weapons are beginning to be seen as such an alien force. But in addition, unnecessary illness and premature death are also alien forces when they don't have to happen. Our duty as physicians to provide health extends beyond those who come to us for help, it extends to every individual everywhere. IPPNW is based on that belief. And to follow on an earlier talk, we should show hate to the injustice of the situation, we should show love for the children who require our help, we should know that there is hope, based on the past, and we should act because a world working together to provide a healthy and happy childhood for the infants of this globe is also a world that will find other ways of doing constructive things together. Immunization may be a small step but it is a positive step in making this a world of peace.

MAINTAINING LIFE ON EARTH – THE MEDICAL CHALLENGE

Bim Mahajan, India

Integrated Development Aid as a Factor in the Politics of Health

I t is my privilege to present the non-physician's point of view as to the medical challenge in the developing countries as some of us see it. The tension and suspicion between the great powers, to which references have been made in practically all speeches here and which have resulted in nuclear proliferation have for decades cast a long and dismal shadow on prospects for providing a decent living for millions of people in the so-called third world. This is not to absolve the countries in the third world of their own defaults but most of these countries, because of the international tensions and suspicions, to which I have just referred, have been forced in the past to choose between one power block or the other and arm themselves to fight adversaries nextdoor belonging to and abetted by the other block. They have received more credits and grants for arms than for development. And in the process great powers and their allies have been abetting tyranny, corruption and mismanagement in the developing countries exacerbating rather than relieving the plight of their destitute populations.

It's painful to recall figures for defence expenditures as per cent ot the gross national product in some countries to bring home this point. The figures I have are for 1984. In U.S.A. and U.S.S.R. the defence expenditures, according to the information I have, worked out to roughly 7 and 14 per cent of their respective GNPs, in West Germany the figure was 3.3 per cent, in Japan fortuitously because of its special relationship with the United States, only 1 per cent, but in contrast among the developing countries and others who do not belong to the above group, Israel for instance, spent 29 per cent of its GNP on defence. Of the other Middle East countries, Saudia Arabia is spending 24 per cent, Libya 17.5 per cent, Jordan 5.15 per cent, Syria 13 per cent, Egypt a little over 8 per cent, Ethiopia, which has been passing through one famine after another, has been spending 11 per cent, Nicaragua 10 per cent, China 8 per cent, Pakistan 5.4 per cent, India 3.5 per cent. Africa as a whole spends 16 billion dollars per year in the military sector, receiving the bulk of the arms imports from the U.S.S.R., U.S.A., France, U.K., West Germany and Italy.

It's painful to note that as against this buoyancy in arms shipment there has been little enthusiasm for development support as distinct from famine relief. A special session of the General Assembly of the United Nations is currently discussing prospects for mobilizing resources for integrated development programmes to ward off threats of famine in the

African countries. The African countries after having listened to and acted on the advice of international organisations and bilateral aid agencies for making international policy adjustments in recent years, not completely but quite substantially made a sacrifice in terms of savings and cutting down their very low consumptions. They are now expected to draw a blank from this session of the General Assembly. It must be underlined in this context that, while unprecedented volumes of resources were committed for relief of famine in Ethiopia and other affected countries in Africa in the last two or three years, these sums did not reflect any significant addition to the resources which had already been committed for other purposes to the same countries. Neither rescources are nearly reallocated for different purposes, in several cases reflecting transfer from developing projects to relief oppressions.

It has been observed by experts that more children die because they are improperly weaned than because of famine. Also more children die because their parents do not know how to manage diarrhea than because of epidemics. And more children die because their parents do not have access to wells, hoes or purchasing-power than because of wars. Warding off death will not ensure, that those who survive can grow to live a life based on self-respect; the fact that between death and nobility there exists a broad twilight zone of morbidity, functional impairment of various kinds, apathy, lack of sense of well-being, poor physical stamina, low productivity etc., can not be ignored. Many of these children, who may escape death eventually, grow into stunted adults of low body size and productivity. And low body sized women with relatively small bicristal diametres beget babies of low body rate which in turn gallop along a low growth trajectory unless taken in hand for special nutrition care in infancy. It is indeed a tragedy that childhood undernutrition contributes still heavily to high child mortality. But an even greater tragedy from the national point of view is that it might generate a pool of substandard survivals who serve to perpetuate the undernutrition scenario to successor generations.

The current situation, as described by my two colleagues, brings to mind an age-old dilemma. Is a glass half full or half empty? An optimist would answer, and with enough justification, that the child mortality rate has been halfed in the last three decades, in fact the figures that Dr. Foege would give are even more encouraging. A pessimist would point to the current famines in Africa and elsewhere. Many of us would be buoyed by the statistical improvement in child health which were just mentioned, but sobered by the fact that thanks to explosive population growth as result, as many children suffer and die today as they did twenty years ago. Per capita food consumption has actually gone down in many countries in Africa during the last twenty years. The progress in child survival has at best offset the grosser problems in these countries.

The third world needs a strategy of what is commonly referred to as integrated development, if the real challenge of development has to be met. This would direct emphasis not on just measures that prevent death but also on food production, supply of clean water, education and, ultimately, health. It is a strategy that can incorporate measures to counter the drought through revegetation of desiccated lands. It is a strategy of investing in people side by side with developing agriculture, industrial transportation, commerce and all that a modern society needs to make life worthwhile for the people. The most effective strategy for countering diarrhea, malnutrition and infections includes nutritional education, breast-feeding, rehydration and immunization. These have been referred to, so I will not dwell on these in detail, and also a lot of successful programmes have already been initiated and are being carried on by several agencies, particularly by UNICEF.

The one point which I did not hear but feel very important to mention here is the strong relationship which has been observed between reducing infant mortality and female education. Countries that have attained both low fertility and low mortality rates also have high female literacy rates. And that is another very important part of the integrated development process that I referred to.

Next comes the provision of clean drinking water and sanitary human waste disposal. Sanitary water supply would eliminate half the diarrhea including 90 per cent of all cholera, 80 per cent of sleeping sickness and 100 per cent of guinea worm infestations as well as a small fraction of several other serious tropical diseases. I hope my colleagues on two sides will be able to bear me out on that. It is shameful to recall that four fifth of the world population, 73 African and Asian countries, do not still have access to clean drinking water. Most have no toilet or latrines. World-wide 1.3 billion people, or about one fourth of the total population of the world, lack clean water and 1.7 billion lack adequate sanitations.

Again, although healthy and better educated people can make better use of available food, and reducing water-born bacteria alone, will not solve malnutrition problems. The food production in Southern parts of Africa for example grows only at historic rates of 1.4 per cent per year, while population grows 3.5 per cent annually. More trouble lies ahead. The current trend in this part of the world has been described as a doomsday threat. East and West Africa face a similar scenario as does much of Southern Africa including countries like Afghanistan and Bangla Desh. Integrated development on a scale sufficient to arrest declining living conditions will be relatively expensive and will be much beyond the current resources available to the development countries in Africa. At the same time, if you take into account the amounts that are being spent globally on armament, and also by the poor countries themselves, the problems should not be beyond the resources currently available to the world as a whole. The African famines have alerted the world to at least some of the people who live on the edge between subsistence and dissolution. But disaster threatens millions more in Bangla Desh and other parts of South Asia including India, Pakistan, Turkey and other parts of the third world. In all, almost 1.4 billion people live in countries where children die more often than adults, where 145 million children are malnourished and where more than two thirds of the people are illiterate. Any discussion on maintaining life on earth must ask in their case: maintaining life for what? They do not just need food shipments, but they must be able to grow their own food, develop their own housing and utilities and be allowed to replace butter for guns as was mentioned this morning. The World's poorest people can themselves hardly increase their savings to provide funds for development, but reducing consumption any further would be virtually impossible while corruption and waste can be corrected through outside pressure which can be linked to aid given by other countries.

The plea that I personally would like to make in this discussion is: Surely immunization and other health measures are extremely important and have been very successful and should be carried further. But the challenge of development will not be met just by taking these medical means unless the emphasis on food production and industrial development of these countries is equally increased at the same time and even more enthusiastically.

MAINTAINING LIFE ON EARTH – THE MEDICAL CHALLENGE

Tarzie Vittachi, Sri Lanka

Interdependence, the Human Conscience and Survival

L adies and Gentlemen, I speak as a non-physician, and as a non-physician in this kind of assembly I feel my lay-status more acutely than ever before, but I take comfort in the fact that 98 per cent of the people in this world are lay people. And these lay people in the world are very, very happy indeed that 150,000 physicians have at last decided to destroy a very ancient myth, a myth that has gone on for at least 100 years, possibly 200 years, that medicine is value-free. This is the myth that you have destroyed. You have destroyed the myth, you have really destroyed that myth and gone back to the origins of your profession, which really acknowledged quite candidly, quite openly, without any shame-facedness that your concern is a human concern and it is a moral concern.

We lay people understand that you physicians, the members of the IPPNW, have diagnosed the disease, that threatens to destroy this world, have diagnosed the disease against the whole of humanity and you have pronounced the diagnosis, that we are in danger of extinction but also your prognosis is (this is what I hear all the time from what has been said on this platform today) that really there is no cure for it yet. We have no answers yet. There are some ways in which we can struggle, but we have no remedy yet. We know that the disease has to be eradicated, eradicated in a society of values. As we let in our personal values it seems we have to get that far and that close to be able to deal with this disease. We are dealing with a powerful psychosis, for which there are no vaccines. This psychosis blatantly defies reason, I mean elementary reason. I often tell my children, when they ask about these questions, and that is the best litmus test I know about our own consciousness, the way we talk to our children about this, that these weapons that have been produced, most of them, or the most expensive of them, are most of the treasure of the earth, 900 billion dollars of it a year, goes on weapons which are by definition useless, because if anyone found a use for it we won't be here discussing it. I think that this is the kind of psychosis that we are dealing with. I also tell my children that while we spend this 900 billion on useless armament, that nearly 900 million people are destitute, I also tell my children, who come from the so-called third world, that we know nothing about destitution in our family, that I have seen destitution, I myself, who come from a poor family, which never knew destitution, but we knew poverty. We cannot imagine destitution, but there it is, the unreason of the whole procedure of trying to go to war, to solve our human disputes. So we live with a psychosis that can tolerate the stupendous fact that while 25 countries of Africa starved in 1984 we had an excess, and we call it a surplus of food, in many other parts of the world. Our minds can tolerate this incredible contradiction that there is a surplus when people are starving. This is the psychosis we are dealing with. Six or seven years ago I was back home in Colombo when the then Prime Minister of India Mr. Moraji Desai arrived to speak to the parliament of Sri Lanka. And I was within six feet of him in this self-described, this cadaverous Ghandian in a Ghandi-cap. He told the parliament of Sri Lanka: "My friends, you will be happy to hear that we in India have produced 28 million tons of surplus food – surplus grain." And I asked myself: "Surplus to what?" Surplus to need? And he answered, without my asking the question he went on to say: "But unfortunately many, many of our people are too poor to buy this." So even for a Ghandian, even the survival need of food must go through the famous market process. This is the psychosis, in which not only the Western world, but my part of the world, lives in. We live in a psychosis, which does not think it is a contradiction, in other words, actually a drawback in evolution, to resort to war to solve human problems, that is to resort to violence to resolve human problems. It's the most primitive way of dealing with a human dispute. We live in a society, in a world, in this psychosis, in which there is a massive attempt to destroy the only set of multilateral institutions that we have to manage our world's problems, with all their defects, with all their problems in those institutions I am referring to, the United Nations family. Many, many weaknesses, much to be criticized, but the attempt is to destroy the whole system and replace it with what? With a bi-lateral, a throw-back to bi-lateralism, to the power politics of the 1914–1918 war. Is that what we are trying to come to now? This is what we are threatened with. This is the psychosis, in which we have to solve this problem that you are dealing with, the problems of nuclear war. We are dealing with the world in psychosis, that rules our world, that imagines that the world consists of two super powers and the rest of us. And I take leave to say to those super powers, I have got news for them, that we are the world, we constitute three quarters of human beings of this world. And you are threatening to destroy our world.

They keep telling us in this super-power world that the world is interdependent. Lovely words, like interdependence. I first heard this word used in public in 1973, in December, when the so-called then Arab oil-embargo had been launched. This is what the Americans called an oil crisis, and the Arabs called it oil opportunity. I remember hearing Henry Kissinger, I remember reading, that Henry Kissinger, then the mighty Henry Kissinger had said to the NATO foreign ministers meeting in Washington D.C. that the world is inter-dependent. And I asked myself how is it possible? Henry Kissinger speaking of the brother-hood and the sisterhood of man? How is it possible? I don't believe this. And I followed this man right the world wherever he spoke, at the Food Conference in Rome, at the Nairobi AMCAD Conference, I heard him say it, "the world is interdependent". And then I began to understand what he was meaning by this. Only meant by this was: Look, you Arabs, you have oil, we have a need for it. If you do not give it to us at prices we consider reasonable, watch it! That was what interdependence was. And I, he taught me a lesson, and I am grateful for that, that interdependence without equity is rubbish. It only means deepening dependency of the poorer and the weaker.

Well, I would like to call your attention to a very significant fact, having said all this. Have you noticed that ever since your work began, in this grouping of IPPNW, and even before, as individual human beings, as physicians, that there has been no public demonstration of any big order, or any significant order, no street demonstrations in any part of the developing world against nuclear war. It is very interesting to recognize this. I think we must ask ourselves why. There are massive demonstrations here in Europe, in Germany, in Hyde Park in London, in various parts of Britain and the United States. There have been no demonstrations by the people of the third world. You may have your own guesses, but I as a veteran reporter, who looks at the third world, looks at the world through reporter's eyes, I have some guesses myself. And these are that people spend all their time surviving. The poorest people in the world have no time for even revolution. They have to survive today. I have a cartoon image of the world in my head, which I recall every day practically in my life. The world wears a broad and very thick steel belt round its bulging middle, from tropic to tropic, of armed dictatorships right round the globe. What is this belt holding down? The ordinary aspirations, the ordinary human aspirations of 900 million people and it can't be suppressed for long. That is that struggle going on all the time underneath this belt. This is why I call your attention as physicians, as people concerned with the human psyche, the psychology of violence. You have to be concerned with this. Just watch for those customers that you have not yet looked at in this way. 900 million of them underneath that belt. And these consist of people, of parents, as Bill Foege was saying, 15 million parents every year who lament the death of an infant child, 15 million mothers that is, and 30 million parents about.

I go home every year, Ladies and Gentlemen, to my village, which I left fifty years ago. I go back every year now, since I began to work with UNICEF, to see if what I am saying in New York City makes any sense down there from where I came. And I know the terrible things that are going on. As I went home along this bird track just three months ago, about six weeks ago, I had to stop the car because there was a funeral going the other way. There were three people at this funeral, the mother and the father and a little sister burying an infant son. It's a terrible thing to find that there are 40,000 of such funerals going on every day. Now this is what I mean by saying that there are no demonstrations against nuclear war. I am not being gloom and doom, I am not telling horror stories, I am also trying to show you that there are some chinks in that armoury of super power. There is some chink, again, in that there is some light through this chink. One of the things that happened, for instance, was recently in an impossible, implausible place called El Salvador. There, through a lot of work that has been done, underground, behind the scenes, from people, so different as the pope and the guerillas in the country, freedom fighters, guerillas, whatever you like to call them, that they stopped fighting for three days to immunize their children. The guns were silent those days.

I think there is some hope, some light, it is not UNICEF advertizing itself, there is some light there, that a common concern for all of us is our children. I remember Roberto Rossellini, the great neo-realist Italian film director, once telling me that for some reason he could not explain, that in every millenium people looked to their children. They were concerned about their children. There may be something in us, programmed in us for the perpetuation of our race, although in many ways we don't deserve it. To be perpetuated the way we behave. There may be something there to look at. I like to point out one important thing from UNICEF, it's from the experience of UNICEF. That which Bill Foege referred to as social mobilisation, really if I may talk to you, many of you are much younger than I, so I dare to do this, as a Dutch Uncle, as they say. I think we need to learn, you need to learn as physicians, something you don't know very well, which is to talk to people. I don't mean just having press conferences. I mean talk to people. It's very easy to have a press conference. I am talking of social mobilisation. I am talking of creating the climate through the media. But, talk to people, people don't live in climates, they live in the weather. I remember Jahawarlal Nehru once telling few of us who were interviewing him once, and he said to us, referring to England, he said: "England – such a wonderful climate, and such lousy weather."

This is what I am referring to. People live in the weather. We must talk to people where they live. And we are willing as UNICEF to collaborate in using the ways we have devised to talk to people, to spread the message of peace. It is the same message that we are trying to persuade. We call it help. The two have to go hand in hand.

I want to say that I am very, very happy that, as Karl Bonhoeffer and Herr Richter said this morning, over and over again they said that the struggle you have is a moral struggle. This is so important. It is not a struggle against weapons, it is not a struggle against governments, it's moral struggle against immorality, against immorality. And I say this, Ladies and Gentlemen, because I am a completely unrepentant, irredeemable and probably uncorrigible Ghandian. Ever since I had the great fortune of meeting him in 1946 as a very young journalist, I being his pupil, I learned so much, our family has learned so much the way we live, the way we feel, the way we think comes from very much the things he did, the way he lived. He is a man who destroyed, if I my remind you (you don't need reminding), the man who destroyed the mightiest empire in history without the use of a single gun. I wrote a piece about him recently, referring to him as the inventor of the first intercontinental ballistic missile. It shocked people when they read the headline and I explained that he sat spinning at his spinning wheel in Wardha and Lancashire, 10,000 miles away, toppled. Those were his techniques, those were his ways of dealing with things. Those ways, non-violent ways.

I must tell you something, a story to wind up. A story that Jahawarlal Nehru told me once when he read that story I had written about Ghandi as the inventor of the ICBM. He said: "You know, you really must understand because you loved him like I did. You must understand how deeply moral his movement was." He told me the story of how in 1942 Ghandi and Nehru and some of his other lieutenants had been put in jail by the British and when he went to jail he announced a Quit India movement. This was at the height of the war, when the Japanese armies were poised to flood into India. He led a Quit India movement. And during this time he had gone on a fast, as usual, and Mr. Nehru said, as you know, he always went on a fast unto death, he had fasted 14 days, and one morning the warden of the prison came to him and said: "Mr. Nehru, Mahatma Ghandi wishes to see you." And he went to Ghandi's cell and saw him there, seated, skin and bone, and he was spinning, very slowly. And he said: "Sit down, my jewel of India" to Nehru, and he sat down, on the floor, of course. And Sadap Patel was there, his other lieutenant. And Ghandi went on spinning for a while and said: "Is it true that some of our non-violent workers have killed two British soldiers yesterday? We have lost this struggle." And Nehru replied: "Yes, Mahatmaji, but they were provoked." And he turned on him and said: "Provoked, did you say? You do not seem to understand the basis of non-violence. The point is that we cannot be provoked. We have lost the struggle." And Partel said: "We have won, Ghandi. I have heard that there is a message coming from Delhi today to release you and us. We have won." And Ghandi turned to him and said: "Won a non-violent struggle at the cost of two lifes? No, Sir, we have lost." And he turned to the warden and said: "Mr. Warden, can I please have a glass of orange juice." And he broke his fast.

This is the moral fibre, my friends, that you, I, all of us must immolate, even if we have no experience of it, we must reach out for that kind of fibre, if we are going to win this battle, this battle against the psychosis. I have one more thing to say and I say it in a minute. The question before all of us is really: Are we as a human race going to have to confess in 15 years' time, when this century finishes, that we failed twice in this century, in our time, to produce the institutions, to produce the understanding, the mutual understanding to manage our globe ecologically, politically, economically and especially politically, twice in this century, are we going to have to confess that, perhaps we may not have, the danger is that we may not be given that opportunity even to confess because we may never get there. But if we do get there, in the way hanging on to this balance of terror, I do not want to confess to my grandchildren, that we failed, I know my daughter does not want to confess to her grandchildren that we failed. We have the technology, as both of you have said, we have the knowledge, as we have said, we have the communication skills, as I have said, have we got the human conscience?

MAINTAINING LIFE ON EARTH – THE MEDICAL CHALLENGE

Suszan Hollan, Hungary

The IPPNW's Medical Prescription:
A Comprehensive Nuclear Test Ban

My task today is to give a concise report on the progress we have made towards a world-wide moratorium on nuclear explosions. As a Hungarian physician I am very proud that it was in Budapest that the 41 affiliates of IPPNW had adopted a call for a moratorium on all nuclear explosions as our medical prescription. At our 4th Congress in Helsinki Dr. Lown urged a policy of reciprocating initiatives compared by public opinion and pointed out that the cessation of nuclear testing would be the most logical first step. Physicians worldwide mobilized behind this idea and the test ban became one of the major public issues of the year. It has not been difficult for us physicians to understand that a cessation of all nuclear explosions is in fact the first essential step reversing the arms race. The compelling logic of this step was spelled out in the medical prescription itself. First, a test ban is verifiable. In an age of profound distrust we must begin with measures which do not require trust. Second, a test ban impedes the development of new generations of less verifiable, more destabilizing weapons. Third, a test ban would enhance, not diminish the security of all nations. Fourth, a test ban would help to prevent the proliferation of nuclear weapons to other countries and reverse the arms race. By preventing the proliferation of nuclear arms the human resources and economic funds spent on weaponry would be available to defeat hunger and disease throughout the world.

The appeals and arguments of our Co-Presidents, Dr. Chasov and Dr. Lown, and the effective Soviet physicians movement played an important role in the fact that, barely one month after we issued our call, General-Secretary Gorbachev announced that the Soviet-Union would unilaterally stop all nuclear testing on August 6th, the 40th anniversary of the bombing of Hiroshima. The moratorium was to continue until the 31st of December unless the U.S. also stopped testing, in which case a mutual moratorium would continue indefinitely. The General-Secretary's announcement was the first sign that our medical prescription was being heeded and it provided the world and IPPNW with a historic opportunity. Action by IPPNW and its affiliates to mobilize public opinion on behalf of a joint Soviet-American moratorium began almost immediately. On the 1st of August, our Executive Director sent out an urgent memorandum to all IPPNW affiliates outlining the strategy and offering specific recommendation. Affiliates were urged to meet with the U.S. and Soviet Ambassadors to their country and with their own heads of government. Letter-writing campaigns, telegrams to heads of states, public meetings and press conferences were all recommended. Within a few weeks every IPPNW affiliate was actively engaged. The list of public activities from Buenos Aires to Den Haag, from Dakar to San José is impressive indeed.

Particularly notable were the efforts of our American colleagues in Physicians for Social Responsibility. PSR was instrumental in bringing the test ban to the fore, as a vital public issue in the U.S. PSR lobbied successfully for the passage of a resolution in the U.S. House of Representatives calling for the immediate resumption of test ban negotiations. All over the United States, American doctors urged the adoption of our medical prescription. In Boston, for example, 500 physicians rallied at the Harvard School of Public Health, wearing their white coats with blue armbands which read: "Stop nuclear testing!" Widely covered by the press, such events were important in bringing public attention to bear on what had been previously an obscure issue.

The Nobel Prize, of course, gave IPPNW a unique opportunity to direct attention to the testing issue. With the world's press focussed on IPPNW affiliate leaders used the chance to repeat the call for a test ban and offer the rationality of our prescription. Our Co-Presidents, Dr. Lown and Dr. Chazov met for nearly three hours with General-Secretary Gorbachev on December 18th, a week after the awarding of the Nobel Prize. The Co-Presidents urged the General-Secretary to extend the moratorium beyond December 31st and, in making their case, the Co-Presidents were able to point to a turning tide of political opinion regarding the test ban, a tide turned in part by our colleagues. When the meeting ended it was unclear whether IPPNW's call would again be heeded. Remarkably it was and on January 15th General-Secretary Gorbachev announced a three months' extension of the Soviet moratorium.

In spite of our success in bringing the testing issue before the world public and in spite of our impact in helping to bring about the opportunity for a mutual test moratorium we must take note of what we have not accomplished. The United States government has refused to join in a mutual halt. Although the Soviet Union has announced yet another extension of their moratorium through to August 6th, we have not yet succeeded in persuading the U.S. government to follow our medical prescription. But time is short. We have only two more months to make the prescription a reality. We have reason to be proud of our accomplishments as we continue to struggle to bring about a test ban and reverse the deadly arms race. Yes, Rome was not built in a day, but it was built. And we, too, shall some day see the full fruits of our labours. Let us redouble our efforts. Let us put our hearts and souls, our imagination into finding new effective ways to achieve a world wide pressure of public opinion for the acceptance of the nuclear test ban. This extraordinarily successful congress strengthens our decision that we will do our best that on August 6th, the 41st anniversary of the tragedy of Hiroshima, we can mark the beginning of a new era of hope.

Maintaining Life on Earth –
The Uses of Space

MAINTAINING LIFE ON EARTH – THE USES OF SPACE

Richard Garwin, U.S.A.

The Uses and Mis-Uses of Space

I will take the opportunity to introduce the topic and then we can argue about some of these points. In the use of space first we have the use of near-earth space, closest to the 4 billion people on earth. Space is extremely valuable in the service of mankind because radio signals and light go almost unaffected through space; thus you have the applications of communications for broadcast of interpersonal communications, telephone, television, videoconferencing – the things which we give no second thought to these days because they have become so common. But they are valuable; they will expand; and they could be imperiled if we don't do these things right.

We have the services of navigation. For two decades we have had the Transit satellite, a rather specialized navigation system, and now we are just beginning to have the operational systems of Navstar, global positioning system in the West and a comparable GLONAS system from the Soviet Union. These will provide within a tenth of a second at very modest cost for anyone equipped with a proper electronic box, position in three dimensions to accuracy of 10 meters or better. So it will tell me that I am here in this room at the bottom instead of at the top, in this corner instead of at the other corner. (Of course it will not work in this room because the radio signals will not come directly inside. But outside it will work any place on earth above the surface of the ocean.) Such systems will be useful also for improving the control of aircraft, providing greater safety and allowing more flexible and less expensive flight without fear of interference between such aircraft.

Space is also useful for observation and you see every day the pictures from the U.S. Landsat satellite which sweeps the earth and provides its pictures to anyone with a ground station equipped to receive them. The French SPOT satellite does a similar job, at better detail.

We've talked about the infrared early warning satellites which look continuously at the entire surface of the earth and say every second that there are no missiles being launched, that we are still at nuclear peace. We have the reconnaissance satellites which in near-earth orbit look over the surface of the earth for activities which might imperil peace. And we have those that are used for treaty verification to establish that nations, the United States and the Soviet Union particularly, which have assumed solemn obligations under the ABM Treaty of 1972 and the Limited Offensive Agreements, are in fact abiding by those agreements. Those treaties are the basis for a grant of immunity to satellites. Not only the immunity of common law but also specific immunity not only not to destroy but not to interfere with the operation of those satellites used in treaty verification.

In the control of commercial aircraft, air traffic control, all three functions of communication to aircraft, precise navigation, and surveillance (independent monitoring of the position of the aircraft) are important and can be provided, and I believe will be provided by satellites but are not yet. Then there are some specialized applications in this case pioneered by the Soviet Union – their search and rescue satellite SARSAT, I forget their name for it – which is very useful in finding people, vehicles, which have been downed by emergencies or lost at sea.

Now there are some lessons from our use of space since 1957. Either we are all permitted to use space at low cost in a peaceful nonweapons manner or no one will be able to do so. Thus far we have done very well in a regime of tacit cooperation in which the limited amount of space – and it is limited for special purposes particularly in the small region available in geosynchronous orbit, that small band a few hundred kilometers wide and deep available to satellites which appear to be stationary with respect to the earth. The international organizations which are concerned with the allocation of radio frequencies have done a good job and so have the other informal negotiations among scientists, technologists, and those who want to use space without interfering with one another. This will all disappear if space is to be used for the deployment of weapons, which must be countered by other weapons, and that is one of the reasons why those who wish to benefit from the use of space, those who wish to make money in space, should pay attention to the non-deployment of weapons in space.

Another lesson is that all of these benefits have been obtained without the presence of people in space. This does not prevent governments and their supporters from great campaigns of persuasion and even propaganda in support of manned space flight. We should not expect anything different in an era in which tens of billions of dollars are spent each year on advertising; and those who are interested in earning money by providing manned spaceflight are not immune to the temptations of advertising or even propaganda. But we should not necessarily believe these arguments. I think that in the United States, NASA (National Aeronautics and Space Administration) made a fundamental error in the early 1970s after the technical success of the Apollo program in demonstrating that we could put a man on the moon within ten years and bring him or them back safely. What NASA did was to continue manned spaceflight – in the feeling, I believe, that it was the only way to ensure the continuation of their budget at the high level to which they had become accustomed. But, as the saying goes, having lost sight of their objective they redoubled their efforts. And so NASA obtained continued budgets for the purpose of demonstrating what had previously been demonstrated – that people can exist and even do some work in space – produced a very high cost means of space transportation, the space shuttle, and hoped that the number of satellites to be launched and the cost of the shuttle would be appropriate for commercial success. Predictably this did not happen and in 1979 the NASA persuaded President Carter to require all future military launches to be on the space shuttle rather than on unmanned boosters. A person who is greatly respected in the United States, Dr. Albert Wheelon, Vice President of the Hughes Aircraft Corporation, spoke in New York in April 1986 and he volunteered that this grant of monopoly in 1979 by President Carter to NASA of military launches, that all should be on the space shuttle, was a national tragedy. It increased the cost of such launches. It has reduced the flexibility and, of course, as is clear for all to see since the Challenger disaster of January 1986 the decision was not a good one. Wheelon went further and said that this was a matter of pandering to the desires of one agency above the good of the entire people of the United States, and I agree with that. In your hotel this morning you may have taken the lift. There was no operator in that lift even though its purpose was to carry passengers. Similarly even for those specialized uses of space which require people, there is no need to have people as pilots. So we should learn the proper role of people in space.

Space is also useful for, as I said, specialized communications applications. For instance, the cooperative verification of treaty compliance. If one has a requirement that submarines carrying nuclear weapons not be allowed in certain areas (deployment area limitations), this can be verified in a cooperative fashion even though the submarines are never visible from space. One can have an arrangement whereby a certain submarine at random time can be commanded by its headquarters to rise to the surface and to transmit its identifying signal. Communication satellites acting like the navigation satellites themselves ("time difference of arrival") can verify that the submarine is indeed where it says it is and therefore not where it is agreed that it should not be.

Finally, I should talk about space science a little bit as a matter of introduction. Space is an excellent place from which to observe what goes on in the universe ranging from gravity waves to x-rays to gamma rays and to particles themselves. The absence of vibration is very distinguished from that on earth and the predictability of the effect of gravity also. The absence of the atmosphere allows radiations to be observed which are not detectable on earth. In the long-term we may even be able to save the earth – if we get to the long-term which will of course be a very great accomplishment – from those extinctions of species which have apparently plagued this planet for billions of years and of which we see the trace in the rocks and the fossils. These extinctions appear to be caused in large part by cometary bodies which every 20 or 30 million years strike the earth with sufficient frequency to destroy much of the life. With enough cooperation, these could be observed in time and diverted but it's not something that we need to worry about right now. Our main need is to survive for enough tens of years and centuries so that our technology and our spirit of cooperation will be strong enough to do the job when the time comes.

In 1968 the Soviet Union initiated the testing of an antisatellite weapon which has now been tested some twenty times. This was, I believe, a considerable error. The testing of this weapon has contributed to the contamination of near-earth space with particles which can be lethal to the use of space for either military of commercial or scientific purposes. Fortunately, in recent years the Soviet Union has had a moratorium on the testing of this weapon, and I hope this moratorium continues indefinitely. It was also not a good idea, in my opinion, for the United States more recently to begin testing our own antisatellite weapon. And I believe that we cannot long continue to test without having the Soviet Union join us in this folly.

I believe the scientific and the commercial and the non-weapon military uses of space are dependent in large part on a ban on antisatellite tests in space and on a ban on the deployment of space weapons. So even though there are no weapons in space – there are no Soviet ASAT tests in space right now – I think it is a matter of the highest urgency for us to do what we can in the soonest future to have a treaty which requires all nations to abjure the testing of antisatellite weapons and the deployment of weapons in space.

MAINTAINING LIFE ON EARTH – THE USES OF SPACE

Roald Sagdeyev, U.S.S.R.

Giotto, Vega and Voyager versus SDI

I appreciate what you said about your incompetence in space issues but at the same time I am willing to start with stressing on my incompetence in medical problems. The only contribution which I tried to bring in this area was the following one: It goes back to international co-operation in space. The natures of law, the natures of orbital mechanics, the Newton's Law essentially, predetermined the space as an arena for co-operation for international efforts, the orbits of satellites are circling around the globe and they are crossing, they are transcending all of the national boarders. So, in this way, technology which we put into space is a kind of joint property. And, within this type of approach, with the spirit for international co-operation several quite outstanding ventures were accomplished during the last couple of decades.

Some of them were mentioned by Dick Garwin, I would especially like to stress again on a very modest but very important project which was called "Search and Rescue Satellites". He mentioned very small objects in space, essentially the cargo for "search and rescue" is very small. It's roughly twenty or thirty kilogramms. It would consist of a radio-receiver and of a special kind of tape-recorder. Then imagine an aircraft or a ship, a small ship, which in remote areas of the ocean is having an emergency. Then, in order to call for help, it would have to use very simple and cheap methods, even in such a fashion so that the crew would not have to intervene in such cases. So they could have a very small special transmitter which would be switched on at the extreme emergency, with very weak special signals, then would be tracked by this search and rescue satellite with very simple approach to modern measurements using radio wave propagation and some small nuances. The spacecraft, this modest cargo, could detect easily the location of the source of the signal, could put it on the tape-recorder and then 10 or 15 minutes later it would report to the ground base station, that they have a certain signal. With this type of approach several hundred of emergency cases have already been handled and it has proved to be quite successful. I cannot report to you that we were able to save thousands of lives, perhaps, we can count only several dozens or maybe hundreds of saved lives but it is a very good beginning. So, the spirit of international co-operation was emanating from the very beginning of space era. I think everyone still remembers very well the large joint docking project in space "Apollo Sojus Joint Flight". Unfortunately this spirit of co-operation between the two greatest space powers is already in the past. There is not yet active co-operation in space between the United States and the Soviet Union, unfortunately. But there are areas where we have still important types of co-operation.

One of them was the dramatic project which was just finished a few weeks ago, a large international project to encounter the Halley's comet. Now I am coming back to my promise to explain what is the connection to medicine. During a couple of millennia, many hundreds of years, man on earth was extremely superstitious, especially about the comets and Halley's comet was the most prominent source of this superstition. Every apparition of the Halley's comet which Sir Edmund Halley suggested was taking place on the regular basis of every 75 to 76 years. Every apparition was in the minds of men, was connected with terrible happenings on earth. The devastating wars, terrible epidemics, and funny enough maybe ten or fifteen years ago some of astrophysicists and exobiologists suggested even scientific foundation for potential epidemics brought by the comets. They suggested that spending most of its time very far from the sun, the comets could contain some unknown new viruses and when they come into the close proximity to the sun and to the earth, they could deliver some of its viruses to the earth to cause epidemics. So nevertheless the team of scientists from different countries about six or seven years ago gathered and decided, let's try to prevent these terrible happenings, let's try to intercept Halley's comet on its way to the closest approach to the earth. So, essentially, what happened? We arranged the project in the following way: Several groups of nations had their own separate projects, seperate spacecrafts, you know of the Giotto spacecraft, which was a product of eleven European nations, united under the umbrella of European Space Agency. The Japanese are newcomers in outer space and they wanted to have their separate contribution, it was a modest small spacecraft which carried only 10 to 15 kilos of scientific cargo but it was very sophisticated, typical for modern Japanese technology and eventually it contributed importantly. And then Russians with their co-operation of Eastern European, socialist countries, with the use of experience of flying to Venus several times during the last decades, also prepared two identical spacecrafts, Vega spacecrafts which were sent first in the direction of Venus, and then using the gravity field of Venus as a trampoline we made a swing-by to Halley's comet. So, the first decade of March was a culmination of these international efforts. We gathered again, the same team of scientists, by that time several hundreds of us, to start witnessing the real-time encounter and we started in Moscow with the Vega encounter, at the same time we had got a message about the encounter of the Japanese.

About two years ago the position of the orbit of Halley's comet was known very vaguely. The exact location at any given time for Halley's comet's nucleus, its most vital essential part which contains, which is a source of all cometary material, was known only with accuracy of something like 20,000 to 30,000 kilometres. Of course, knowledge was improving with more and more astronomic observation of Halley's comet from the earth with telescopes in observatories, but even on the eve of the Vega's encounter with Halley's comet we could predict its position only with an accuracy of 1000 or 2000 kilometres. But the encounters of our spacecraft, which carried scientific instrumentation from ten countries, dramatically improved our knowledge about the position of the comet. Our European friends having their control centre for Giotto space craft in quite close proximity to this very place, in a small German city – Darmstadt – they were extremely eager to find out, what the findings were, as to where the comet's nucleus would be during their encounter, and everything was arranged in advance, with a joint team, which was doing all the computations. This team fortunately included a very experienced and well-equipped computer team from Pasadena, California, from the Jet Propulsion Laboratory. Whithin hours finished calculations and data were sent to Darmstadt. And 24 hours prior to encounter the Giotto spacecraft made a last manoeuvre. It used the Vega as a pathfinder and was able to hit the comet at a very close distance of only 500 kilometres. This succession of very well orchestrated missions and the general spirit of co-operation, was, I think, really exemplary and we even succeeded in a post encounter project. Just a week ago the first collection of papers and scientific publication, were published together in a special issue of *Nature* magazine. So imagine this special issue containing almost forty scientific articles on Halley's comet encounters. And of course we were very proud, we felt that even if modern man does not believe in such superstition, we thought it's probably still a good contribution to keep peace before the comet would come in closest proximity to the earth. But unfortunately we were unable to prevent all the catastrophes or the disasters on earth as you now know. So that means we should never stop international efforts. There are many more outstanding projects of this kind. Out of different formidable tasks which have to be performed, probably one of the most important and urgent is the task to do something about ecological problems.

The Chernobyl type of disaster is one more important signal to all of us to unite, to do something together. A few years ago, the group of scientists in different countries, in America, in Europe, in Russia, in Japan, through the International Council of Scientific Unions originated an interesting approach, an approach which had to lay a basis, a fundament, to establish a special kind of global ecological programme from space. The goal of the programme was to make detailed assessment, what kind of environment, the biosphere, the human kind of the 20th century is going to pass on to the next generation, which would have to live in the third millenia. This type of global inventarisation of space resources, the state of atmosphere, the state of oceans, the soils, the resources, the level of contamination of environment due to the intervention of man. It could be established within the next fifteen years if we could join our efforts. I think, it would not be enough, certainly, to have only one, two, three, even five spacecrafts just as we used to study this small celestial object, Halley's comet, for such an enormous object like our planet. It would be needed to bring together the efforts of many countries to launch, maybe not even dozens but hundreds of specialised satellites.

But we have to do it, it is an extremely important global ecological problem, because there are predictions that even without a nuclear holocaust, within forty or fifty years humankind is going to face terrible ecological problems. Because the ecological equilibrium is always shifting and it is shifting now gradually, with small steps, but there is very evident acceleration in global changes, for example in climatic changes and nobody knows, unfortunately modern science cannot predict yet, at what moment of time, at what state this continously shifted equilibrium could become completely unstable and collapse, leading to unpredictable changes in the environment, in the biosphere. These changes certainly could threaten also ecological equilibria in the micro-biological world, which then would bring a lot of terrible problems in medicine, in agriculture and everywhere.

I would like to touch now one issue, which sometimes is also labelled as area for co-operative efforts. This is the area of Star Wars. It was extensively discussed by Dick Garwin yesterday. But, you know, talking many times in Star Wars issues, meeting different kinds of people, all of us who are dealing with this subject have discovered an outstanding problem. When you try to build a series of arguements why Star Wars are dangerous, destabilizing, could lead to the increase of nuclear danger, you have to go into detail, you have to start with technical arguments, why the technology suggested for Star Wars wouldn't work. Then you would immediately meet a scepticism of the kind "these guys are trying to undermine American technological genius". No, we are not doing that. In fact, I think America made an extremely outstanding contribution in the space age, and the last confirmation of that contribution was the marvellous encounter with Uranus. Imagine at such a distance, when the radio signal is propagating during dozens of hours, a tiny world in the dark outskirts of the solar system was encountered with this extremely sophisticated and clever unmanned spacecraft Voyager. The question is not undermining technological genius of human kind, the question is that the world which would be opened with this type of technological competition would be extremely fragile and unstable. And this type of strategic instabilities could be analysed in a very logical way. But you know the difficulty. When you start explaining these things, you see that listeners are becoming bored because from the other side, they get much simpler arguments like, "defense is human, defense is moral". I found for myself, that even when I talk to my wife it is difficult to persuade her of what is wrong in such a simple argument. So I always asked why we, the opponents of Star Wars, couldn't find a very simple and clever argument and, recently, I am glad to report to you, a friend of ours, Carl Sagan, I think found a very simple argument. Talking recently on one of the American TV networks, he said in very simple terms "If you cannot construct an ideal shield, if any shield is leaky, it is no better than a leaky contraceptive". I tried to analyse the impact of this comparison he made through the results of American public opinion polls and there is a very interesting correlation: the polls which indicate the results from female audience are now becoming much more positive for us against SDI. Out of many aspects of Star Wars or SDI, there is one particularly interesting aspect, which was brought on the eve of Geneva summit.

Realising that there are a lot of difficulties, of a technological competitive character, of strategic instability, especially the difficulty of extreme vulnerability of this space-based SDI system, some of the proponents of SDI suggested a kind of international co-operation. They said, when we develop the technology, we will share it with Russians, so we would have a joint family, sharing SDI technology. So what could we answer to this type of proposal for this kind of international co-operation in space? Right now, it is very difficult to imagine that this type of sharing could take place, because, as you know, often even a little bit more sophisticated personal computers are under embargo. And in my view, this type of embargo is extremely dangerous and harmful. If, abstracting from any kind of discussion on the Chernobyl accident you just would pick up a small nuance out of it. Are technology, electronics or computers reliable or not? The same technology, the same electronics are, one could guess, probably used to control the rockets in the silos. And you know how many nervous outbreaks we encountered during the last few years in America, when from time to time there were leakages. The computer for early warning system failed and there was a false alarm. People were very nervous. And especially people on the American continent were extremely nervous with this type of breakdowns, but I think the accident which we had recently should alarm people that each of us, in the best spirit of common security should also be worried with potential false alarms on the opposite continent. I think, if I would be alarmed with such a kind of situation in America, and certainly I am alarmed, so this is the reason why I do not impose embargo on Russian computers for Americans. So, coming back to the proposal, to share technology, there are many different arguments why it is naive, unrealistic.

I would like to finish with an argument of a serious character. An argument which is based on strategic stability. Suppose after such type of nice presents from one side to the other, both sides at a certain moment of time would posses two equal space-based defensive shields and the fire power of types of nuclear weapons from the strategic triad. Then, the question is what fraction of this fire power would be sufficient to kill instantly its sister in space, the space-based defensive sister of the other side, which has objects, space stations, lasers, mirrors, just neighbouring, the orbits would be shared. And, in fact very simple calculations of the type which were discussed by Garwin yesterday would bring you to the result that very tiny fractions of fire power would be enough, maybe less than one per cent. The reason is quite simple. The number of space-defense battle stations would be much smaller than the number of dangerous intercontinental ballistic missiles and, of course, even less than the number of warheads. Their orbits would be predetermined, they would be known in advance with great precision, so this is an extremely unstable situation. No matter, how you get such precious things, even if you spend your own money for your own technology or it was the result of a generous gift, it is extremely vulnerable, in a matter of seconds it could be annihilated by the other side and then the situation would be completely as in the beginning. It would be absolutely without any protection. So these kinds of considerations are usually very important and the general problem is now that we are really speaking in different languages. We simply have no chance to talk together to the proponents, with the proponents of the SDI. And I think the reason is that in fact they are not very much interested in serious discussions. They consider SDI as a kind of political process to push forward the whole spectrum of the arms race.

MAINTAINING LIFE ON EARTH – THE USES OF SPACE

Hans-Peter Dürr, Federal Republic of Germany

The Uses of Space in the Light of Pressing Global Problems

We are today at the threshold of a serious escalation in the militarization of space. According to the ideas of some highly influential people there shall be not only numerous military satellites circling around the globe in various orbits, which watch over everything, which communicate on everything and which assist in navigating military equipment to everywhere, but there shall be, in future, powerful weapons on space-based platforms designed for the destruction of missiles and satellites. The threat of annihilating mankind on earth will be carried into a new dimension.

Life on Earth is highly jeopardized. Maintaining life on earth – in view of these tremendous dangers – has gained highest priority. Maintaining Life on Earth is therefore the topic of this congress.

The question we ask ourselves in this session is whether space can be used to help us in maintaining life rather than to increase the dangers of destroying life. In this context we refer to space as of something "waiting for man to be used by man, to be conquered by man." But space – we should recall – is actually the Universe, huge and ample beyond any human imagination, in which light can travel ten billions of years to transverse it. The earth is just a tiny, tiny little spot in it populated by some strange species of whom some members arrogantly believe to be the center of the world.

Tiny and nearly invisible as this earth actually is, something very rare and precious has happened on this earth, something which – to our present knowledge – seems to be rather unique in this Universe. On the thin and special crust of this earth "life" has developed during the last four and a half billion years – with us, the homo sapiens sapiens, as its last offspring.

Life on earth appears like one big organism. Human life is only part of this organism. Human life depends vitally on the other life, and all life depends on the very special conditions on earth, on her soil, her waters and air, all comprising a highly vulnerable system. Maintaining life on earth hence requires, first of all, the protection of this very vulnerable crust. The highly amplifying techniques of man, connected with the unleashing of large hidden energies, have grown to a size to upset the natural forces on earth and to destroy her delicate dynamical equilibrium.

To look up to the starred sky, to penetrate the sky and to look into the vast space beyond the earth, to investigate by the arriving light from other celestial bodies, this has captivated the mind of man from early history. Astrophysics and space reasearch still play an eminent part in our basic research program today. The atmosphere of the earth, we realized, is only transparent to part of the electromagnetic radiation which arrives from outer space. Hence by leaving the atmosphere and performing observations from satellites outside the atmosphere one can obtain much richer and crucial information about our universe, its structure and its origin.

Understanding the universe, similar as understanding the dynamics in the atomic and subatomic domain, has always fascinated man. The very big and the very small designate the important frontiers of the physical sciences where, as one hopes, new fundamental insights about nature can be gained. Basic research in astrophysics as well as in elementary particle physics, the physics of the subatomic region, require complicated and expensive equipment: large telescopes, space satellites in astrophysics, and high energy accelerators and complicated detectors in particle physics. Both fields are particularly suited for international cooperation and joint ventures. In elementary particle physics international cooperation and collaboration of scientists from Western and Eastern countries in experimental and theoretical research was always very intensive and extensive. In space research such a cooperation is still approached with some hesitation. Such a cooperation is not completely absent as, for example, indicated by the fact, that Professor Roald Sagdeyev, from the Soviet Space Research Laboratory in Moscow, who is here with me on the panel today, is a non-resident scientific member of our Max-Plack-Institute in Munich. In contrast to many efforts, however, to intensify collaborations on space research world-wide and in particular across the political demarcation lines, the prospects of a more extended military use of space threaten to destroy any international cooperation in this field, today. And not only that: particle physics, where this cooperation has worked out so well up-to-now, – because of its possible significance for SDI – may also run now the risk to be affected by military rationale. We should be very aware of the alarming signs indicating a beginning erosion of international cooperation and collaboration in basic science, this small island of common trust and mutual respect in an ocean of distrust, intolerance and misperceptions. In fact, great efforts should be made to turn the tide and to make space in an exemplatory way a really and truly international cooperative venture. In particular, West and East should join their efforts to carry out together the important and very costly experiments and investigations in space.

In our session, today, the subject of interest is not space research or scientific and philosophical questions connected with a better understanding of the universe and our planetary system. The subject in question is: the uses of space. We may ask immediately: "The uses of space for what purpose?" And, perhaps, supplement it by the statement: "for the benefit of mankind, for our own good." But what does this mean? What is really good for mankind? What do people actually need? How do we and others want to live – now and in the future? And who is interested in these questions, at all? Who will decide on this?

What we really need and how we want to live is, of course, visualized by different people in very different ways depending on their personal and cultural background. But these differences should not be exaggerated to the extent as to suggest that there does not exist *any* agreement on such issues among people:

- We all have to proceed on the basis of a limited earth with limited resources in its accessible crust.
- We all are convinced that every human being should at least be given the opportunity of the most primitive conditions for a decent life.

– We all are vitally interested in a survival of mankind and the survival of the biosphere on earth.

The survival of mankind, however, does not only depend on whether we succeed in solving human conflicts in future in a new and unconventional way – i. e. without wars – but whether we learn to understand that man – despite of his great talents and competence and his resulting relative independence from his fellow-man and from nature – that man remains, in a complicated and vulnerable fashion, a part of nature, a part of his environment.

The vitality, the adaptability and evolutionary ability of the biosphere derives from a high-dimensional dynamical equilibrium of forces and counterforces which is controlled and stabilized by closed processes. Brute force interferences, as inflicted today by man through means of his powerful and highly amplifying techniques, threaten to disrupt this sensitive fabric.

The driving force behind many of the vast technological developments and innovations is not predominantly generated, I gather, by a desire to offer man more extended chances in life or a better quality of life but rather, I am afraid, by the zeal to increase the profits of an economical elite and to strengthen the power of a few over the many. Our daily experience seems to indicate that basic necessities of our life get more and more subjugated to technique and material conditions rather than conversely, that technique and material conditions are used and developed for the solution of the difficult and really challenging problems of our time. There are a great number of burning problems at our hands, as we all know, for example

– The protection of our environment, which is greatly endangered by the pollution of the air and the water, and the contamination of the soil through our expanding industrial activities and the production of radioactive fall-out.
– The protection of natural resources, in particular the provision of a long-term supply by tapping only inexhaustible or predominantly inexhaustible energy sources.
– The mounting problems of the so-called Third World with her overpopulation, her poor health, her malnutrition and increasing poverty.
– The reconstruction of the world economy such as to provide a fair and just distribution of wealth, and to find an adequate treatment of unemployment.

All these problems, this is quite obvious, will ultimately condense into world-wide catastrophies if we do not try to solve them sonn and resolutely. They all will jeopardize our security. They all will lead to unrest, uprisings, and wars. They all, hence are initimately connected with the issue of peace.

Why, therefore, should we not concentrate on these problems first? Why, in particular, should it not be possible to make these really urging problems of our time for once, directly and explicitly, the main object of a huge research and development program, the object of a world peace initiative? Such a world peace initiative could be, indeed, a program, in which West and East and all other countries in the world could whole-heartedly participate, because the solution of these problems is in the very best interest of *all* og them. A common effort in this direction would provide a sound basis for East and West to acquire confidence and trust into each other.

I realize, of course, that this proposal sounds rather utopian. But I wish to emphasize that it is not nearly as utopian, in substance, as President Reagan's Strategic Defense Initiative

SDI. In addition: such a common initiative would be so much more worth-while, so much more reasonable and so extremely suitable for broad agreement among all people.

In order to set this utopia on realistic grounds one probably has to do something similar as Reagan did in case of SDI: He appointed the Fletcher Commission, a group of some 50 experts in various fields, who worked for 4½ months to transform his irrational dream into a collection of some hundreds of different and seemingly rationally founded projects.

Applied to our case this would mean: To start off our utopian project, we should take all these urging problems of the world and ask an international group of outstanding minds to cut them up intelligently and appropriately into a large number of smaller and more concise problems which then can be offered to various individuals, groups and institutional communities to be investigated in detail. (To set up such a commission, of course, it helps to be a president). Some of these problems, one can be sure, will require for their solution certain new scientific investigations and/or technical developments. These investigations and developments should then be undertaken with high intensity and determination. In this consideration we may discover that space, indeed, could be used, in one way or the other, to solve some of the problems.

At this point, hence, I arrive at the subject of our session, on the uses of space. The meaningful uses of space I claim can only be determined within the larger context of all these urging problems which confront us. Bcause of the severe financial constraints under which all these problems have to be solved and – what may be even more decisive – because of the rather limited number of very bright, intelligent and creative minds who actually have to find and work out these solutions, space research and space techniques should not be looked at as isolated activities but should be regarded always in direct competition with all other projects proposed for solving these problems. Obviously, if we do one project, some other project cannot be done at the same time. We have to state priorities and then make our choices accordingly.

Let me shortly indicate some possibilities for space projects which may be worth-while:

– Installation of meteorological satellites to provide for a more reliable weather forecast. This is important for agriculture and hence the food production.
– Installation of reconnaissance satellites with sensors in various wave lenght ranges of electromagnetic radiation for the observation of the surface ot the earth, in particular to recognize ecological changes, e. g. in the vegetation, and to discover new resources etc.
– Setting up satellites for world-wide communication, i. e. telephone, television, radio, computer links and networks, which could have important influence on education and could intensify human contacts of people at very different locations.
– Installation of satellites for improving navigation on sea and in the air.
– Establishing space laboratories, probably unmanned, for special research projects and industrial techniques which require absence of gravitation (microgravitation).
– Space installations which may improve the utilization of sun energy, and perhaps many other projects.

I personally prefer to deemphasize some ot the other motives which sometimes are mentioned in connection with the uses of space, for example:

– Extensive space travel or the use of outer space as a chance for man to settle on other planets, or
– Import of certain raw materials from the moon or other planets, which are scarce on earth.

It is my impression that settling on the South pole would prove for man far more comfortable than leaving the earth, and all methods for digging out raw materials on earth, even under very unfavorable conditions, will still prove far more economical than employing space transportation.

Of course, I do see that the ambitious and enterprising man, which our education loves and favours, will consider the conquest of space a great and exciting challenge. I would very much hope that we can offer him other challenging tasks on earth to prove his courage and endurance.

Some may view space travel as an escape from earth, some even as a last refuge, after they have destroyed the earth or transformed it into a garbage can. I suggest, we better watch out for these people.

Perhaps the solution of these urgent global problems may not quite require such extreme technologies and high-tech as, e. g., necessary for tackling SDI. Hence some people may be afraid that these problems will not be intellectually ambitious enough to catch the imagination and the enthusiasm of our scientists and technicians, and that they are not glamourous enough to nourish their vanity. Most of them will certainly prefer to see their name attached to a star rather than to a waste utilization plant. We should recognize, however, that in view of the increasing threats and dangers to man, and to mankind in general by man, many people – and in particular our young people – have developed during the last decades a strong desire to devote their intellectual and moral energies to the higher aspirations of man, in particular

- to the possibility of the survival of mankind in a harmonious and healthy environment, and
- to the common goal of a peaceful coexistence of all people on the globe in justice and selfdetermination.

With these high goals in mind we should not forget, however, to think about the very tiny little first step which points towards these goals and which we ourselves will undertake tomorrow, after we have returned home from this stimulating congress.

The Congress Lectures

THE CONGRESS LECTURES

Leon Eisenberg, U.S.A.

Rudolf Virchow: The Physician as Politician

We come together in a cause that transcends national boundaries: the continuing struggle to abolish the nuclear threat to life on earth. In his Nobel Peace Prize Lecture[1], our Co-President, Dr. Lown, summarized our work in these terms: we are writing "a prescription for hope" based on our conviction that "what humanity creates, humanity can and will control." We do so as physicians, because we know, in a way that few others do, how devastating a nuclear holocaust would be, how delusional it is to believe in an effective medical response to such a catastrophe, and how far the hopes for humankind rest upon prevention as the sole prescription for survival. That knowledge places a special responsibility upon physicians, one that goes well beyond our general responsibility as citizens.

Sir Charles P. Snow, in an address to the Annual Meeting of the American Association for the Advancement of Science in 1960[2] on: "The Moral Unneutrality of Science," highlighted the responsibility of scientists in these words: "Scientists have a moral imperative to say what they know. It is going to make them unpopular in their own nation-states. It may do worse than make them unpopular. That doesn't matter. Or at least, it does matter to you and me, but it must not count in the face of the risks ... There are going to be challenges to our intelligence and to our moral nature as long as man remains man. After all, a challenge is not ... an excuse for slinking off and doing nothing. A challenge is something to be picked up ..."

Responding to that moral imperative, some 6500 scientists and engineers in the United States have declared that they will not work on the "Star Wars" arms program for space because it can only escalate the nuclear danger by promoting a false belief in a fail-safe defense system. We salute them as we assemble here in this Congress of the International Physicians for the Prevention of Nucelar War to redouble our efforts to make sure "the final epidemic"[3] never occurs.

Because we meet in Cologne, I have thought it fit to exemplify the moral unneutrality of medicine by recalling the life and career of a physician in the highest tradition of German medicine, one who, more than a century ago, recognized that: "if disease is an expression of individual life under unfavorable conditions, then epidemics must be indicative of mass disturbances of mass life"[4].

The Rudolf Virchow[5] whose name I invoke earned many enemies during his lifetime (from 1821 to 1902). Indeed, he made no effort to avoid them when they opposed scientific progress or human rights. At 25, barely three years out of medical school, Virchow attacked the theories of Rokitansky, then the dominant figure in pathology. At 27, he was an activist in the German Revolution of 1848; in consequence, the government suspended him from his post at the Charité; he was obliged to vacate his office. He found it prudent to accept an invitation from the University of Würzburg in Catholic Bavaria where he immersed himself in scientific work. When he dared return to Berlin for his wedding in 1850, he was excorted back to the border by the Prussian police. In 1865, he earned a place on Otto von Bismarck's "enemies list." Having been elected four years earlier to the Prussian Landtag as a member of the Progressive Party, Virchow led the opposition to Bismarck's proposal for a military budget. The Chancellor chose to interpret a speech by Virchow as an insult to his honor and sent a formal note demanding satisfaction by a public retraction or by a duel[6]. The duel was averted only through behind-the-scences negotiations by Bismarck's intermediaries, General von Manteuffel and Count von Roon, the Prussian Minister of War[7].

Yet, that very same Virchow was later to become Rector of the University of Berlin and to receive worldwide recognition for his contributions to medical science and public health. As a "senior statesman," the physician who had manned the barricades forty years earlier was offered a title of nobility by the Imperial Government. It is a measure of his integrity that he remained a committed republican to the end; he refused to become "von" Virchow, unlike such scientific contemporaries as Behring and Helmholtz.

Few of us can hope to match Virchow's achievements. But his courage in speaking out for fundamental human rights provides an example to sustain us at a time where the propriety of what we do here is under attack as a "misuse" of medicine for political ends. Recall that Virchow, at one and the same time, helped to provide the scientific foundation for medicine, advanced the thesis that medicine is as much a social as a biological science, applied the fruits of his scientific investigations to public health measures, and ran for political office to fight the rise of Prussian militarism, the sworn enemy of every value he held as a physician. It is the irony of history that his name, when it is recalled at all in Germany or elsewhere, is invoked only as the father of a biomedicine which dismisses the social determinants of health and disease as "political" matters beyond the physician's purview. Let me outline his contributions to biology briefly before reviewing his social activism.

It is no exaggeration to herald Virchow as the principal architect of scientific medicine. It was he who established the pathophysiology of thrombosis, pulmonary embolism, leukocytosis, leukemia, the mycoses, abnormal heme pigments, amyloid bodies, echinococcus liver tumors, and trichinosis, among others. Still, even these major contributions pale when measured against his role in establishing cell doctrine in pathology with William Henry Welch[8] was to hail as "one of the greatest events in the history of medicine."

In 1838, Theodore Schwann had discovered that nucleated cells were the basic biological units of all animal organisms. But what was the origin of these cells? Schwann believed that they arose by spontaneous generation from an undifferentiated homogeneous substance termed the "blastema." Extended to pathology, this doctrine held that when an inflammatory exudate became "organized" (that is, acquired a cellular structure), the cells developed out of the fluid matter of the exudate. Indeed, this belief had led Rokitansky to formulate his theory of the "dyscrasias;" namely, that all pathology stemmed from the blood. By detailed experimental study of inflammation, Virchow disproved blastema theory and asserted unequivocally in *Cellular Pathology*[9], published in 1858: "... We can now go so far as to establish, as a general principle, that no development of any kind begins de novo, and consequently to reject the theory of spontaneous generation just as much in the history of the development of individual parts as we do in that of entire organisms ... Where a cell arises, there a cell must have previously existed (omnis cellula e cellula), just as an animal can spring only from an animal, a plant only from a plant."

In public health, Virchow's contributions were no less extraordinary. The discoverer of the pathophysiology of trichinosis led a successful ten-year campaign to establish compulsory meat inspection in Germany. At the request of the Berlin City Council, he designed and supervised a sewage disposal system which set the pattern for similar actions in Germany and beyond. He was a tireless exponent of health education for the general public: "As long as [education] does not aim to maintain and increase, ... by the power of independent thought, a sound, genuine and unadulterated human understanding ... the layman will lack the basis to form his own judgement on his physicians ... Not only the uneducated, but also the educated layman will remain servilely subordinate to medical authority; a resounding title ... will constitue a most lucrative shingle for the medical quack ..."[10]

I turn now to the Virchow who coined the appealing, if grandiose, aphorism: "Medicine is a social science, and politics is nothing more than medicine on a large scale"[11].

In the summer of 1847, Upper Silesia had been devastated by an epidemic of "famine fever" (now known as relapsing fever). The local authorities were unable to stem the plague. The public scandal prompted the central government in Berlin to appoint a Commission of Investigation, with Virchow as a member, a major tactical error as they were soon to discover. In a scathing report[12] he insisted that the causes of the epidemic were more social than medical. It was the conditions under which the workers were forced to live, most particularly bad housing and malnutrition, which made them vulnerable to disease. Nothing but universal education, absolute separation of church and school, regional and local self-government, a just system of taxation, and industrial development could bring about an improvement, and these could only be achieved upon the basis of "*free and unlimited democracy*"[12, p. 315]. His investigation was undertaken twenty years before Obermeier discovered the spirochete *Borrelia recurrentis* in the blood of relapsing fever patiens and fourty years before Flügge identified the human body louse as its vector. These later findings did not in any way vitiate Virchow's theory that epidemic diseases result from "mass disturbances of mass life"[4]. As the most recent review of the literature on louse-borne relapsing fever[13] notes: "[It] is usually seen in epidemics, [which] have characteristically occurred in the wake of large-scale disasterous events, such as wars, famine, floods, etc. ... [marked] by overcrowding, lapses in personal hygiene and frequently by malnutrition ... Case fatality rates in epidemics have been higher than those in endemic disease."

Sir William Osler, in commenting on Virchow's political career[14], wrote: "In Germany the struggle for representative government attracted many of the ardent spirits of our profession, and it was then that Virchow began his political career. The revolution [of 1848] was a failure, and brought nothing to the young prosector but dismissal from his public positions. His participation might have been condoned had he not issued a medicopolitical journal *Die Medicinische Reform*, the numbers of which are even now very interesting reading, and contain ideas which today would be called liberal, but were then revolutionary."

What were the revolutionary ideas promulgated by Virchow and his colleagues? They included: public provision of medical care for the indigent (including free choice of physicians in place of "paupers' doctors"), prohibition of child labor, protection for pregnant women, reduction of the working day in dangerous occupations, removal of toxic substances, and adequate ventilation at work sites. Medicine was to be reformed on the basis of four principles: first, that the health of the people is a matter of direct social concern; second, that social and economic conditions have an important effect on health and disease, and that these relations must be subjected to scientific investigation; third, that the measures taken to promote health and to combat disease must be social as well as medical (Virchow went so far as to proclaim the right of the citizen to work as a fundamental principle to be included in the constitution of a democratic state); fourth, that "medical statistics will be our standard of measurement"[15]. Revolutionary in mid-nineteenth century, liberal by the end of that century, given lip service on all sides today, those principles have yet to become the norm.

The medical reformers of 1848 understood that medicine, if it is to reduce morbidity and mortality, must attend at one and the same time to the biological *and* to the social roots of disease. As Virchow[16] recognized: "The improvement of medicine will eventually prolong human life, but the improvement of social conditions can achieve this result more rapidly and more successfully."

The truth of that thesis has been abundantly demonstrated. Better living standards and improved sanitation account for the greater part of the gains in longevity in the past century[17]; the persistence of class-related inequalities in disease prevalence continue to document the health effects of the way people live[18, 19]. As physicians, we must fulfill our role as "the natural advocates for the poor"[20] by exercising the leadership necessary to eradicate those inequalities through social action. The privileges we enjoy entail corresponding obligations to place what we know in the service of the public good. In Virchow's words[21]: "Medical instruction does not exist to provide individuals with an opportunity of learning how to earn a living but in order to make possible the protection of the public!"

Virchow's commitment to "the protection of the public" led him to seek public office and become a politican in the literal sense. He stood for election and served in a series of legislative bodies: the Berlin Town Council (from 1859 until his death), the Prussian Landtag (from 1862), and, after the unification of the German State, the Reichstag (from 1880 to 1893). I have already described the personal risk he took in opposing Bismarck's military budget. Had Virchow been forced to duel the Iron Chancellor – and he could not have refused the challenge without compromising his public honor beyond redemption in mid-nineteen century Prussia – it would have been slaughter, given the discrepancy in size and in martial skills between the two. Indeed, Virchow's colleague Twesten had lost the use of his right arm as the result of a duel with von Manteuffel four years earlier[5]. Bismarck's political associates averted the affair, not because they had any greater regard for the trouble-making legislator, but because the Chancellor would have made himself ridiculous by a public duel with a parvenu.

Four years later, on October 21, 1869, undeterred by the risk, Representative Virchow took on the Junkers once again by introducing the following motion in the Landtag[22]: "Whereas the permanent state of war-readines in almost all the countries of Europe is not the result of enmity between their peoples ... Whereas the reduction of military expenses is absolutely necessary to balance the budget without a further burden on the people and in order to find the means for crucial purposes the government itself admits have been too long deferred ... Therefore, we urge the government to reduce military expenses, and to use diplomatic means to bring about general disarmament ..."

In the debate on his resolution, he pointed out that expenditures for education in Prussia had remained stationary because military expenditures consumed an ever increasing share of the budget. He contended that there had hardly been a time with so little reason for the several states to confront each other fully equipped for war because they were engaged in major internal reconstruction projects. The nations of Europe had come to recognize that only by domestic programs could they gain the security they need for cultural progress. He went on: "We must announce our principles in honest and open opposition. We must defend them as being in the best interest of our country. We cannot abandon them, even if we are blamed for lack of patriotism . . . The size of our army provides a pretense for other countries to strengthen theirs . . . General disarmament is necessary for the task of bringing civility to Europe. Only with reduction of the military budget will there be a chance for the continuing education of peoples in the various countries."

Virchow's motion was rejected by the House of Representatives, 215 to 99. Just eight months later, in July 1870, the first of three major wars began, wars which brought in their wake destruction, suffering and death.

In the years after the defeat of his disarmament motion, the right wing supporters of Bismarck continued to attack Virchow in every forum for being "unpatriotic." After all, he had acknowledged having met with French scientists in his international anti-war efforts. In a speech before the Reichstag on January 12, 1887, Virchow reiterated proudly[22]: "I shall always consider it a special honor to propose a similar motion, and to give the German people the chance to display in practice their manifest love of peace."

In his incessant struggle for that goal, Virchow fought staunchly against the virulent anti-Semitism of the 1870's and '80's, a movement which Bismarck assiduously cultivated behind the scenes as a political weapon against the German Progressive Party, but from which he maintained a calculated public distance. In the elections of 1881, Virchow ran against, and resoundingly defeated, the notorious anti-Semite, Adolf Stoecker, the court chaplain. Pastor Stoecker was widely viewed as representing crown and church, a man whom Bismarck privately endorsed in a letter to his son as an "extraordinary, pugnacious, useful comrade-in-arms"[5]. Virchow was himself a leading figure in physical anthropology and a founder of the Berlin and German Societies for Anthropology. On the basis of careful anthropometric measurements, he attacked the concept of the racial purity of the German nation, a concept which was to be a plague visited upon Germany and to lead to the debacle of World War II. Just how far-sighted his vision was is evident from his remarks in the Annual Report of the Smithsonian Institution for 1889 (p. 563): "If different races would recognize one another as independent co-laborers in the great field of humanity, if all possessed a modesty which would allow them to see merits in neighboring people, much of the strife now agitating the world would disappear."

Having said all this, I verge on idolatry. Social medicine did not spring forth, fully formed, from the head of Virchow. He had predecessors and contemporaries in France (Cabanis, Villerme and Guepin) and in England (Thackrah, Gaskell, Chadwick and Engels), and such staunch co-workers in Germany as Neumann and Leubuscher[4]. Nor, of course, did he single-handedly create scientific medicine; indeed, he acknowledged himself to be the student of the great physiologist, Johannes Müller. Virchow was human and therefore fallible. His self-confidence about his views made him a pugnacious opponent and often verged on arro-gance. As a scientist, he remained a skeptic about the findings from the new science of bac-teriology and the evidence in favor of Darwinism well beyond the time when the accumu-lating facts should have been persuasive to him. As a clinical pathologist, his incorrect evaluation of the biopsy material taken from the throat cancer of Frederick III contributed to the mismanagement of his case[23]. As a politican, his long-standing anti-clericalism and over-riding concern for the separation of church and state led to his most serious political error: he sided with Bismarck in the latter's fight against the Catholic church!

Yet, these mistakes, and there were others, fade into insignificance against the majesty of his accomplishments in establishing cell doctrine as the basis of pathology, in recognizing the social causes of disease and in identifying the responsibility of physicians for the health of all citizens, matters which continue to be central to contemporary medicine. He remained a steadfast republican. It is to his everlasting credit that he never, as did so many others, repudiated the goals he had advocated during the revolutionary 1840's, even though those goals were beyond attainment in the conservative years of the last half of the century. Virchow, the man, may be dead; the record of his life remains as a beacon to guide ours.

When Virchow was forced to discontinue publication of *Die Medicinische Reform*, he wrote in his final editorial[24]: "The medical reform that we had in mind was a reform of science and society. We have developed its principles. They will make their way, even without the continued existence of this organ. But every moment will find us engaged in working for these principles and ready to fight for them. We do not abandon the cause, merely the approach . . ."

Today, the leading principle in the "reform of science and society"is the prevention of nuclear war. Unless we make it a reality, there will be no science and no society. Let us fight for that principle in the spirit of Rudolf Virchow.

BIBLIOGRAPHY

1 Lown, B. Nobel Peace Prize Lecture: A prescription for hope. New Eng. J. Med. 314: 985–987, 1986.
2 Snow, C.P. The moral un-neutrality of science. Science 133: 255-259, 1961.
3 Adams, R. and Cullen, S. (eds.) *The Final Epidemic –Physicians and Scientists on Nuclear War.* Chicago, Educational Foundation for Nuclear Science, 1981.
4 Rosen, G. What is social medicine? Bull. Hist. Med. 21: 674–733, 1947.
5 Ackerknecht, E. H. *Rudolf Virchow: Doctor, Statesman, Anthropologist.* Madison, University of Wisconsin Press, 1953.
6 Bismarck, O. *Die Gesammelten Werke,* Vol. XIV, part 2, *Briefe.* Berlin, O. Stolberg, 1924-35, pp. 695; 1154.
7 Stern, F. *Gold and Iron: Bismarck, Bleichröder and the Building of the German Empire.* New York, Random House, 1979, pp. 55.
8 Welch, W. H. Rudolf Virchow, Pathologist. Boston Med. and Surg. J. *CXXV: 453-457, 1891.*
9 *Virchow, R. Cellular Pathology.* Translated from the second edition of the original by F. Chance. New York, Robert M. DeWitt, 1860, p. 54.
10 Virchow R., *Collected Essays on Public Health and Epidemiology,* Vol. 1. L. J. Rather, ed. Canton MA, Watson Publishing International, 1985, p. 53–54.
11 Virchow, R. *Collected Essays,* Vol. 1. *Op. cit.,* p. 33
12 Virchow, R. Report on the typhus epidemic in Upper Silesia. In *Collected Essays,* Vol. 1. *Op. cit.,* pp. 205-319.
13 Southern, P. M. and Sanford, J. P. Relapsing fever: a clinical and microbiological review. Medicine 48: 129–149, 1969.
14 Osler, W. Rudolf Virchow, the man and the student. Boston Med. and Surg. J. *CXXV:* 425-427, 1891.
15 Virchow, R. Cited in Rosen, G., *Op. cit.*
16 Virchow, R. Cited in Ackerknecht, E. H. *Op. cit.,* p. 127.
17 McKeown. T. *The Role of Medicine: Dream, Mirage or Nemesis?* London, Nuffield Provincial Trust, 1976.
18 Kittagawa, E. M. and Hauser, P. M. *Differential Mortality in the United States: A Study in Socioeconomic Epidemiology.* Cambridge, Harvard University Press, 1973, p. 151.
19 Department of Health and Social Security. *Inequalities in Health: Report of a Research Working Group,* London, 1980.
20 Virchow, R. *Collected Essays,* Vol. 1. *Op. cit.,* p. 4.
21 Virchow, R. Cited in Ackerknecht, E. H. *Op. cit.,* p. 140
22 Virchow, R. Cited in Hanauske-Abel, H. M. and Obermair, G. Zivilisten haben keine Chance. Die Zeit, 18 September 1981.
23 Lin, J. I. Virchow's pathological reports on Frederick III's cancer. N. Eng. J. Med. 311: 1261-1264, 1984.
24 Virchow, R. *Collected Essays,* Vol. 1. *Op. cit.* p. 76.

Ian Prior, New Zealand

The Pacific Ocean and Nuclear Weapons

S ince the destruction of Hiroshima and Nagasaki by the Allies in 1945, nuclear
weaponry has had a greater direct effect on the Pacific region than on any other part of
the world. The aim of this paper will be to review briefly some of the direct effects of
atmospheric testing on small Pacific populations such as the Marshall Islanders, to examine
strategic missile testing in the Pacific, and how this is promoting or contributing to the
Strategic Defence Initiative or the Star Wars scenario. Most crucial to 1986, I wish to
highlight the way in which the Reagan administration in the past five years has revolutionised
naval warfare.

Put forward in 1986, the new strategy represents a move away from the "passive defence
strategy" of the past. Lehman's formula for "maritime superiority" actually threatens to be
provocative and destabilising, with the focus on "high threat areas", and more so as they
confront the Soviets in the Pacific in a way that is different from any other region. In doing
so, they concentrate on areas of Soviet weakness.

The nature of direct confrontation is such that senior U.S. Naval staff, including Admiral
Robert Lang in 1983, when relinquishing his position as CINPAC, told astonished Japanese
journalists, "The Pacific region, I believe, is where we will witness confrontation with the
Soviet Union."

Researchers Bello, Hayes and Zarsky of the Nautilus Pacific Action Research in the *South
East Asian Chronicle* described the array of U.S. weaponry, force deployments and
contingency plans in the Pacific as being as terrifying as the region is vast. Describing the new
Lehman "Forward Defence Strategy" at a Congressional Hearing in March 1984, Admiral
James D. Watkins, Chief of Naval Operations, simply stated in layman's language: "We go
for the jugular", and as one learns more and more about the strategy, it is quite clear that
major involvement of the carotids is also being planned for as well as the jugular, in order to
achieve maximum effect. In adopting this strategy, Japan, a nation already traumatised by
the Hiroshima and Nagasaki experience, is no longer simply a regional power concerned
with its own defence, but has become the tangible extension of a forward deployed offence-
oriented U.S. Naval strategy, over which they have no control. I repeat: over which they
have no control. The fact that the nuclear component of much of the U.S. armaments is
concealed by the "neither confirm nor deny" policy, and the reluctance of Japanese leaders
to question this crucifixion of their hard-won three non-nuclear policies will, we hope, build
up as a matter of political concern as the public gets stronger in their non-nuclear demands in
Japan and throughout the Pacific. The three non-nuclear prinicples in the Constitution are:

– No manufacture of nuclear weapons
– No introduction of nuclear weapons
– No possession of nuclear weapons.

It has been said that the citizens of New York and San Fransisco have similar concerns about home porting nuclear powered and nuclear weapon carrying vessels in their city ports.

The part being played in destabilising the Pacific by the new nuclear Tomahawk sea-launched cruise missiles (SLCM) and its Soviet counterpart 85-WX-21 will also be considered, together with comments on the complete absence of any moves toward arms control discussions or agreements by the Supperpowers in the Pacific region.

Finally I wish to discuss moves being made by people and governments within the region to try and shift political and moral dependence on deterrence by nuclear arms of the super-powers to a declaration of abhorrence of nuclear weapons and an unwillingness amounting to a total rejection of "protection" by them. The "protection" is in quotes since such protection is clearly an illusion. Is there a Pacific way that can encourage moves towards regional security measures and ways of putting forward a philosophy of "common security" as set out by Olof Palme and this committee that could be our goal? A philosophy? Wittgenstein recently stated: "The aim of philosophy is to show the fly the way out of the fly bottle." – Not only to get out, but surely also to prevent the fly getting into the bottle. – We need to work out how to put the genie of nuclear weapons back in the bottle.

Directions for IPPNW must also be related to these proposals so that we can continue to grow as a force in the world politic that can really show the way, or one of the ways towards prevention of nuclear war and bilateral disarmament and stable world peace. Clearly, there will be no single way whereby cooperation not confrontation can be achieved and translated from a professional level to a political level in the best sense of Virchow, as so well put forward by Dr. Leon Eisenberg this morning – medicine is social science, and politics is nothing but medicine on a grand scale. More than that, we have to rekindle and keep rekindling the awareness of ordinary people of the role they must play in doing it. The time has come for a new era of understanding between people, and IPPNW must take up the challenge of bringing this about.

Summary

1.   The 1981 change of strategy by the U.S. with adoption of the Lehman formula for maritime superiority has resulted in an extraordinary build-up in Air, Naval and Submarine U.S. forces in the Pacific. The Pacific as a U.S. lake with all the means to force the Soviets to increase their forces in the Pacific region and to ensure diversion of Soviet forces to the area so they can defend their territory, has been achieved.

2   The arms race is uncontrolled with no efforts at arms control between the Superpowers.

3.   The Cruise Missile deployment by both Superpowers will certainly destabilise the region still further.

4.   The close contact by U.S. and Soviet forces on a day to day basis could lead to an altercation, to limited nuclear war and then to general nuclear war.

5.   The involvement of Japan in bases and communications control and command systems places them in the front line for a war they may not wish.

6.   The placement of nuclear weapons, the admission of nuclear capable and carrying vessels to Japanese ports has violated the three Japanese constitutional principles of no manufacture, no admission and no possession of nuclear vessels. The blind acceptance by Japanese leaders of the "neither confirm nor deny" principle adopted by such countries as the U.S. and the U.K. has allowed this charade to continue. 82 per cent of Japanese people are aware of this but are either unable or unwilling to challenge the Government.

7.   The anti-nuclear stand taken by New Zealand and the introduction of legislation which will prevent by legislation any entry of nuclear powered or nuclear capable vessels or aeroplanes to New Zealand represents a major step forward in arms control in the region. This is based on support from more than 74 per cent of the population who on a recent poll stated that there were no circumstances whereby they would accept the protection by nuclear weapons.

8.   Mr. David Lange, Prime Minister, has on many occasions articulated clearly how this was not only for our own safety, but that there was also a very strong moral imperative which had made people of New Zealand make this choice and elect a government committed to this major step.

9.   The New Zealand Government has been put under considerable pressure by the U.S. Government because of the effect this would have on the long-standing ANZUS Treaty between Australia, New Zealand and the U.S. This is not a nuclear alliance, and Mr. Lange has said New Zealand would participate in a conventional but not a nuclear alliance. 82 per cent of the U.S. Naval vessels travelling to New Zealand are nuclear capable, and 95 per cent likely to be carrying nuclear weapons, and this raises questions as to whether the U.S. could accept a non-nuclear alliance. High U.S. officials have said ANZUS is dead unless we change.

10.   The quality of diplomats has improved notably since New Zealand took the stand, and a much more professional approach towards New Zealand and the South Pacific is being adopted. Countries like Fiji are also subject to pressure, having had a non-nuclear policy in the past and then changed to welcome the U.S. The South Pacific Nuclear Free Zone Treaty has been accepted by the majority of South Pacific Forum countries, but some, including Vanuatu and the Solomons believe this is not strong enough in its excluding of nuclear ships transiting in the region. It is a step forward, however, and the nuclear powers are being approached to ratify it.

* * *

The stand by New Zealand has been applauded by people in many countries and it is the strong hope that other countries will follow in the best way they can. A goal would be total exclusion of nuclear weapons from all countries except the five nuclear nations together with moves to implement a comprehensive test ban treaty. There is strong feeling that the nuclear superpowers, particularly the U.S., will require an extraordinary change in outlook toward the "security" offered by nuclear weapons before real progress can be made. The goal of "common security" so clearly envisaged by Olof Palme, and moves to an effective detente would be very consistent with a Pacific way of tackling this problem.

IPPNW together with other scientific groups such as SANA, engineers, represent *the* most highly skilled and effective groups working towards nuclear wind down, balanced reduction of nuclear arms and stable world peace. IPPNW by its East/West nature has a major responsibility to do all it can to help improve East/West relations. Bernard Lown has recommended the establishment of highly competent groups to start examining the areas of disturbed imagery we harbour of one another. Before we treat, we diagnose. – To do this, the IPPNW as a Federation and its members must seek for what Goethe said all men and women needed: material and spiritual independence.

The Pacific way – based on how small societies function in the Pacific – depends on discussion, listening and respect for the individual – communication and interchange at many levels of our societies is paramount if Dr. Lown's idea is to be effectively implemented and if it is to change in any way why people want to be a party to an arms race that is bleeding the world dry. How was it that Bob Geldorf and his team were able to get 30 million people for "I Run the World, the Race Against Time"? Because of the extraordinary inequality that exists – made worse by the arms race. IPPNW must extend its *base* of support if we are to move on to material and spiritual independence.

– IPPNW Education and Research Trust is a move we have made to extend our base of support in the community. Ordinary people, business houses and bequests are all being sought. Already the Trust is helping IPPNW in its activities.
– Why not similar Education and Research Trusts in other countries in the Eastern bloc and Western bloc to help us meet our goals? We have the opportunity to make this meeting the start of a New Era, and that could be an easily understood explanatory description: "IPPNW Education & Research Trust – towards a New Era".
– The Asian Pacific Meeting, February 9/10, 1987.
  We invite you to this meeting.
– Finally, a Pacific tradition is to exchange gifts – without any mention of when repayment will occur.

Our Co-Presidents have given all of us a great deal; they have stimulated us into action, into committment and into listening. On behalf of our Pacific groups, I would like to give you each a Fiji club – not a strange gift really. A reminder that they were used for conflict resolution by Fijians but on a one to one basis, not like a nuclear weapon of comparable size, killing indiscriminately. But also because they will have many other uses – but I will leave these to their ingenuity. Perhaps as a *gavel* for council meetings, but most of all as a reminder that they come with our aroha and love, and we look forward to their visit to the Pacific in February 1987.

THE CONGRESS LECTURES

Harmut Hanauske-Abel, Federal Repbulic of Germany

Medicine under National-Socialism

A lbert Schweitzer. In the fifties one of the most outspoken critics of nuclear weapons development and deployment. His almost forgotten Radio Oslo broadcasts entitled "An Appeal to Mankind"and "Peace or Nuclear War" present a series of arguments that today are re-emphasized by IPPNW: the illusion of disaster planning and civil defense under the special conditions of thermonuclear explosions; the potential for accidental nuclear war and for failure of control, command, communication; the disastrous biological consequences of radioactive fall-out. In this country, according to a recent poll, Albert Schweitzer is by far the most respected personality of the century, and he is considered to be *the* physician, to represent the archetypical healer. Germans love to think of him as being German. Indeed, the language of all his manuscripts in final version was German – with one remarkable exception: Albert Schweitzer, the Nobel Peace Prize Laureate, considered it inappropriate to give his Nobel Address in German, he deliberately chose to speak French. In 1795, Immanuel Kant had written his treaty "On Eternal Peace", in which he studied how "to by all means condemn War as a legal procedure, whereas make the condition of Peace in immediate obligation", written in German of course – but in 1954, the German language did not suit the message of Schweitzer's speech, the preservation of Peace. The very sound of Kant's native tongue, his "den Krieg als Rechtsgang schlechterdings verdammen, den Friedenszustand dagegen zur unmittelbaren Pflicht machen", globally enforced associations of horror unprecedented in human history, horror organized by commands in German. Never before Schweitzer's decision was any language considered unqualified to express the desire for mankind's peaceful development, never before had any Nobel Prize Laureate hesitated to give his traditional Lecture in German.

But then again, it was a German government, a decree in German that, in January 1937, made it a criminal offense to accept Nobel Prizes – and indeed, Domagk and Butenandt had to refuse to be decorated for the discovery of the sulfonamides and for the elucidation of steroid hormone structure, respectively; it were German executives who denied the release of a concentration camp interned citizen for the sole reason of being a Nobel Peace Prize Laureate, and instead made his emprisonment an affair of national interest; it were German physicians who very early diagnosed the potentially fatal illness of this state prisoner and who did not implement proper treatment even in the late stages of his disease.

Carl von Ossietzky, Nobel Peace Prize Winner of 1936, was editor of the legendary magazine "Die Weltbühne" and most critical of post-World War I Germany with its relentlessly persistent, antidemocratic nationalistic tradition. Writing about Hitler's rise, he concluded in 1931 that this man and his "Drittes Reich" would "perish", dragging the entire nation into disaster, and he predicted in "Die Weltbühne": "Never again will Germany exist as a united nation". In 1933, the new administration immediately arrested him, and in a unique move, ordered the German Ambassador in Oslo to warn the Nobel Peace Prize Committee against nominating Ossietzky, just to "avoid the impression of an intentionally anti-German demonstration" – Ossietzky was nominated nevertheless, and he dared to accept. Ossietzky suffered from latent pulmonary tuberculosis. During years of imprisonment without trial in concentration camp and state penitentiary, the aggravation of his physical condition was professionally monitored. To quote from his 1936 medical record: "Severe open tuberculosis, with masses of mycobacteria in the sputum, extremely increased erythrocyte sedimentation rate, etc. The entire left upper lobe is affected, cavitation is prominent." By 1937, the Gestapo had to recognize that Ossietzky's disease was endangering – his guards. Only because of "the considerable risk of infecting Government officials" was Ossietzky transfered to a specialized hospital, were he died under close custody a few months later.

The Administration inaugurated January 30, 1933, was welcomed by the German Chamber of Physicians, the national association of the medical doctors, as the advent of a new time. In July of 1933, with high-handed nation-wide mass imprisonment for half a year, Ossietzky at this time was in the concentration camp at Sonnenburg, the "Law for the Reconstitution of Civil Service", custom-made to eliminate all "non-Aryan" official, was already for three months effective, Jewish physicians were boycotted and the SS warned patients against entering their waiting-rooms, the German telegram-offices refused to accept the spelling of Jewish names – in July 1933, the *Deutsches Ärzteblatt*, the official organ of the German Chamber of Physicians, carried this title page. That lay-out is extraordinary: the cover usually presented as a monochrome dark-blue page, optically non-aggressive. The swastika-embroidered red flag, proudly flying side by side with and in front of the German tricolor in black-white-red, and, as you may read in the right lower corner, the presentation of this July edition as "Number 1" unmistakably symbolize the beginning of the long desired national resurrection.

To understand the historic trait that produced this title page, one has to consider the tremendous national sentiment among German scientists, and German physicians in particular, becoming more and more prevalent after the Prussian victory in 1871 and after the consecutive formation of a German state. In late 1914, at the outset of the Great War, this sentiment motivated the formulation of a singular document, the "Manifesto of the Ninety-three". The citizens of Louvain had joined their troops in fighting the Imperial German Armies that did invade Belgium despite its declaration of neutrality. The Germans retaliated by shooting the local dignitaries, shelling the city and the ancient cathedral and burning the University Library. The international outcry was countered by this Manifesto, stating: "Our voice shall be the herald of truth. It is not true that we have broken the neutrality of Belgium. It is not true that the life or the property of a single Belgian citizen was even touched by our soldiers. It is not true that our High Command has disrespected International Law. It is not true that our troops rampaged the city of Löwen. However, we strictly refuse to pay the price of a Germen defeat just to preserve artistic or cultural objects. It is not true that the fight against our so-called militarism is not, at the same time, a fight against our culture. Without German militarism, German culture would have been wiped out. To protect our culture, it gave birth to our militarism. German army and German people are one and the same. This we guarantee with our names and our word of honour." The Manifesto was signed by the

Slide 3:
Deutsches
Ärzteblatt
1933

intellectual elite of Wilhelmine Germany, and among the ninetythree were Wilhelm Röntgen, Emil von Behring, August von Wassermann, Albert Neisser, Paul Ehrlich, Emil Fischer, Fritz Haber, Walter Nernst, Wilhelm Ostwald, Max Planck. Only two leading scientists protested against this manifesto: Albert Einstein; and one of the pioneers of electrocardiography in Germany, private cardiologist to the German Imperial family, distinguished Professor of Physiology and Internal Medicine at the Charité and the University of Berlin, Georg Friedrich Nicolai. The Prussian authorities did not dare to trouble the Swiss Einstein, but Nicolai was a German citizen – immediately he was detailed to a military infirmary. When he publicly critized the unlimited submarine warfare and the use of poison gas by the German Imperial Army, calling it "as criminal as idiotic", he was as-signed to an infantry unit as a common soldier and ordered to swear the oath of enlistment. Nicolai conscientiously refused and escaped, causing a nation-wide man-hunt by the civil-ian, military and secret police. It was Albert Einstein who, in his private house in Berlin, Ha-berlandstraße 36, hid his fugitive friend for several weeks, and enabled him to flee to Scan-dinavia in the summer of 1918. There Nicolai was welcomed as a representative of the Other Germany, he was nominated for the 1919 Nobel Peace Prize. Upon resuming his academic duties at Berlin University in 1920, his first lecture was interrupted by the medical students: a "deserter" should never be allowed to educate the future generation of German physicians, they claimed, and, to underline their academic argument, they produced the evidence of – revolvers, knives, and brass knuckles. The Rector of the University, one of the signers of the "Manifesto of the Ninetythree", offered Nicolai to install a peer committee of inquiry for restoring "trust and confidence", and Nicolai agreed. The committee concluded –: that the students' charges were justified and correct in all points, a traitor to his country should never educate German physicians, that Nicolai's conduct was detrimental to national interest during the war, that, irrespective of his achievements as a clinician-scientist, his character was incompatible with the dignity of the University of Berlin. For these reasons, the committee unanimously suspended him. Nicolai emigrated in the early twenties.

Slide 4:
G. F. Nicolai

At the same time, a physician in Munich, Dr. Gutberlet, financially secured the acquisition of a newspaper by the recently founded NSDAP, the Nationalsozialistische Deutsche Arbei-ter Partei. That newpaper received the name *Der Völkische Beobachter*, it immediately became the party's propaganda platform and was instrumental for the spectacular rise to power within just a few years. Numerous physicians rapidly assumed pivotal roles in the hier-archy of the swastika party and its affiliated organisations, and of all university graduated party members, physicians constituted the largest group. Among German medical doctors, swastika party members definitely were a minority, the number of supportes and sym-pathizers was much larger, however, and professional opposition both inside and outside the various physicans' organisations was isolated and fragmented. Indeed, the adaptation of the major organisations to the priorities of the new administration occured as an amazingly smooth process, achieved within a few weeks and at times indiscernible from self-submission. Essential for that collusion was the pervasive, traditionally national sentiment of the profession. As a vignette: The medical student who organized the disruption of Prof. Nicolai's first post-war lecture at the University of Berlin in January 1920 was Leonardo Conti, and he praised himself for contributing to the "expulsion of that Jewish deserter"; Dr. Leonardo Conti became the highest ranking physician of the new administration; he was Reichsärzteführer, the top executive of all German physicians, and – he personally initiated the medicalized killing in several concentration camps, he personally supervised the "Euthanasia Program" designed to extinguish patients as "life unworthy of life". In this

Slide 5:
Brandenburger
Tor 1933

republic, the events during spring 1933 still are subject of the most controversal debate, and fifty years later, in 1983, the *Deutsches Ärzteblatt* published a series on this period. In these articles, I could not find a single expression of human concern or mourning. All the insight presented is: it totally was a question of social security and insurance technicalities, the offers of the new administration were irresistable. On sixteen pages, Dr. Conti is mentioned twice; Dr. Haedenkamp is mentioned 31 times, with ten per cent of the text from his original 1933 articles, quoted in the most favorable way.

Dr. Haedenkamp was a leading administration specialist and editor of the *Deutsches Ärzteblatt* before and after the inauguration of the new administration. He had written one of the programmatic articles of that "Number 1" July 1933 edition, and as a technocrat, he was instrumental in implementing the "de-Jewing" of the German physicians. After 1945, as a technocrat, he was instrumental in reconstructing the German Chamber of Physicians, and in 1954, was awarded one of the highest civilian decorations of this country. The series that started with this cover may be deciphered as a pro-Haedenkamp plea. "Would it have changed anything if the physicians' organisations had resisted the pressure of the new administration, and if they had not resigned voluntarily?" The question implies that there was no choice except not to act. Not to act, however, is to act. That lay-out is extraordinary: the front title, in an idiomatic German expression, states that the process of adaptation was an over-night affair, coming by surprise, a twist of fate, inevitable, unanticipated. This is corrective surgery, and in a Freudian slip, the cover announces corrective surgery – of carniofacial dysplasias.

Dr. Haedenkamp's career should not be used to discredit him. Dr. Haedenkamp was a professional in his field just like Dr. Wernher von Braun was a specialist in his, one made any administration run, the other made any rockets fly – their challenge was "how", not "what for". The philosophy of such proefessionalism is that by doing your job, you do nothing else but your job, and this is entirely a question of performance, not of responsibility. After all, would it have changed anything if Drs. Haedenkamp and von Braun had resisted the pressure of the new administration, and if they had not joined in voluntarily? Exactly that
philosophy was prevalent among the German medical community when the new administration was inaugurated. Physicians don't have any political mandate, do they? They have to care for patients, not for parties. They have to cure, not to criticize. Medicine starts with a patient stepping into the physicians's office – you don't practice medicine in your waiting room, and even less in the streets or in the factories. Virchow and his "Politics is nothing else but Medicine on a grand scale"? Good grief, he was a pathologist with all those mortal remains around, so somehow he had to pep up his conception of medicine – if he ever had seen living patients, he would have known better: Real medicine starts when a real patient enters your office.

With that attitude, there was no preparedness to react when the new administration started to single out individual colleagues, stigmatizing them as "Bolsheviks" or "Jews". With that attitude, German medicine allowed the amputation of its elite and was unable to organize any protest. Up to summer 1933, already 235 professors of medicine and biology had left the country; the Charité in Berlin lost, within a few years, 138 members of faculty; among the German emigrants were Sigmund Freud and numerous future Nobel Prize Laureates of the biological sciences like Chain, Loewi, Krebs, Perutz, and also of the physical sciences like Bethe, Stern, Born, Penzias, just to name a few and not to speak of those that already were Laureates, like Meyerhof or Einstein. Some argue that to this very day, German medicine and science could not compensate these losses.

Placards like that could be seen all over this country. It warns against consulting Jewish physicians or lawyers, and gives their names. Other posters put the names of German patients to the pillory who ignored the call for boycott and continued to expose themselves to un-German physicians. According to the conception of the new administration, medicine no longer had to preserve the integrity of an individual body; medicine had to serve the benefit of the collective body of the German people, and that mission was in complete agreement with the relentlessly persistent, tremendous national sentiment prevalent in the medical community. Exclusively "Aryan" physicians, according to the new administration, where qualified to secure German racial health – within a few years, over ninety percent of "non-Aryan" physicians were "eliminated", with considerable economic benefit for the remaining "Aryan" colleges, and by 1938, "non-Aryan" physicians were prohibited from having "Aryan" patients and from carrying the title "medical doctor", they were designated "treater of the sick", Krankenbehandler. This "New German Medicine" also provided the criteria for differentiating between "Aryan" and "non-Aryan", most convincingly evidenced by skull geometry or shape of ears. German professors were working on in vitro tests for diagnosing the "non-Aryan" genome from a blood sample, and racial biology and racial hygienics became essential parts of the curriculum for medical students. In the interest of continuous medical education, the *Deutsches Ärzteblatt* published articles on the differential diagnosis and phenotypic appearance of genetic inferiority, like this one, entitled "Identification and eradication of those unfit for the collective", Erkennung und Ausmerzung der Gemeinschaftsunfähigen. "Non-Aryan" individuals, foreign to the "Aryan" constitution of the German people, had invaded its collective body and infected its organs – Ossietzky was one of those pathogens, that is why his guards, as representatives of the collective German body, had to be protected against him. Accordingly, such microbes had to be dealt with in exactly the way health professionals cope with living pathogenic agents: in Ossietzky's case it was isolation, but in general, disinfection was the therapeutic imperative – and the word "disinfection" indeed was routine to designate the industrialized slaughter of human beings. "They have been disinfected" stood for: they have been gassed. In this imagery of killing in the name of healing, it was just a coincidence that the Krankheitserreger, the pathogenic microbes displayed human anatomy. The treatment of these infectious agents was not supposed to collide with the Hippocrate Oath or with reverence for human life. In the words of Dr. Klein, physician at Auschwitz where these two children were killed: "Out of respect for human life, I would remove a purulent appendix from a diseased body. When you find a gangrenous appendix, you must remove it." So these physicians did their job – and by doing their job, they did nothing else but their job, and this entirely was a question of performance, not of responsibility. The machinery was disassembled into individual elements, and each one was expected to just function professionally. Would it have changed anything if one wheel had resisted the pressure of the machinery, and if it had not turned voluntarily? The transports were arranged professionally by a conventional travel agency, with group discount and special excursion rates of course, and the trains' route, in this case to Auschwitz-Birkenau, professionally planned by the railway board. All the specialists just did their jobs, and so did the physicians: selection of arriving transports, here at the Birkenau ramp, with more than seventy percent "to be disinfected" immediately: on the way to the chambers, the escorting physicians were riding in a red-cross marked vehicle together with medical technicians; these "disinfectors" inserted the gas pellets, doctors had to declare the successful completion of the mission. In this process of treating the sick racial body of the German people by mass murder therapy, doctors assumed a number of key functions, and

Slide 8:
Placard

Slide 9:
Textbook
Photograph

Slide 10:
Article in
*Deutsches
Ärzteblatt*

Slide 11:
Microscope

Slide 12:
Auschwitz-
Children

Slide 13
Ramp of
Auschwitz
before triage

Slide 14:
Ramp of
Auschwitz
after triage

Slide 15:
Document

and the first commandant of Treblinka was a physician, Dr. Eberl. – "Material: head of a body"; in parentheses: "Twelve year old child". "For histologic sections"; "Department of origin: gypsy camp at Auschwitz", signed "Dr. Mengele". In his twin studies, this German physician occasionally had one or both children killed, for experimental reasons. He had started his investigations at the Institute of Racial Biology, Faculty of Medicine, University of Frankfurt/Main. That Faculty of Medicine was established by a donation of Jewish citizens in 1914.

Slide 16:
Article from
Münchener
Medizinische
Wochenschrift

Reports on experiments with humans were published in the German medical literature, like this one in the *Münchner Medizinische Wochenschrift*, still today one of the leading journals of this country. In the passage, one can read in extra bold print "experiments in man-to-man infection", the publication is concerned with hepatitis. The text does not, for instance, indicate the voluntary participation of a thirty year old woman whose tuberculosis became reactivated already "after the first application". Prof. Gutzeit, who initiated this study, was the highest ranking internist of the German Army, and he participated in planning such investigations at the Sachsenhausen concentration camp. Dr. Conti initiated and organized large scale experiments in the Natzweiler and Buchenwald concentration camps to study rickettsioses and the effect of anti-rickettsial vaccination – and to propagate *R. prowazeki*, human beings were used as culture medium. Dr. Conti committed suicide while awaiting his trial in Nuremberg.

Slide 17:
Prisoner with
oxygen-mask in
a hypobaric
chamber

For his appointment as university lecturer, Dr. Rascher, at the Dachau concentration camp, performed experiments on adults to study hypothermic and hypobaric trauma and to investigate the pharmacological acceleration of blood coagulation. He coined the notion of "terminal experiment" – the death of the test person was an integral part of the experimental protocol. On three occasions in 1942, results of his studies, without mincing matters, were presented to a professional civilian and military audience; no protests. In the blood coagulation studies, humans were deliberately shot and left unattended, in order not to interfere with the post-mortem findings. A Russian prisoner of war was, in a hypobaric

Slide 18:
Autopsy of this
prisoner

chamber, exposed to an altitude of 21 kilometres, his death was filmed, even the autopsy was picturized. When American troops advanced towards Dachau, Dr. Rascher and his wife, by order of Himmler, were executed.

Slide 19:
Leika Klyger-
mann

For his appointment as university lecturer, Dr. Heißmeyer, at the Neuengamme con-centration camp, performed experiments on children to study the effect of cutaneous tuberculosis in cases of pulmonary tbc-infection. To histologically document the iatrogenic disease, axillar lymph nodes were excised and examined. The name of this child was Leika Klygermann, she was eight years old and born in Poland. When British troops had reached the outscirts of Hamburg, Arnold Strippel, the commandant, ordered the execution of all the children. The physician in charge, Dr. Trzebinski, narcotized each of them with morphium, and they all were strangulated.

The British military government executed Dr. Trzebinski; the German Democratic Republic sentenced Dr. Heißmeyer to a penal servitude for life. Arnold Stippel escaped the British and stayed in the Federal Republic. After a first verdict in 1949, the appeals and counterappeals dragged on for decades; in 1970, Arnold Strippel, as compensation for "innocently endured imprisonment", received 150,000 DM.

When, in 1947, Prof. Alexander Mitscherlich, in later years one of the most out-standing of all post-war German physicians, edited the medical documents of the Nuremberg trial, an entire book on medicalized killing, he was denounced by the leading medical authorities as a traitor to his country – his presentation of facts was detriment to the reputation of German medicine, they argued, and they tried to dequalify and discredit him. The gazette of the University of Göttingen personally attacked him repeatedly, but the editors were reluctant to publish his answer. Since Nicolai, that non-sensible, relentless national sentiment – personally, I think it is *one* element even in the most recent decisions and publications of the German Chamber of Physicians – that unconvincible, relentless, stubborn national sentiment had remained unaltered. Prof. Mitscherlich's collegues lacked the willingness to understand how mass murder could silently be accepted as an expression of the collective's healing process, how medicine could become an integral part of the Auschwitz system, how physicians could function in the world that Paul Celan, survivor of the Czernowitz getto and one of the geniuses of German language, described in his 1948 "Todesfuge", "Death Fugue":

Slide 20:
Gate of
Auschwitz
Concentration
Camp

Black milk of daybreak we drink it at sundown
we drink it at noon in the morning we drink it at night
we drink and we drink it
A man lives in the house he plays with the serpents he writes
he writes when dusk falls to Germany your golden hair Margarete
he writes it and steps out of doors and the stars are flashing he whistles his pack out
he whistles his Jews out in earth has dig them dig for a grave
he commands us strike up for the dance
He calls out jab deeper into the earth you lot you others sing now and play
he grabs at the iron in his belt he waves it his eyes are blue
jab deeper you lot with your spades you others play on for the dance
He calls out more sweetly play death death is a master from Germany
he calls out more darkly now strike your strings then as smoke you will rise into air
then a grave you will have in the clouds there one lies unconfined
Black milk of daybreak we drink you at night
we drink you at noon death is a master from Germany
we drink you at sundown and in the morning we drink and we drink you
death is a master from Germany

Willi Graf, member of The White Rose. – Would it have changed anything if the physicians' organisations had resisted the pressure of the new administration, and if they had not resigned voluntarily? He never would have asked a question like that. If I, a German medical doctor, still can face an international audience of physicians, it is because of men like him. Sophie Scholl, member of the White Rose. – Would it have changed anything if the physicians' organisations had resisted the pressure of the new administration, and if they had not resigned voluntarily? She never would have asked a question like that. If I, a German medical doctor, still can face an international audience of physicians, it is because of women like her.

Slide 21:
Willi Graf

Slide 22:
Sophie Scholl

They just had time to formulate six leaflets, a total of thirteen pages, in 1942 and early 1943. They were all students of medicine, biology, or chemistry, supported by Prof. Kurt Huber of the University of Munich.

"We *must* attack the evil where it is most powerful. Do not hide your cowardice under the cloak of sophistication. Everybody is in a position to contribute to the fall of this system. What matters now is, not to allow oneself any rest until everybody is convinced of the utmost importance of his fight against this order. Just as an example do we mention the fact that, since the conquest of Poland, threehundredthousand Jews have been murdered with extraordinary bestiality. We see the most horrible crime against the dignity of man, a crime that is unprecedented in all of human history. Why is apathy the reaction of the German nation? Almost nobody seems to care. Should that indicate that Germans are brutalized in their basic attitudes? We warn against any optimism. Everybody strives to acquit oneself of complicity, everybody does it and then sleeps with a clear and peaceful mind. But none can be exonerated, everyone is *guilty, guilty, guilty!* We will not be silent, we are your bad conscience, the White Rose will not grant you any rest."

Slide 23:
Riot at the
University of
Munich January
1943

The leaflets were distributed nationwide. Their effect stunned that German government, and despite an all-out effort, the Gestapo did succeed only in identifying the city of origin, Munich. The impact of these leaflets was dramatic: on January 13, 1943, during the celebration of the 470th anniversary of the Maximilians University, the Munich students felt encouraged to interrupt the provocative speech of Paul Gießler, who held one of the most prestigious positions of the swastika party, Gauleiter of Munich and Upper Bavaria. The students disarmed the police in the building, and marched downtown in protest against the regime. Munich was put under martial law, and although telephone and telegram service was discontinued immediately, the unrest spread to Frankfurt, Vienna and the Ruhr region.

Slide 24:
Hans Scholl

To unify the German resistance movement, Hans Scholl planned to meet, in Berlin on February 25, 1943, Dietrich Bonhoeffer and Klaus von Dohnanyi, who later were killed by that German government. Just a week before the crucial meeting, on February 18, 1943, Hans Scholl and his sister Sophie were arrested while distributing leaflets on the Munich campus. Four days later, they were sentenced to death, four hours later they both were executed. Also executed were Willi Graf, Christoph Probst, Alexander Schmorell, Hans Leipelt, and Prof. Kurt Huber. In one of his last letters, Hans Scholl wrote:

"I am overwhelmed by a dedication to heal. I feel that I can achieve the ultimate in medicine. A physician must be a philosopher and politician at the same time. That is why the recent years were more a gain than a loss. Whatever textbook knowledge I may not have acquired, I can make up the deficit easily. But I am now able to discern man's role in both the world and the state, man, who is the sole center of medical thinking."

Slide 25:
The Original
Text

"Ich sehe, daß ein Arzt Philosoph und Politiker sein muß. So waren also die verflossenen Jahre eher ein Gewinn als ein Verlust. Denn was ich an rein fachlichem Wissen verloren habe, werde ich rasch nachgeholt haben. Dafür aber kann ich den Menschen, der immer im Mittelpunkt des ärztlichen Denkens steht, in die Welt und in den Staat einordnen."

As physicians, we cannot under any circumstances avoid responsibility. For the sake of our patients, we have to be professionals. But for the sake of our patients and our people in this nuclear age, we must understand that not to act is to act, and that by just doing our job, nothing is done at best. Will it change anything if the physicians' organisations resist the nuclear arms build-up in East and West, and if they do not resign voluntarily?

We *must* attack the evil where it is most powerful. Do not hide your cowardice under the cloak of sophistication. Everybody is in a position to contribute to the fall of the nuclear system. What matters now is, not to allow oneself any rest until everybody is convinced of the utmost importance of his fight against this disorder.

BIBLIOGRAPHY

Allensbach poll, March 1985; reprinted in: *Stern* 26: 52–58.

Bringmann F. Kindermord am Bullenhuserdamm. Frankfurt: Röderberg-Verlag, 1979.

Celan P. Gesammelte Werke. Vol. 1. Frankfurt: Suhrkamp, 1983; 41–42.

Chagoll L. Im Namen Hitlers. Kinder hinter Stacheldraht. Frankfurt: Röderberg, 1979.

Editorial. Einspruch der DDR-Sektion! *Deutsches Ärzteblatt* 1986; 83: 917.

Frei B. Carl v. Ossietzky. Berlin: Arsenal, 1978.

Gilbert M. Endlösung. Reinbek: Rowohlt, 1982.

Ginzel G. B. Jüdischer Alltag in Deutschland 1933–1945. Düsseldorf: Droste, 1984.

Hanser R. Deutschland zuliebe. München: Deutscher Taschenbuch Verlag, 1984.

Jachertz N. Die neuen Herren kamen über Nacht. *Deutsches Ärzteblatt* 1983, 80: 23–26.

Kant I. Zum ewigen Frieden. Stuttgart: Reclam, 1953.

Klee, E. "Euthanasie" im NS-Staat. Frankfurt: Fischer, 1985.

Klee E. Dokumente zur "Euthanasie". Frankfurt: Fischer, 1985.

Kudlien F. (Ed.) Ärzte im Nationalsozialismus. Köln: Kiepenheuer, 1985.

Kudlien F. Der Ärzte-Anteil an der frühen NS-Bewegung. *Medizinhist. J.* 1984; 19: 363–384.

Lanzmann C. Shoah. Düsseldorf: Claassen, 1985.

Lechler Kl. Erkennung und Ausmerze der Gemeinschaftsunfähigen. *Deutsches Ärzteblatt* 1940; 70: 293–297.

Lilienthal G. Der "Lebensborn e. V.". Stuttgart: G. Fischer, 1985.

Lingens-Reiner E. Prisoners of Fear. London: Gollancz, 1948.

Lifton, R. J. Medicalized killing in Auschwitz. *Psychiatry* 1982; 45: 283–297.

Mitscherlich A., Mielke F. Medizin ohne Menschlichkeit. Frankfurt: Fischer, 1985.

Mitscherlich A., Mielke F. Das Diktat der Menschenverachtung. Heidelberg: Schneider, 1947.

Mitscherlich A., Mielke F. Wissenschaft ohne Menschlichkeit. Heidelberg: Schneider, 1949.

Mitscherlich A. Unmenschliche Wissenschaft. *Göttinger Universitäts-Zeitung* 1947; 2: Nr. 17/18, 6–7.

Mitscherlich A. Protest oder Einsicht? *Göttinger Universitäts-Zeitung* 1948; 3: Nr. 10, 6–8.

Mitscherlich A. Absicht und Erfolg. *Göttinger Universitäts-Zeitung* 1948; 3: Nr. 3, 4–5.

Mitscherlich A. Ein Leben für die Psychoanalyse. Frankfurt: Suhrkamp, 1984.

Müller-Hill B. Tödliche Wissenschaft. Reinbek: Rowohlt, 1984.

Nicolai G. F. Die Biologie des Krieges. Zürich: Orell Füssli, 1917.

Ossietzky, C. v. Rechenschaft. Frankfurt: Fischer, 1984.

Rein, F. H. Wissenschaft und Unmenschlichkeit. *Göttinger Universitäts-Zeitung* 1947; 2: Nr. 14, 3–5.

Rein, F. H. Vorbeigeredet. *Göttinger Universitäts-Zeitung* 1947; 2: Nr. 17/18, 7–8.

Seaver G. Albert Schweitzer. New York: Harper, 1955.

Scholl H., Scholl S. Briefe und Aufzeichnungen. Edited by I. Jens. Frankfurt: Fischer, 1984.

Scholl I. Die Weiße Rose. Frankfurt: Fischer, 1982.

Schweitzer A. Friede oder Atomkrieg. München: Beck, 1985; 33–91.

Schweitzer A. Gesammelte Schriften. Vol. I–II. Edited by R. Grabs. München: Beck, 1974.

Stanic D. ... und draußen blühen Blumen. Kinder im KZ. Berlin: Elephanten Press, 1982

Stuchlik G. Goethe im Braunhemd. Frankfurt: Roederberg, 1984.

Voegt, H. Zur Aetiologie der Hepatitis epidemica. *Münch. Med. Wschr.* 1942; 89: 76–79.

Verhoeven M., Krebs M. Der Film Die Weisse Rose. Das Drehbuch. Karlsruhe: v. Loeper, 1982.

Wuttke-Groneberg W. Medizin in Nationalsozialismus. Tübingen: Schwäbische Verlagsanstalt, 1980.

Zuelzer W. Der Fall Nicolai. Frankfurt: Societät, 1981.

THE CONGRESS LECTURES

Richard Garwin, U.S.A.

Nuclear Weapons and Space

I want to begin my talk about nucelar weapons and space with a little personal history. I was involved in building the first hydrogen bomb in the years 1951 and 1952 and I've worked on offensive and defensive weapon systems for the United States government including ICBMs, intercontinental ballistic missiles, air defense, ballistic missile defense, and the like. I served for eight years on the President's Science Advisory Committee for Presidents Kennedy, Johnson and Nixon. In addition to working on weapons and making technical contributions I have also tried to help with the formulation of policy – not only more weapons but *fewer* weapons if that is in the national and world interest. And so I've had a lot of experience and involvement beginning in 1958 in the Conference on Prevention of Surprise Attack and the 1963 Limited Nuclear Test Ban Treaty which ensures that all explosions of the signatories are underground now; the 1972 Treaty banning all effective defense against strategic ballistic missiles by the United States and the Soviet Union, and the SALT I agreement of that year. Then there was the 1979 SALT II Treaty which was signed by the leaders of the United States and the Soviet Union, never ratified by the United States and now very much in doubt. But still holding firm are the 1967 Outer Space Treaty which bans the placing of nuclear weapons, or weapons of mass destruction, into orbit and the 1963 Draft Treaty which is the Limited Nuclear Test Ban Treaty. Now it is too bad, in my opinion, that we don't have a total ban on nuclear explosions and I will explain why I think we ought to have one soon.

There *have* been nuclear explosions in space, but a lot of you are too young to remember or maybe you weren't interested at the time. In 1958 there was a series of nuclear explosions by the United States – small ones in the South Atlantic, a marvelous technological achievement at the beginning of the space age with the rockets carrying them into space launched from an aircraft carrier. In 1962 we had a very substantial test series with large nuclear explosions up to some four megatons in the South Pacific. And the Soviet Union has also had space nuclear explosions – neither of us since the signing of the Limited Test Ban in 1963.

There have been previous considerations of nuclear weapons permanently in space in addition to the thousands or tens of thousands that will fly through space at the beginning of a nuclear war on their missile carriers. But the Soviet Union in the early 1960s tested not the nuclear explosive but the rocket carrier in the so-called fractional orbit bombardment system

(FOBS) and a multiple orbit bombardment system. This is a foolish way to plan to deliver nuclear weapons in comparison with the simple way of having them sit safely on a rocket at one end until you want to use them, and then fly a quarter world away to destroy people in the target area. Orbital dynamics are really very simple, you just have to think about it a moment. A nuclear weapon in a low-earth orbit certainly comes close to some place on each orbit but not to the same place. If you want to bring it down from its orbit it takes very little energy to do so – in fact a forward firing rocket will do it, but it will bring it down only on those patches of earth below the ground track. So if you want to bring a particular weapon down on a particular city you may have to wait six hours to do it whereas you only have to wait thirty minutes in the normal ICBM mode. In the United States we were worried about the Soviet FOBS capability, because in the 1960s we were planning a defense against ballistic missiles that would look North to destroy in their terminal phase ballistic missiles carrying nuclear weapons launched from Soviet launch areas. If the Soviets could send a weapon around the other way – launch it South from Siberia over the South Pole to attack our radars on their blind side – that would totally nullify the defensive system. I'll get back to that in a moment, but why are you asking me in 1986 to talk about nuclear weapons and space?

I suspect it's because on March 23, 1983, President Reagan gave a famous speech in which he disclosed his dream of a defense which would be so effective that it would render nuclear weapons on strategic ballistic missiles impotent and obsolete. He went further and explained why he had this dream. It was not because we were in danger of nuclear destruction from Soviet nuclear weapons, because (as he said) deterrence of nuclear war by threat of retaliation has worked for more than thirty years and will continue to work. But he felt that the American people, and presumably our allies deserved something better, more moral, than basing our security on the threat to destroy another nation. So he asked for a long-term research program to see whether we could find a way to destroy these nuclear weapons on ballistic missiles before they touched our soil or that of our allies. That was the President's dream. He frankly calls it a "dream", and well he might because what has been happening in the three years since his enunciation of this programm is a Strategic Defense Initiative which is spending a lot of money, $ 5 billion requested for the coming year plus about $ 600 million more, in the Department of Energy in the United States, for nuclear weapons to help this so-called non-nuclear defense. So it is a non-nuclear defense "if possible" against nuclear weapons.

The goal of the SDI program though is no longer a defense adequate enough that we can abandon our nuclear weapons and allow the Soviets to send theirs over if they want – that is, a defense which allows us to base our security on our own initiative and not on persuading the leaders of the other major nuclear power not to launch their missiles. The SDI goal is *not* that. It is to strengthen deterrence, to make our nuclear weapons more effective by protecting them from destruction before they could be launched. So nothing could be more different than the President's dream, and yet somehow this is called the *President's* Strategic Defense Initiative.

Sometimes before we get into the discussion of why the President's dream is infeasible and why the SDI program is unnecessary and inapt, people say, "But suppose an SDI, a space defense, were deployed and suppose it worked and there were a nuclear war and all the nuclear weapons were destroyed or disabled in space. Would they explode? What if they did? And if they didn't explode what would happen to the plutonium in these nuclear weapons as they reenter the atmosphere?" It is only on television that you see these missiles struck by lasers disappear totally; in reality, they don't disappear, they're broken a little bit. But the laws of physics mean that they will also reenter at about the same place that they would have struck anyhow. Certainly with any of the non-nuclear defenses, it is up to the attacker to decide whether the weapon should explode or not. That's called "salvage fusing," and in nuclear war where the defense has to have a clear view and a clear head nothing is more confusing to the defense than to have nuclear explosions all over the field of view. So you could be sure that these nuclear weapons for the most part will not die quietly but they will explode with full yield – up to 10,000 megatons of explosive yield in space. So what? In fact space is a pretty good place to have nuclear weapons explode. There will be damage on the earth from electromagnetic pulse, there will be worldwide fallout, but there will not be nuclear winter. The plutonium which is produced if the weapons explode vastly exceeds the plutonium which is put into the weapons in general because you have excess neutrons which are absorbed in the uranium and that makes more plutonium. Even if the weapons didn't explode, the plutonium would be distributed all over the earth, but in comparison with nuclear war with the weapons exploding on their targets this would not be much of a problem.

However, you should not be happy about this because that is not the way the world is going to evolve. An attempt to place effective weapons in space is likely to lead to nuclear war on *earth* – not in space. And so that's why the title of my talk is not "Nuclear Weapons in Space" but "Nuclear Weapons and Space." The deployment, the thinking about putting weapons in space, particularly defensive weapons is extremely hazardous. Paradoxically it is less threatening to put offensive weapons in space than defensive ones because we already have plenty of offensive weapons on earth and you cannot add very much to the offensive capability by putting them in space. What you can do is to increase the cost and thereby at a constant budget *reduce* the threat to the other side. But I'm not in favor of offensive weapons either in space.

Now let's go back to the President's dream of a defense which is so perfect that we could abandon our own nuclear weapons. The President said that under those circumstances, since we wouldn't have any nuclear weapons we could even share this technology of defense with the Soviet Union so they could be quite sure to defend themselves against our weapons. There are problems, of course, because ballistic missiles are not the only way to deliver nuclear weapons to their targets and to threaten the survival of society or even to destroy military targets. There are aircraft, cruise missiles, trawlers, smuggled nuclear weapons, diplomatic pouches, and the like. On May 23, 1985, Dr. Edward T. Gerry (who is the head of W. J. Schafer Associates, an SDI contractor, and was in charge of boost-phase systems studies for the Fletcher Committee which several months after the President's speech in 1983 began to look to see whether it was feasible to do what the President asked) and I published 15 Agreed Propositions. He is in favor of the SDI program; I am against it. But these propositions show a lot of agreement. One of them is that the United States will have to retain an effective nuclear retaliatory force as long as the Soviet Union is able to deliver nuclear weapons against targets by *any* means including aircraft, ship or smuggled nuclear weapons. The SDI has nothing to do with eliminating that capability; so for the foreseeable future no matter how optimistic you are about a space defense, we will have to make sure we have offensive retaliatory force and that it will penetrate to its target.

So you have a logical problem – we imagine a perfect defense against strategic ballistic missiles, but we must ensure that the Soviet Union cannot have a perfect defense. In fact that logical paradox is resolved by pointing out that it is not feasible to have such a defense. The

SDI program, though, is not looking for a perfect defense; it is looking for a defense to strengthen the U.S. retaliatory capability by defending silos and command posts and things like that. Such a defense is unnecessary. The best kept nonsecret of the Reagan Administration is the report of the Scowcroft Commission which President Reagan appointed January 1983, led by Lt. Gen. Brent Scowcroft, former National Security Advisor. The panel included two former Secretaries of Defense, and many other worthy people – every one of them approved by President Reagan. It reported first one month after the President's Star Wars speech in April 1983 and again in March 1984, and it urged the most extreme caution in proceeding with defensive technologies. It said that our national security could be preserved for the indefinite future by supplementing the existing missiles in the long-term with single-warhead, so-called Midgetman missiles either in silos or mobile so that they could not be destroyed, and by having small submarines to carry the nuclear weapons at sea instead of the large Poseidon and Trident submarines which carry about 200 warheads each. Too many eggs in one basket, no reason to have such vulnerability in the system. These recommendations are going to be important to me and to you in a few minutes.

So the SDI defense is unnecessary for the purpose of preserving the retaliatory force.

In fact, the SDI is not in the U.S. interest or in the interest of the allies if the Soviets are thereby permitted to deploy a defense. The Office of Technology Assessment of the United States Congress in the Fall of 1985 published two volumes on space weapons, missile defense, and antisatellite weapons. In a very interesting example, they say, "Let us imagine that the United States and the Soviet Union have very capable defenses against ballistic missiles, each one capable of subtracting 4000 warheads as they fly toward their targets. Right now let us assume that the United States Minuteman (1000 missiles in their silos), are totally vulnerable to Soviet attack. If we have this imagined "4000-warhead subtractive defense" then the Soviet attack on Minuteman could destroy very few of those missiles and all of those warheads, 2100 warheads on the Minuteman, could go back against their targets in the Soviet Union for retaliation." (The Soviet Union, seeing this, of course, would never have attacked in the first place so it's not all quite as bloodthirsty as it sounds.)

But does this strengthen retaliation? The answer is no. Without the ballistic missile defense every submarine-launched ballistic missile warhead strikes its target in the Soviet Union. It turns out that with all the Minuteman destroyed almost 5000 warheads strike their targets in the Soviet Union. With a ballistic missile defense, an equal defense on both sides, all the Minutemen warheads are sent back but many of them are stopped by the Soviet defense and only 3000 warheads strike their targets in the Soviet Union. So the defense is not in our interests; we are better off if we and the Soviets have no such defense because frankly if they have a defense we will build more weapons to overcome it and they will build more weapons to overcome ours. But if you should for some reason want to have a defense of the Minuteman silos, then you could have it sooner, better and cheaper without the SDI program. We know how to do that, and another agreed proposition with Dr. Gerry May 1985 is that in the continuing context of deterrence of nuclear war by threat of retaliation the defense of the Minuteman silos can be done sooner and more cheaply without layered defense in space.

Well, why this emphasis on space? It is because the ballistic missiles start from silos or submarines and as they go up through the atmosphere the rocket has a large flame which is even now visible from early warning satellites in geosynchronous or high-earth orbit. It is difficult to hide the flame; it is difficult to simulate the flame with lots of decoys. After they are launched the missiles evolve into a large number of warheads – the MX and the SS-18

Soviet missile into ten warheads – and they could have an enormous number of decoys as well. So that if one waits for five minutes or ten minutes after the missile is launched, then each booster, each of the missiles, may turn into a thousand targets in space which have to be destroyed. And that's why people would really like to destroy these missiles immediately after they have been launched while they are still visible, still fewer, and still more fragile than the warheads themselves.

There is one problem – the ICBMs are launched from deep within the Soviet Union and it is not easy to see them from New York, South Dakota or even Cologne. You can see them only from space. That means that the boost-phase intercept must be done from space, must be done from satellites. Satellites are vulnerable to antisatellite weapons because the satellites follow predictable orbits and are very visible; in particular satellites are vulnerable to space mines. A space mine – nothing in space just sits there, the only way it can remain in an orbit is to continue to move – is a small satellite with one purpose, namely to explode when it receives a radio signal or when it is tampered with. Each of the large defensive satellites, typically satellites with lasers on them, are expected by their proponents to cost $ 2 billion or $ 3 billion each. Each of these large satellites would be accompanied by one or two enemy space mines always within lethal distance. You say that will nullify the effectiveness of the defense and so the United States would not tolerate a space mine in the vicinity of the defensive satellite. But the Soviet Union would not stand for a defensive satellite which nullifies its retaliatory capability. And that is why when one imagines that one can have an effective defense in space, the first response will be to accompany each of these satellites as it goes up with a space mine which will forever threaten to destroy it at the outbreak of war. If the owner of the defense destroys the space mine, this just insures that the war will begin in what would otherwise have been peacetime.

Well, ignoring all these arguments, some in the U.S. Defense Department even argue now that deterrence won't work anymore, contrary to what the President said. Deterrence won't work "because the Soviet Union is building defenses and the only option that the United States has is to build defenses ourselves." These arguments can be turned around too. I'm sure that similar things are said in the Soviet Union but you don't hear about them. Maybe because they do not get so much publicity in the press and there is no popular pressure on their Congress, the Soviet leaders can make better decisions than we have been able to do recently. But in any case, the U.S. Defense Department says that working on defense is necessary, is not optional. This is the same Defense Department which spends about $ 200 million a year for offensive countermeasures to penetrate Soviet defenses and which we have always been confident will work. And if $ 200 million is not enough there's a lot more money in the SDI budget – $ 5 billion or $ 6 billion – 30 times as much to strengthen the offensive countermeasures program.

Some say, well there are advantages to defense because the satellites can be lifted into orbit gradually and so we will be able to use the latest fantasy – the transatmospheric vehicle – to get those up there at low cost, whereas the warheads will always have high-cost rockets to take them up. Logically, if you can get defensive satellites into space cheaply you can also get into space cheaply nuclear warheads, decoys, shielding mass – there is nothing in this that favors the defense. In fact the defense must work almost perfectly and the offense must work hardly at all for the defense to be desirable.

Now what is the reality? If we want to reduce the Soviet threat from some 35,000 nuclear weapons which they have now – among them some 10,000 strategic warheads – to 1000 weapons total, and I think that would be a big advance to have 1000 nuclear weapons on the

Soviet side, then the Unites States will also have to reduce to 1000 weapons. Now it may be in people's minds that if they have an effective SDI, they could have the Soviet Union reduce all the way to zero, while we don't reduce at all (which is tantamount to surrender), but that's not the Soviet Union which I have observed all these years. So I would like 1000 weapons on the Soviet side, something like a 97 % reduction in number of nuclear weapons, and I would be willing also to reduce U.S. weapons to 1000 as well. In Europe one should note that the United Kingdom and France and China have hundreds of nuclear weapons each and if they build many more, if they go above say 300 each, than they could certainly prevent this happy day (or happy interim reduction) to 1000 weapons in each of the superpower armories.

I don't care how the Soviet Union bases its 1000 nuclear warheads. They could put them on one big missile for all I care, and they could certainly keep them on 100 SS-18s with ten warheads each if they wanted to do so. I'm not going to design the Soviet force. But the potential damage of the Soviet force, the number of warheads, will be limited.

I think the U.S. nuclear force should be 400 single-warhead Midgetman missiles in silos – the same silos we have now – 400 single-warhead missiles on 50 small submarines so the submarines would carry eight warheads each instead of the present 200, and 200 nuclear-armed air-launched cruise missiles on 100 aircraft. Right now we have about 130 aircraft with twenty nuclear armed cruise missiles each and that's too many eggs in one basket.

To make these reductions possible we will have to respect on both sides the 1972 ABM Treaty. Nobody is going to vastly reduce the number of offensive weapons in the face of increasingly effective defenses. We will have to ban antisatellite tests in space and ban space weapons with a treaty like the May 1983 Draft Treaty that I presented to the Senate Foreign Relations Committee and which the Soviet Union presented in similar form in August 1983 to the U.N. General Assembly. We will have to have a total ban on nuclear explosions to prevent the proliferation of nuclear weapons to additional nations. It will be easier to reduce further ... I know 1000 nuclear weapons on either side does not arouse the enthusiasm of a lot of people in this room who might like fewer – maybe even none. I don't see how to get none from 60,000. I think we will be much nearer none when we have 1000 on either side.

Now what keeps us from achieving this? There is a saying in the arms control community that the U.S. and the Soviet Union make precisely the same proposals in arms control but never at the same time. And many suspect the problem is that they don't really want agreement or reduction. Certainly there are many people in both countries who do not want reductions, and it is up to those of us who care, who really care about national security and survival rather than about weapons, to ensure that we are the leadership, that the military in either country take their orders from the civilians, which they in general do. The problem is that the civilian leadership has not done a good enough job in under-standing the problem and in asserting itself to make policy. The military provide options. For instance in a 1981 Military Space Symposium there were papers submitted with phrases like "Where two men meet there is conflict, and so of course there will be war in space." Well there is no conflict in this room. I don't see people murdering one another right here and there are many more people present than two. That's what law is all about and civilization, and that's why we have to pay attention to whom we have in charge of our weapons and to the policy that they are following. So I think that the nations and the people of the world should emphasize to the Soviet government that whatever the origin of the decision to build the large radar at Krasnoyarsk, it will be a violation of the 1972 ABM

Treaty when it is ready for operation and construction. And they should explain to the President of the United States that it is intolerable that at the same time that the 1972 ABM Treaty is in force to have a program whose very charter it is to destroy it – the SDI. We in the United States should work through our Congress (if we can't work through our Administration) to ensure that we get just those weapons that we want and we preserve those treaties that we want and that our leaders do what we want them to do. At least we should try. So that's what I've been doing in talking to you.

The Core Curriculum

Frank Barnaby, Great Britain

Contemporary Nuclear Policy

When, on 23rd March, 1983, President Reagan introduced his Strategic Defense Initiative he complained that Soviet and American nuclear policies relied "on the spectre of retaliation, on mutual threat". "And", he said, "that's a sad commentary on the human condition. Wouldn't it be better to save lives than to avenge them?" The President based his remarks on the assumption that the Superpowers are operating a policy of nuclear deterrence based on *mutual assured destruction,* a policy commonly known as MAD.

The President went on to explain that he wanted to change America's nuclear policy by embarking "on a program to counter the awesome Soviet missile threat with measures that are defensive". "What if", President Reagan asked, "free people could live secure in the knowledge that their security did not rest upon the threat of instant U.S. retaliation to deter a Soviet attack, that we could intercept and destroy strategic ballistic missiles before they reached our own soil or that of our allies?"

President Reagan wants, in other words, to shift from MAD to nuclear defence because he believes that MAD, based as it is on the threat to kill hundreds of millions of Soviet citizens including women and children, is immoral, as indeed it is, whereas a purely defensive nuclear policy is more morally acceptable. The President also believes that a policy of nuclear defence would improve American, and world, security by freeing "the world from the threat of nuclear war".

President Reagan's stated goal is a perfect nuclear defence to eliminate "the threat posed by strategic nuclear missiles. This could pave the way for arms control measures to eliminate the weapons themselves". He asked the scientific community "to give us the means of rendering these nuclear weapons impotent and obsolete". It would then be possible, the President argues, to negotiate them away.

Other Star Wars advocates claim that a less than perfect strategic defence would strengthen MAD and would, therefore, be worth having if a perfect defence is unattainable. They also argue that new American strategic offensive weapons – such as MX intercontinental ballistic missiles (ICBMs), new small ICBMs called Midgetmen, Trident II submarine-launched ballistic missiles (SLBMs), B-1B strategic bombers, new cruise missiles, and so on – should be deployed "to safeguard stability during the initial phase of a defensive transition".

These new offensive weapons are, the advocates say, also necessary if a total strategic defence is deployed to maintain what they call "deterrence stability" during the decades of transition from MAD to nuclear defence. Star Wars advocates, therefore, want no slackening of the pace of the development and deployment of new offensive strategic nuclear weapons while defensive strategic nuclear weapons are being developed and deployed. On the contrary. The Strategic Defensive Initiative, its advocates stress, necessitates the modernisation of offensive nuclear forces to maintain strategic stability during the transition to a policy of nuclear defence. The call is, then, for all types of nuclear weapons – offensive and defensive.

The current debate about nuclear policies raises urgent questions. Are the Superpowers now really operating MAD policies? What effects are new nuclear weapons having on nuclear policies? Are nuclear policies worked out before weapons are developed and deployed? Or, do political leaders change nuclear policies to rationalise weapon deployments? In short, are the political leaders in control of weapons development and deployment and the evolution of nuclear policies, or is the technological tail wagging the political dog? If the nuclear arms race is out of political control, how can it be brought back under control?

These crucial questions are best considered against the background of current developments in nuclear weapons and their supporting technologies. These will now be described.

Nuclear-weapon Modernisation

Relatively few changes were made in American nuclear weapons during the 1970s but dramatic changes are planned for the 1980s. Projected nuclear-warhead production in the U.S.A. may involve the production, during the 1980s and up to the mid-1990s, of some 30,000 new warheads. Of these about 14,000 are for weapons in current research and development programmes. The likelihood is that the U.S. will deploy 23,000 or so new nuclear warheads during the 1980s.

About 17,000 nuclear warheads will be withdrawn from the stockpile or replaced during this period. And so by now the American nuclear stockpile will contain about 32,000 weapons. Today, the Americans have about 25,000 nuclear weapons.

From what little we know of Soviet plans, and from what we can surmise from the history of Soviet nuclear-weapon deployments (which have, in general, tended to follow those of the U.S.A. although with a time delay of a few years), we must expect the Soviets to increase their nuclear arsenal to an extent similar to that of the Americans. Today's Soviet nuclear arsenal contains about the same number of nuclear weapons as the American one, 25,000.

Huge though these increases in the numbers of nuclear weapons are, they are, from the point of view of world security, much less important than qualitative improvements in nuclear weapons. There is already so much "overkill" in the nuclear arsenals – there is no rational reason, military, strategic or political, for having 25,000 nuclear weapons – that even large increases in numbers are of little relevance to the nuclear policies of the Superpowers – they simply make an irrational situation somewhat more irrational.

In this connection, it should be remembered that only a small number of nuclear warheads is needed for a credible policy of nuclear deterrence based on mutual assured destruction (MAD). There are at most 200 cities in each Superpower with populations greater than about 100,000 people. Assuming two nuclear weapons are needed to destroy a large city, about 400 warheads would be more than enough for an adequate nuclear deterrent, more than enough, in fact, to kill roughly 100 million people in each Superpower and destroy about a half its industrial capacity.

There is, therefore, an absurd amount of overkill in the nuclear arsenals. An adequate nuclear deterrent could be had with 400 or so nuclear warheads and yet each Superpower has about 10,000 strategic nuclear weapons targeted on the other Superpower!

As has been said, qualitative improvements in nuclear weapons are more important than the increases in numbers. The most crucial qualitative advances in nuclear weapons are those which improve their accuracy and reliability. The more accurately a warhead can be delivered on its target the smaller the target that can be destroyed. This means that, as nuclear weapons become more accurate, increasing numbers are targeted on military targets. Many of the new strategic nuclear weapons being deployed may, therefore, be seen as more suitable for fighting a nuclear war than deterring one by MAD.

The accuracy of a nuclear warhead it normally measured by its circular error probability, or CEP, defined as the radius of the circle centred on the target within which a half of a large number of warheads of the same type fired at the target would fall (in other word, there is a 50 per cent of landing a warhead within a distance to the target equal to the CEP). Both the Americans and the Soviets are reducing the CEP's – and, therefore, increasing the accuracy – of their nuclear-weapon systems, including their ICBMs, SLBMs, strategic cruise missiles, and tactical nuclear weapons.

The Americans, for example, have improved the guidance system of the Minuteman ICBM, particularly by improving the pre-launch calibration of the gyroscopes and accelerometers that guide the missile during the boost phase. These improvements have reduced the CEP from about 400 metres (its value at the end of the 1970s) to about 200 metres (its current value). At the same time, the design of the Minuteman warhead was improved so that for the same weight, volume, radar cross-section and aerodynamic characteristics, the explosive power of the warhead was increased from the equivalent of the explosive power of 170,000 tons of TNT to that of 330,000 tons of TNT.

It is interesting to compare the efficiency of the new Minuteman warhead with the Hiroshima bomb. The latter exploded with a power equivalent to that of about 12,000 tons of TNT and the bomb physically weighed four tons. The ratio of the explosive yield to weight, the measure of the efficiency of a munition, was 3,000. The new Minuteman warhead has an explosive power equal to that of 330,000 tons of TNT and a weight of about 300 kilograms, giving a yield-to-weight ratio of more than 1,000,000. This vast increase in the efficiency of nuclear weapons, achieved in just over 30 years, is just one indication of the incredible rate at which military technology advances.

We should, however, not be surprised at the revolutionary developments being made in military technology. Given the huge resources devoted to military science it would be surprising if they were not. About 500,000 scientists work worldwide on military research and development. The total number of scientists in research worldwide is about 2,250,000 and so about 25 per cent of the world's research scientists are fully employed developing new weapons and improving old ones. If only physicists and engineering scientists – those at the forefront of technological advances – are included, more than a half are working on military research and development. Governments are funding military science to the tune of nearly $100,000 million a year, far more than they give for peaceful research.

The new higher-yield Minuteman warhead, delivered with the increased accuracy, is able to destroy a Soviet ICBM in its silo (hardened to withstand an over-pressure of about 2,500 pounds per square inch) with a probability of success of over 50 per cent. If two Minuteman warheads are fired at the Soviet silo the probability of destroying it is about 90 per cent.

The American new ICBM, the MX, will be even more accurate than the Minuteman. The guidance for the MX uses a new system, called the advanced inertial reference sphere, an all-altitude guidance system that can correct for movements of the missile along the ground before it is fired. A CEP of about 100 metres, a half of the CEP of the Minuteman, will be achieved with this system. The MX warheads may also be fitted with terminal guidance, in which a laser or radar set in the nose of the warhead scans the ground around the target as the warhead travels through the earth's atmosphere towards the target. The laser or radar locks on to a distinctive fixed feature in the area, such as a tall building or a hill, and guides the warhead with great accuracy onto its target. With terminal guidance, MX missiles will have CEPs of 30 metres or so.

The MX ICBM is a large missile, having a launch weight of about 86,000 kilograms, about 2.4 times the launch weight of the Minuteman. It can carry warheads weighing a total of 3,500 kilograms, enough for ten MIRVs, each with a yield equivalent to that of 330,000 tons of TNT (330 kt). The three MX booster rockets will use advanced solid propellants, very light motor cases and advanced nozzles to propel the MX twice as efficiently as the Minuteman is propelled. The boost phase of the MX is 100 seconds, much shorter than that of the Minuteman. MX ICBMs will be deployed in existing Minuteman silos, starting at the end of 1986. The Americans are also developing a new small, mobile ICBM, carrying a single warhead, to replace the MXs in the 1990s; it will be called Midgetman.

The most formidable Soviet ICBM is the SS-18. The CEP of the SS-18 is, or soon will be, about 250 metres. A typical SS-18 warhead probably has an explosive yield of about 500 kt. This warhead would have about a 50 per cent probability of destroying an American ICBM in its silo. Two warheads fired in succession would have about a 90 per cent chance of success. The U.S.S.R. has 308 SS-18s in service, most, if not all of which, carry ten MIRVed warheads each. The SS-18 ICBM force, 3,000 or so warheads strong is, therefore, a significant threat to the American 1,000-missile strong ICBM force. In theory, three SS-18 warheads could be targeted on each American ICBM.

The Soviet SS-19 ICBM was thought, by American intelligence agencies, to be as accurate as the SS-18 and, with a similar warhead, as great a threat to American ICBMs. Each SS-19 may carry six MIRVed warheads so that the total force of 360 missiles may be able to deliver 2,160 warheads. But the CIA has recently revised its estimates and now says that the SS-19 is not accurate enough to be a serious threat to American ICBMs. There has been, however, no change in American intelligence estimates of the accuracy of the SS-18 which is still seen to be a threat to American ICBMs.

Because of the increasing vulnerability of land-based ICBMs, greater attention is being given to strategic nuclear submarines and the missiles they carry. Both Superpowers are busily modernising their submarine fleets. The U.S.A., for example, plans to deploy about one new Trident submarine a year for the next few years, at a cost of about $ 200 million per submarine. The U.S. Navy envisages a fleet of some 25 Tridents early in the 21st century. Seven Tridents are already operational and the eighth began sea trials in May 1986.

These first eight Tridents will be fitted with Trident C-4, also called Trident-1, SLBMs. But the ninth Trident, currently due to become operational in 1988, will be equipped with the Trident-2 SLBM. The Trident-2 will have a longer range than the Trident-1 and, therefore, the submarines carrying it can operate in much larger areas of the oceans and still be in range of targets in the Soviet Union. The submarines will then be less exposed to Soviet anti-submarine warfare (ASW) systems. If the U.S. Navy's plan to operate early in the next century 25 Trident submarines comes about, they will carry 600 Trident-2 SLBMs equipped with about 6,000 nuclear warheads. Each warhead will probably have an explosive power of about 500 kt.

Trident-2 warheads will be very accurate. Whereas the CEPs of the Minuteman and the Trident-1 missiles are about 100 metres the CEP of the Trident-2 will be about 200 metres.

The improved accuracy will be achieved by mid-course guidance and more accurate navigation of submarines. Navigational accuracy and missile guidance will be greatly improved by NAVSTAR, the American 18-satellite navigational system due to become operational in 1988.

The use of terminal guidance will increase the accuracy of Trident-II SLBMs even more. With it, CEPs can be expected to come down to roughly 50 metres. Within a few years, then, American SLBMs will be as lethal as ICBMs.

The U.S.S.R. is also improving the quality of its SLBM force. Soviet SLBMs are thought to be less accurate than their American counterparts. The CEP of the SS-N-18, for example, is probably about 600 metres, although the SS-N-20 and the SS-NX-23, now under development, are almost certainly more accurate.

CEPs of 50 metres or so are the best attainable in practice for ballistic missiles. Once this plateau is reached by the U.S.A., it is only a matter of time – probably three or five years – before the U.S.S.R. catches up.

The Modernisation of Tactical Nuclear Weapons

Both superpowers are modernising their tactical nuclear arsenals. Tactical nuclear weapons generally have a shelf-life of twenty or so years after which they must be replaced or withdrawn from the arsenal. The weapons deteriorate because the fission and fusion material in them, particularly tritium, decays and some of the non-nuclear materials deteriorate. Modernisation is, therefore, inevitable if nuclear weapons continue to be deployed.

Among the new types of tactical nuclear weapons being deployed by the U.S.A. in NATO countries are Pershing-II ground-to-ground missiles and ground-launched cruise missiles. Both types are fitted with terminal guidance and are extremely accurate, with CEPs of about 50 metres. The Pershing-II missiles have a range of 1,800 kilometres and the ground-launched cruise missiles have a range of about 2,500 kilometres. Both carry warheads with explosive yields of a few kilotons. The deployment in Western Europe of 108 Pershing-II and 464 cruise missiles is planned.

These American missiles were deployed in NATO European countries, it is said, in response to the Soviet deployment of the SS-20 missile. In turn, the Soviets have deployed new ground-to-ground missiles, the SS-21, SS-22 and SS-23, in response to the American deployment of Pershing-IIs and cruise missiles. The Soviet missiles are, however, less sophisticated and accurate than the American ones. The SS-20, for example a mobile missile with a range of about 5,000 kilometres and carrying three MIRVed warheads each with a yield of 150 kt, has a CEP of about 400 or 500 metres. The lethality (i.e. the probability of destroying a target of a given hardness) of the SS-20 is about the same as that of an American Poseidon SLBM. Pershing-II missiles, however, are many times more lethal than the SS-20, and the two weapons cannot be regarded as comparable. The Soviets have deployed about 400 SS-20s, about a half of them west of the Urals, targeted on Western Europe, and the others east of the Urals, aimed at targets in Asia.

From MAD to NUTS

Until the early 1960s, NATO's official military policy was massive retaliation. If the Soviets attacked Western Europe, NATO would respond by dropping nuclear weapons on Soviet cities and destroying the Soviet society. But in the early 1960s the policy was abruptly changed to flexible response. The reason for this change was simple. The Soviet nuclear arsenal had grown to make massive retaliation no longer sensible. It was all very well to threaten the Soviets with nuclear destruction when their nuclear arsenal was so inferior that they couldn't reply in kind. But when they could, NATO had to change its policy.

The new policy is called flexible response. Basically, the idea of flexible response is that if the Warsaw Pact attacks NATO then NATO would try to beat off the attack, and win the war, with conventional weapons. But, if the Warsaw Pact broke through into West Germany, NATO would stem the advance by using tactical nuclear weapons. There may then be a nuclear exchange but, hopefully, one limited to low-yield nuclear weapons.

Flexible response advocates argue that at this stage sanity may prevail and NATO and the Warsaw Pact might negotiate an end to the war. But if the fighting continued NATO would be prepared, if necessary, to escalate the conflict and use higher-yield nuclear weapons. The final stage in this ladder of escalation would be the use of strategic nuclear weapons against the homeland of the Superpowers. Massive retaliation has not been abandoned, just delayed. And since both sides can now do it, it has become mutual.

The theory is, of course, that the threat of mutual massive retaliation is enough to prevent one side from attacking the other in the first place. Hence, the policy of flexible response depends upon a strategy of nuclear deterrence based on mutual assured destruction.

Morton Halperin, who served on the U.S. National Security Council under Henry Kissinger, summarised NATO's policy of flexible response as follows. First, we will fight with conventional weapons until we are losing. Then we will fight with battlefield nuclear weapons until we are losing. Then we will blow up the world!

MAD depends on the belief that the enemy will not attack suddenly (pre-emptively) if he knows that most of his cities and industry will be destroyed in retaliation. If the enemy no longer fears that his cities are at risk MAD no longer works.

A paradox of the nuclear age is that a policy of MAD only works with inaccurate nuclear weapons. When accurate nuclear weapons are deployed in large numbers the enemy will assume that the other side's nuclear weapons are targeted on his military forces and not on his cities. The cities then cease to be the hostages. Accuracy, in other words, kills deterrence. With accurate nuclear weapons, nuclear warfighting based on the destruction of hostile military forces becomes the preferred policy.

Current American (and, presumably, Soviet, too) nuclear policy is a confusing mixture of MAD and nuclear war-fighting (also known as Nuclear Utility Targeting Strategy, or NUTS!). SLBMs provide the MAD element, being still inaccurate enough to be targeted on cities, while ICBM are nuclear war-fighting weapons, accurate enough to be targeted on enemy strategic nuclear forces and other military targets. But when Trident-2 SLBMs are deployed in the late 1980s they will be accurate enough to be targeted on military targets in the U.S.S.R. and American nuclear policy will go totally from MAD to NUTS.

If a large number of tactical nuclear war-fighting weapons (such as enhanced-radiation weapons, often called neutron bombs, as anti-tank weapons) is deployed in Europe, they will be integrated into military tactics at low levels of command. Then, not only will a war in Europe almost inevitably escalate to a nuclear war but the military will more easily come to believe that a nuclear war is "fightable and winnable", and that a "limited nuclear war" is possible. This belief in the fightability and winnability of nuclear war will make such a war more likely. And this is the danger of the deployment of strategic and tactical nuclear weapons seen to be useful mainly for fighting a nuclear war.

A range of military technologies is being developed that will strengthen the belief that a nuclear war can be fought and won. Two such believers, Colin Gray and Keith Payne, have argued "the United States should plan to defeat the Soviet Union and to do so at a cost that would not prohibit U.S. recovery". "A combination of counterforce offensive targeting (i. e. attacking military targets), civil defense, and ballistic missile and air defense should", they go on, "hold U.S. casualties down to a level compatible with national survival and recovery."

The most important of the "war-winning"technologies now under development are those related to anti-submarine warfare (ASW), anti-ballistic missiles and anti-satellite warfare systems. The aim of strategic ASW is to detect and destroy within a short time all the enemy's strategic nuclear submarines withing range of one's homeland. There is much secrecy about ASW developments. For example, the U.S. Navy is working with blue-green lasers, possibly deployed on satellites, to detect submarines but little is known about the results of this work. From time to time statements are made by, for example, U.S. Naval spokesmen implying capability to detect and destroy Soviet strategic nuclear submarines, at least those close to the U.S. coast but we have few details about current strategic ASW capabilities. But even in the absence of a technological breakthrough – which may, of course, be made – we can be sure that steady progress in limiting the damage that can be done by enemy SLBMs will be made.

When one side can severely limit the damage that the other side's strategic nuclear forces can inflict in a retaliatory strike, and believes it can destroy any enemy warheads that survive a surprise attack by ballistic missile defences, then the temptation to make an all-out first strike may become well-nigh irresistible, particularly during an international crisis.

An important factor here is that the side that first perceives that it has a first-strike capability may well believe that it should use it to prevent the other side from getting it, too. If both Superpowers achieved such a capability, international affairs would be so unstable as to be unacceptable.

Nevertheless, there are those who argue that all efforts should be made to improve the quality of nuclear weapons to achieve a strategic nuclear superiority. The main motive for acquiring such a superiority is not necessarily to wage nuclear war but to gain the advantage over the other side in the Superpower struggle for global influence. Advocates for nuclear superiority argue that parity paralyses American foreign policy. America would be more likely to act adventurously if it were strategically superior, knowing that the U.S.S.R. would not dare to oppose it.

The danger is, of course, that the other side will not allow its adversary to gain strategic nuclear superiority. The attempt to do so may well provoke the other side into making a preemptive, or preventive, nuclear attack.

The first action in a nuclear surprise attack would be to destroy the other side's military satellites, the "eyes and ears" of the military in space. This is why great efforts are being made to develop effective anti-satellite weapons.

The combination of accurate and reliable nuclear weapons with effective anti-submarine warfare, ballistic missiles defence and anti-satellite warfare technologies is a particularly lethal one. The development and deployment of these weapons and supporting technologies will lead to a very high risk of a nuclear catastrophe, too high a risk to be acceptable to rational people.

In summary, current developments in military science are much more likely to lead to a nuclear first-strike capability, a very offensive and destabilising posture, than to the nuclear defence advocated by President Reagan. The President's vision of the perfect defence against nuclear attack may well become a nightmare.

Controlling the nuclear arms race

Since World War II great efforts have been made to control the nuclear arms race and achieve some nuclear disarmament. But these efforts have failed. We have learnt that whereas military technology advances very rapidly, diplomacy moves very slowly. By the time arms control treaties can be negotiated they are out of date.

Given this situation, the best way forward would be to negotiate a nuclear freeze in which the nuclear-weapon powers would agree to stop the testing, production and deployment of nuclear weapons. The most important elements of a freeze are:

- A comprehensive ban on all nuclear-weapon tests.
- A ban on the testing of ballistic missiles.
- A cut-off in the production of fissile material for military use.

Of these measures, which could be negotiated separately, a comprehensive nuclear test ban is the most urgent. Such a ban would achieve two very important objectives. Firstly, it would prevent the further modernisation of nuclear weapons. Modern nuclear weapons are so complex in design that testing is necessary to check that they work effectively.

Secondly, the military from time to time takes out a nuclear warhead from the nuclear arsenal and tests it. If this were no longer possible, the military would in time lose confidence in the reliability of its nuclear weapons and be unwilling to use them, particularly in a nuclear first strike. A comprehensive nuclear test ban would, therefore, prevent the further deployment of nuclear-weapon systems that may lead to the very destabilising situation where one side or the other perceives that it has a nuclear first-strike capability.

A nuclear freeze should, of course, not be seen as an end in itself but the first step to ending the nuclear arms race and beginning the process of nuclear disarmament, beginning with the destruction of nuclear-war fighting nuclear weapons. Unless we succeed in getting rid of these weapons before long there is a considerable risk that they will get rid of us.

THE CORE CURRICULUM

Conn Nugent, U.S.A.

How a Nuclear War Might Begin

U sually it is the job of IPPNW to describe how a nuclear war ends, with human and biological devastation. This afternoon I would like to try to describe various ways in which such a holocaust could begin. No one knows. In 1914 no one foresaw the assassination of Franz Ferdinand in Sarajewo. Immediately thereafter very few thought that the incident would kindle a general Europe war and, once war was declared, very few predicted four years of relentless and unprecedented blood-letting. In hindsight historians know that the assassination of Franz Ferdinand was not the cause of the First World War, rather it was an excuse by which elaborate symbiosis of military plans, political alliances and nationalist fervours began to take effect. Those forces were latent, dramatically underrecognized, but so potent that they overwhelmed the once optimistic civilization of La Belle Epoque.

Perhaps it is not so very different today. We do not know the Sarajewo of the atomic age and we must always keep this radical uncertainty in mind. History teaches or persuades me that, given enough time, the very existence of nuclear weapons will cause their use, perhaps in a manner unimagined by human beings. This is not to argue against incremental acts of prudence, which can dramatically extend our period of grace, our time frame in which to confront the menace of nuclear weaponry but we must remove the menace. We must utterly abolish the weapons for there is to come a time when a lecture with this title can never be given.

Let me divide today's lecture into three broad topics. One, and Dr. Barnaby has touched upon it, the characteristics of contemporary nuclear weapons and the ways in which those characteristics by themselves give rise to the risk of nuclear war. Two, potential crises which might impel a nuclear war, and three, social attitudes and opinions which engender or tolerate those weapons and which engender or tolerate those crises.

First, the weapons themselves. It is important to realize that nuclear weapons are a political issue. That is to say a political issue in themselves, regardless of the warmth or the frigidity of the relations between nuclear nation states. The mere posession of nuclear weapons is always an issue. Because of their appalling potential and because there must always be a certain imbalance, a certain asymmetry between states in the numbers and capabilities of their nuclear weapons, the weapons themselves induce fear and distrust in the heart of the adversary. The weapons of one side become the raison d'etre for weapons on the other, and of course for the military which seeks them, controls them and ponders their use. The weapons become an issue and they create issues. And thus they themselves have provoked and will provoke crises in which they might be employed. It is a vicious circle of the first order.

The second comment to make about nuclear weapons and their role in the risk of nuclear war is to briefly discuss recent technocratic, technological developments in the characteristics of the nuclear weapons which increase the risk of war. I don't mean to repeat too much of what Dr. Barnaby has already said, but I will outline them in, I hope, shorter form. The destructive capacity of nuclear weapons as we now know has not significantly increased since the 1950s. More important have been recent changes in accuracy and in the time in which a nuclear weapon can reach its target. First, let's talk about accuracy. The accuracy of the new generation of nuclear weapons presents the risk that a first strike can destroy the retaliatory capacity of an enemy. Now it seems to most observers that this is not now a genuine risk, but military planners on both sides are beginning to feel the risk and the perception of risk (for this is essentially a psychological game, once we take a few steps) is really more important than the fact. In this regard so-called defensive systems, be they on earth, or in space, can be seen as provocative strategies for first use because they could be employed to deny this retaliatory capacity. The accuracy of these new generations of weapons threatens most of all the military communication systems. They risk that a first strike could deny command control to the adversary. It is tempting to the provocateur, frightening to the side that fears provocation.

The new generation of missiles also strike their targets within a shorter time. There are two prime examples of this, one is the submarine-launched ballistic missiles, that Dr. Barnaby alluded to, the other is the new generation of intermediate and short-range strategic missiles, Pershings, SS 20s, that are land-based. The very capability of striking a target in a short time increases the risk of the probability of a nuclear war, primarily because it implies reduced time in which to excercise judgement. We have seen an evolution since the Second World War, in the means of the delivery of nuclear weapons from man to bombers to intercontinental ballistic missiles to short-range missiles. And in that evolution the time to react has shrunk from many hours to one hour to a matter of a few minutes. It is no longer possible for the President of the United States, generally imagined to be Henry Fonda by Hollywood, to spend 2½ hours getting things straight with the Premier of the Soviet Union, generally played by an unseen actor with a heavy but rather attractive slavic accent. Now we have a situation in which the decision to fire nuclear weapons can take place, must take place within six to eight minutes. The response of military planners to this shortened time has been to decentralize and automize elements of command. The great fear that we face is the policy of "launch on warning", in which the short time a potential missile is in flight gives rise to decentralized authority by local commanders to fire a launch-on-warning attack.

We all know that contracted time frames impose great burdens on both machines and on man. On machines even though many observers believe that the mechanical systems to prevent a purely accidental nuclear war are safer now than ever before, albeit Chernobyl and a few other such acts of confidence gives one pause. The time available to correct a potentially fatal mechanical error is pitifully short. But perhaps more important is the effect on human beings. It is well known that human beings are prone to bad judgement when they are rushed. It is also known that this is true especially when those human beings are in a small group. Most nuclear crises are handled by groups of about 15 men, middle-aged, cut off from all normal patterns of social intercourse. Within six minutes those 15 men (if we are lucky) will have to arrive at a decision on which rests the fate of Europe.

A third characteristic of the new generation of nuclear weapons which gives rise to increased risk of nuclear war, is in their mobility and their capacity to be concealed. Cruise missiles are an example. Thus their existence or non-existence is difficult to verify, for both arms control negotiations and, equally important, nervous military leaders. If there were an atmosphere of trust between the Superpowers the problem might not be so enormous. But again, we have a vicious cycle. Distrust leads to concealable weapons, concealable weapons give rise to distrust.

A kindred problem is that many of the so-called tactical nuclear weapons are no longer easily distinguished in their explosive impact from some of the new advanced non-nuclear weapons. As new low yield battle field nuclear weapons are developed, so, too, are high yield precision targeted conventional weapons. According to the Armed Forces Journal of the United States the damage radius of one of the American skeet systems can extend to eighty per cent of the radius of a one kiloton neutron bomb. Of course the visual display is different, the radioactive effects are different, but imagine yourself to be a military commander, fifty kilometers away from the front, you have just received word that all your men and all your weapons within a radius of fourhundred metres have been annihilated. You might surmise that you are under attack from nuclear weapons, and you might seek approval for retaliation. Indeed, you might feel compelled to retaliate on your own authority. This problem, what Michael Claire has described as the vanishing fire break between nuclear and conventional weapons, is exacerbated by the fact that, unlike before, today's nuclear weapons are dispersed throughout the conventional forces of the nuclear powers, in their conventional armies, their conventional navies and their conventional air forces. We must assume that any significant deployment of military forces by the great powers will involve a deployment of nuclear missiles. In short, the military forces of the nuclear powers are on hairtrigger standing.

Now it is time to explore some of the situations, political crises, in which this hairtriggerness might provoke a nuclear war. On this topic we owe a good deal to Professor William Jury of the Harvard Law School and an excellent book I recommend to you called "Beyond the Hot Line". Jury talks about four characteristics of a nuclear crisis. The first characteristic of a nuclear crisis is little time, little time for making crucial decisions. It's the fundamental aspect of all crises. And crises have often been defused when intelligent leaders do little more than allow their adversaries some time to think and negotiate. The second characteristic of a nuclear crisis is high stakes, or expressed negatively, the expectation of severe loss to the national interest, however that is perceived. The third characteristic is high uncertainty, not enough clear information. Now that can be uncertainty of data. How many troops or ships does my enemy have? Where are they? What's going on? Or it can be uncertainty of his intent. What does the deployment of those troops, of those ships mean? What is he doing with all that? And this is the start of escalation. The fourth characteristic which Jury describes is that to nuclear crises decision makers few usable options seem available. In crises leaders feel that the number and the variety of actions that they can take are more limited than in normal times. The operative words here are "usable options", for political leaders are always constrained by political considerations and options available. Again the impression of limited options by political leaders in their particular situation, in their particular bunker, surrounded by their particular twelve friends or advisors in government is far more important than what we would consider to be the objective fact of the availability of wider and more intelligent options. All of these characteristics conspire to create an atmosphere what Jury calls "a felt need to act", to do something. And this atmosphere is contagious. And it is reflected as in a mirror in the minds of the adversary. It may be important to note in this regard that with very few exceptions those who have begun wars in the past have always felt that the other side started it. That feeling of being acted upon leads directly to that "felt need to act".

So where and how could crises occur? What events in what places might contribute to the atmosphere of crisis? The first possibility is bilateral confrontation, U.S.S.R. versus U.S.A. On a two-dimensional map it appears that the United States and the Soviet Union are distant partners on the planet, the globe of course as always gives a truer perspective. We are neighbours, a view from the North Pole reveals where the United States and the Soviet Union end their strategical race, especially if one includes the American strategic deployments in the North of Canada. They face each other directly, and not just in Europe. We both have great navies, which sail the world, laden with nuclear weapons. There is always the possibility for a direct American/Soviet bilateral confrontation. There is always the possibility of a confrontation of the two great powers through a secondary crisis of their allies. One example is in Europe. A series of crisis events in Europe, for instance between European states, or perhaps more likely political upheavals within a European state that are seen as threatening the national interest of the larger great power ally. The same analogy could be made of the Middle East. The same analogy can be made for Central America and the Carribean, for Korea, for Afghanistan, for the Indian sub-continent. Hilyard Roderick describes this type of potential crisis as entrapment. One or several NATO or Warsaw Treaty states are entrapped by the military actions of an ally engaged in a local or regional war or an internal revolution. This of course was the story of the First World War, and to my mind remains the most likely of all for nuclear crises.

As nuclear weapons proliferate there is always a possibility of a "small" and "nuclear war" between two nations, fought not for reasons of the East/West discord but for local or regional reasons. Such a war can then create a Soviet/American crisis. Less likely, not impossible would be a nuclear crisis resulting from the explosion of a nuclear bomb by terrorists. Again, such an explosion need not lead to a Soviet/American crisis but the potential is clear. Finally, there is the risk of a purely accidental nuclear attack of whatever magnitude. I stated before the consensus of contemporary opinion is that a purely accidental war is unlikely, but that random factors of human and mechanical failability acting in synergy with the tension of an international crisis could impel what might better be described as an inadvertent nuclear war.

The third and final topic of enquiry is what I described as the social attitudes which allow such grotesque weaponry and such dangerous risk to exist. Let's be basic: why in the world would the U.S.S.R. and the U.S.A. ever fight a war? Let's go back to the textbook causes for war that we learned as schoolchildren. The United States and the Soviet Union do not dispute each other's national boundaries. On the question of natural resources, though the United States has an addiction to imported petroleum and the Soviet Union has an addiction to imported grain, nonetheless in terms of natural resources they are better endowed than 95 per cent of the other states of the earth. In terms of economic competition, one of the great traditional textbook causes of war, there is no significant economic competition between the Soviet Union and the United States. As alluded to earlier, the nuclear weapons themselves constitute a sort of casus belli and, as Professor Galbraith pointed out yesterday, the weapons systems spawn a military establishment to run them, to plan them. A military establishment needs a perceived enemy to justify its existence.

But there is another less tangible factor. We have a rivalry here of two religions, or if you like, a more 20th century antiseptic term, two ideologies. One calls itself marxism-leninism, the other democratic capitalism, whose adherents each believe that they should win universal application ordained both by morality and the logic of historic development. Both American zealots and Soviet zealots believe that their system is the one ineluctably dictated by history.

They show a curious hybris if you will. Both the United States and the Soviet Union are young, multi-cultural states, whose very glow is their ideology and who have a messianic zeal for promoting those ideologies throughout the world. Now this messianic zeal can ebb and flow in both societies. In my country lately it has been on the rise. There are encouraging signals from the Soviet Union that a new, more ample point of view has gained prominence in the U.S.S.R. Ambassador Falin's speech yesterday is an excellent example of that. But as a subscriber to Prawda, I can assure you that demonisation of the enemy exists just as well today in Moscow as in Washington.

But are nuclear weapons really useful in this competition for world influence? How many of the so-called gains in the spread of influence of either of the two great powers can be traced to nuclear weapons? Let us grant to the two great powers, their need to be missionaries. But even from the missionary point of view it could be argued rationally that mutual nuclear disarmament would help, not hinder their seperate efforts to excercise influence. Now I think at bottom, Ladies and Gentlemen, there are some serious primeval human non-tangibles involved in the stock-piling of nuclear weapons: pride and fear, pride to feel and to be seen as a great historical power. This kind of pride, especially among adolescents, often gives rise to ambition. And until human culture totally anathematizes nuclear weapons we run the risk that this ambition will demand nuclear weapons for they have become a symbol, a totem of the great power. Now this is not just a future issue of possible nuclear proliferation but a real issue now, expecially if one considers the small but extremely dangerous arsenals of the UK, France, and China.

But once a nuclear state secures nuclear weapons and once a potiential adversary has done likewise, pride and ambition are joined by fear, fear of national annihilation, and fear is a conservative force in human affairs. It always maintains the status quo no matter how potentially lethal. The fear combined with the pride and with the ambition cause us to endow our political and military establishments with dreadful authority to devise plans for the extinction of our enemy and thus of course for our own extinction. It is a curiously mutual process. Soviets and Americans for example need each other to ratify their pride, and to justify their dread. We dance this deadly dance together.

Herbert Abrams, U.S.A.

Chernobyl – and the Short-Term Medical Effects of Nuclear War

T he history of the Twentieth Century is a continuing confirmation of the wisdom that the impossible is always possible. Whether in the destruction of the Challenger, or in the meltdown at Chernobyl, the seeds of disaster were planted long before the event, and the repercussions will be felt long after. Chernobyl represents the largest experience in recorded time of the effects of whole body radiation on human subjects, uncomplicated by blast and/or burn. It warrants discussion in this Congress as a means of introducing the short-term medical effects of nuclear war and of placing them in perspective.

Casualties

At the outset, Soviet authorities believed that one to two thousand people living or working near the reactor might have received substantial doses of radiation (Table 1). These people were carefully examined and 299 were hospitalized[1]. They were mostly fire fighters and plant workers exposed to estimated levels of radiation ranging from 100 rads to over 800 rads. One hundred and twenty-nine were transported to Moscow by air early on April 27, and the remainder the following day.

Among them, 210 were diagnosed as suffering from acute radiation sickness, 51 of the most serious degree. 35 patients were exposed to doses thought to exceed 800 rads and were considered in "grave condition"[2]. Two patients had died acutely, one in the explosion and another after having been hit with burning debris[3]. In the second week two died of radiation sickness; in the third week nine (Table 2). There were no deaths in the fourth week. Ten additional deaths occurred in the fifth week for a total of 21 radiation deaths and 23 total deaths as of Monday, May 30, 1986. In the sixth week an additional three deaths were reported, and two further deaths by the twelfth week (July, 20, 1986) brought the total to 28.

Number Examined for Acute Radiation Sickness	1000–2000
Number Requiring Closer Evaluation	400– 500
Hospitalized	299
Diagnosis: Acute Radiation Sickness	210

Table 1: The casualties from Chernobyl

WEEK	CONDITION		
	Serious	Grave	Radiation death
1	51	18	—
2	?	16	2
3	?	24	9
4	?	24	—
5	55	14	10

Table 2: The condition of patients during the first five weeks

By the fifth week, 55 remained seriously ill, while 14 were in grave condition. Many of the patients experienced severe radiation burns, and there were also the anticipated gastric and intestinal injuries, as well as platelet destruction leading to spontaneous bleeding[4].

Medical Response and Evacuation

Military and civilian workers, firemen, specialists and health workers gathered from across the country. Other personnel included 1,300 doctors, nurses and other medical specialists. Supplies and equipment poured in from across the Soviet Union and 5,000 trucks, 800 buses, 240 ambulances, helicopters and special trains were mobilized. Vehicles inside the 30 kilometer zone were scrubbed down twice before they reached the zone's border to pick-up supplies from outside. Armored personnel carriers were used to minimize contact with radioactive dust[5].

Although evacuation did not begin until 36 hours after the accident, preparations began almost immediately. Local police converged on Prypiat in order to set up road blocks and maintain order. Hundreds of buses arrived throughout Saturday, April 26th.

Evacuation of the ten kilometer zone around the Chernobyl plant began Sunday afternoon, April 27th. At 1:50 p.m., the local radio announcer started the evacuation of Prypiat while party workers fanned out through all of the city buildings to alert residents. At 2:00 p.m. 1,100 buses began picking-up the 40,000 residents from the entries of each building. Marshalling points were avoided to prevent panic. By 4:20 p.m. the city was empty except for workers who remained to maintain basic services. They left three days later[6]. Three small agricultural villages were also evacuated, bringing the total to 49,000.

The danger zone was expanded from ten kilometers to thirty kilometers sometime around Saturday, May 3rd. A second evacuation took place over the weekend, which included the town of Chernobyl. An additional 35,000 people were reported to have been evacuated, bringing the total to 84,000. This figure was later increased to 92,000.

* * *

Besides Chernobyl, there have been at least 38 major radiation accidents since 1945, with 14 known deaths[7]. On August 21, 1945 and on May 21, 1946 at the Los Alamos National Laboratory, two serious accidents occurred as a result of temporarily uncontrolled chain reactions[8]. Ten persons were exposed, two seriously enough to die: one in seven days, the other in twenty-four days.

Of the two who died, one was a 26 year old man hospitalized 25 minutes after the first accident. While his hands received 5,000–40,000 rads, he had a total body exposure of approximately 590 rads. He became nauseated within 1½ hours, and vomited intermittently for the first 24 hours. On the second day there was slight improvement and he felt better from the third to the sixth day in spite of slight fever.

By the fourth day, his hands appeared red and swollen. From the sixth to the twenty-fourth day he became increasingly toxic and lost weight. On the ninth day, there was evidence not only of swelling, but also of skin loss, massive ulceration, seepage of fluid, and visible blisters throughout the upper extremities. Beginning with the tenth day, his tongue became ulcerated and he developed massive inflammation of the mucous membranes in his mouth. Shortly thereafter his abdomen became distended, and diarrhea, which persisted until death, became a prominent symptom.

On the twelfth day the lesions had progressed, and his abdomen and trunk were now red and inflamed. On the seventeenth day the clinical signs of pericarditis were noted. By the nineteenth day, his hair had begun to fall out, and on the day before death, the trunk had the appearance of a massive burn. In addition to a systemic reaction which led to death with terminal temperatures over 106°, there was widespread local tissue destruction, particularly of the skin of the upper extremities and the abdomen.

Autopsy showed fluid in the lungs, inflammation of the pericardium and intestine, ulceration of the colon, and bone marrow depletion and extensive destruction of soft tissues.

During the entire period, his hemoglobin dropped only moderately, while the white cell count rose and then fell. The lymphocytes disappeared rapidly, and of those that remained, many were abnormal.

* * *

This brief case history of a man followed closely from the moment of the accident illustrates the combination of effects associated with both the total body radiation and the local skin radiation that many of the most severely exposed in Chernobyl experienced.

Radiation Injury

Radiation produces its effects through the ionization of atoms, causing cell damage by altering important intracellular components. The changes that occur may destroy the cell or diminish its capacity to function. The extent of the ultimate damage depends on the magnitude of the initial insult balanced against the cell's ability to repair injury.

Damage may reflect the direct action of the ion pairs on essential molecules, or the effect of reactive free radicals formed by the ionization of water. Free radicals may produce cell poisons, or they may disorganize atomic bonds, with the consequent formation of smaller molecules, or different molecular conformations. If the damage is minimal, repair will occur, but if critical molecules like DNA are affected, the impairment may be profound.

The sensitivity of different cells varies strikingly, and is also dependent on the phase of the cell cycle[9]. Dividing and metabolically active cells and those that reproduce rapidly, such as lymphocytes and intestinal crypt cells, are more sensitive than highly differentiated cells.

Bone marrow, lymphoid tissue, spleen, the male reproductive organs, and the gastrointestinal tract are particularly susceptible tissues. If the exposure to radiation is protracted, recovery processes may occur and the organism can then handle larger exposures.

The LD 50 Dose

The LD 50 is the dose of whole body radiation that will kill 50 % of those exposed to it. For humans, it probably lies within the range of 200 to 450 rads[10, 11], although a recent analysis suggests that it may be less than 200 rads[12]. This problem has generated a good deal of controversy, much of it associated with the difficulty of estimating dose precisely[13]. After the nuclear release, the dose must be calculated from direct radiation from the reactor; the passing cloud; inhalation of passing cloud; ground contamination; ingestion of contaminated food and drinking water; and exposure to contaminated water and shoreline. Even the doses received in Japan remain a matter of dispute; the doses thought to be associated with acute symptoms differ considerably depending on the estimation method[14].

The Response to Acute Whole Body Radiation

An acute sudden whole body exposure to hundreds of rads of radiation is followed by four periods: The prodromal syndrome; the latent period; a febrile period with many symptoms; and a final phase of death, or convalescence with subsequent recovery[15].

The Prodromal Syndrome.   Among those who absorb large doses – like many of those hospitalized at Chernobyl – there is an initial prodromal phase that occurs in minutes to hours, characterized by anorexia, nausea and vomiting. This triad of symptoms is self-limited. It is probably a neurogenic response and is not caused by the interruption of cell production that will ultimately produce the most severe effects in patients who die. The symptoms subside in 24 to 36 hours, frequently followed by a period of relative well being.

The latent period.   Between the termination of the prodromal symptoms and the onset of health impairment, a latent period occurs, in which patients may experience relative comfort for about 2–3 weeks. Cessation of production of new blood cells begins at the time of exposure, but depending on the size and life span of the various cell populations, cells may continue to mature and function for several weeks. Lymphocytes decrease within hours while red blood cells may not reach their low point for many weeks.

Although there is no rigid separation of the response to acute radiation exposure by dose, and much overlap occurs, it is generally accepted that there are three dose dependent syndromes: the Hematopoietic (bone marrow), the Gastrointestinal, and the Central Nervous System.

Hematopoietic Syndrome (The Bone Marrow).   With doses over 200 rads in a 24 hour period, nausea and vomiting are virtually immediate symptoms. They are commonly accompanied by loss of appetite and diarrhea. The white cell count drops, and both frank hemorrhages and small bleeding points are seen, as well as mouth ulcers. The marrow syndrome dominates the picture in patients who have received 200–600 rads[16]. The course usually is as follows: Apathy, nausea, and vomiting become maximal within 6–12 hours. Symptoms subside by 24–36 hours. The lymphocyte count decreases within a few hours, that of other white blood cells and platelets within a few days.

The effect on the white cell count of a nuclear accident is no different from that of exposure to an atomic bomb, a hydrogen bomb, or therapeutic radiation involving the marrow[17]. Although it takes some days before the white count drops, the marrow begins to feel the effect and the general condition deteriorates with marrow depression. If the exposure is less than 200 rads, hospitalization need not be required, but over 300 rads it is almost invariably necessary. Over 75 % of those who receive 400 rads must be hospitalized in the early stage, and 100 % of those during the later period.

At about the third or fourth week, patients develop chills, weakness, headache, fatigue, loss of appetite and shortness of breath which worsen steadily. Sore throat and pharyngitis develop, accompanied by gum swelling, skin hemorrhages, and a tendency to bruise easily. Bleeding and ulceration of the gums and tonsils follow, diarrhea returns and fever develops. Loss of hair (epilation) usually begins one to four weeks after a single large acute exposure, most often in the second and third week. It is a characteristic radiation effect, dose related, and was apparent in many of the hospitalized victims of Chernobyl. Increased susceptibility of infections is caused by the alterations in the immune system. Death may occur within 25–35 days[18, 19].

At autopsy, these patients have varying degrees of destruction of bone marrow and lymphoid tissues. Their lungs may show destructive types of pneumonia and lung abscesses, and inflammation of the colon has been observed.

In recent years, our understanding of the altered immune response produced by radiation has been enhanced by increasing knowledge about the function of the different types of human lymphocytes. The so-called B lymphocyte differentiates into antibody secreting cells, while T-lymphocytes influence the immune response of these cells. Ionizing radiation decreases T-cell function and the antibody response to antigens. An acquired immuno-deficiency state follows that is similar to the condition caused by the AIDS virus in humans[20]. Among the known agents of infection in patients with acquired immuno-deficiency states are many viruses, fungi, protozoa, microbacteria and bacteria. Many of these are difficult to treat, and may be lethal.

The Gastrointestinal Syndrome

With doses at 700 rads or above, nausea, persistent vomiting, and hemorrhagic diarrhea dominate the clinical picture[21]. These symptoms are associated with destruction of the intestinal epithelium. They develop in 30 minutes to several hours after exposure, depending on dose. They may disappear for a few days, only to recurr when the patient appears to have improved. Weakness, anorexia, nausea, and vomiting reappear, preventing normal food and fluid intake. Simultaneously, high fever and persistent diarrhea develop. Exhaustion and delirium may follow; dehydration develops; the circulation fails, and coma and death follow a week or so after exposure[22].

In the patients who died in the first 14 days after the explosions in Hiroshima and Nagasaki, the main pathologic changes consisted of atypical cells in the intestinal crypts and the stomach mucosa along with hemorrhage and edema. Several cases were characterized by inflammatory changes and ulcer formation in the intestine[23]. After large doses of therapeutic irradiation to the intestine, profound changes in the blood vessels have also been observed[24].

The two patients who died a radiation death at Chernobyl within the first week were examples of this syndrome, with total body doses of 700 rads or more. Furthermore, some of the nine patients who died in the third week probably represented the gastrointestinal effect, although all of them had severe bone marrow exposures as well.

The Central Nervous System Syndrome

At or above 2000 rads exposure, severe nausea and vomiting develop rapidly. These are followed by mental cloudiness, listlessness, drowsiness and weakness. Convulsions, tremor and lethargy occur[25]. Alternate states of stupor and hyper-excitability with unavoidable death follow within a few days[26]. This may be due to vascular damage which results in increased intracerebral pressure[27] or may actually be the result of cardiovascular collapse[28]. Hemorrhage, swelling, and inflammation are seen in the brain at autopsy[29].

None of the patients at Chernobyl died of the cerebral syndrome, in which death follows massive acute total body exposures of 2000 rads or more in hours or days. Our knowledge of this phase of acute radiation sickness is based more on animal experiments than on experience with patients.

Treatment of Acute Radiation Sickness

In patients with doses below 150 rads, diagnostic studies should be performed and the patients followed carefully as outpatients. At higher levels, hospitalization may be required, and general supportive measures are particularly important when nausea and vomiting are manifest.

During the *prodromal stage,* sedation may be helpful and occasionally anti-nausea drugs may be indicated. Fluid replacement is rarely required unless vomiting is unusually severe.

In the *hematopoietic syndrome* therapy initially focuses on monitoring the white cell count and infection. Perhaps the most important single safeguard for those with severe bone marrow damage is protection from pathogenic organisms. This requires isolation, sterilized food, and as sterile an environment as possible.

Prophylactic antibiotics may be important if the dose is high, although the possibility of developing resistant organisms requires a careful appraisal of its desirability.

Transfusion of platelets may be helpful in those with hemorrhagic manifestations[30]. The administration of whole blood is probably best avoided, unless bleeding mandates its use, so as not to interfere with subsequent grafting.

Perhaps the most important potential addition to therapy in the past few decades has been the application of bone marrow transplants. Prior to Chernobyl, there were relatively few opportunities to assess its effectiveness in acute marrow destruction due to radiation. An accident at Vinca in Yugoslavia provided the chance to try it in five patients, four of whom survived[31]. Bone marrow transplantation should be considered in patiens known to have received a dose in excess of 200 rads[32].

Unfortunately, in the Chernobyl accident, the effect of exposure sometimes complicated treatment. Tissue-typing was often impossible because radiation had already destroyed blood components. As a result, a marrow substitute extracted from fetal livers was used in six cases. Some patients, having swallowed or inhaled radioactive materials, required special procedures to protect doctors, nurses and laboratory workers. Two such patients died from liver and lung failures caused by radioactive particles[33].

The goal of treatment is to carry the patient through the period when his marrow is too depressed to furnish the necessary blood elements. This is also the primary objective of marrow transplantation, to provide support until residual islands of marrow regeneration begin to produce cells.

In the *gastrointestinal syndrome,* nausea, vomiting, and diarrhea are so profound that nutrition can only be maintained by the administration of intravenous fluids and plasma. The same aseptic precautions and antibiotic therapy are essential, and massive hemorrhage will require platelet transfusions and whole blood or packed cells in order to avoid shock. It is unlikely that any of the measures will prevent death if the dose has exceeded 700–800 rads.

In the *central nervous system syndrome,* treatment will not alter the rapidly lethal course of the illness.

Medical Problems of Survivors

Because of the immediacy of Chernobyl, the problems of radiation sickness have been dealt with at length. Clearly, thermal injury and blast will have devastating effects that go beyond those of radiation in the locale of nuclear weapons explosions. Elsewhere I have discussed in detail the medical problems that survivors will encounter[34]. A brief summary of these problems provides some insight into the dimensions of such a disaster.

Much of the information on the public health in the wake of a thermonuclear war is based on the Hiroshima-Nagasaki data, or on extrapolations of the sixties. There are now on hand the equivalent of one million Hiroshima bombs. In one scenario for a massive nuclear exchange derived from federal sources[35], the U.S. would undergo a 6,500-megaton attack. Approximately 4,000 megatons would fall on urban areas and population centers. Within moments, 86 million people – 40 percent of the U.S. population – would be dead, and an additional 34 million – would be seriously injured. During the post-attack shelter period, an estimated 48 million would die, for a total of 134 million fatalities in the United States alone. Furthermore, many millions of survivors would suffer from moderate to high radiation doses and would experience residual blast and burn injuries.

The World Health Organization has also considered the effects of an all-out nuclear war involving a 10,000 megaton exchange[36]. Half of the bombs were assumed to be air bursts which were detonated over cities with populations of over 60,000; the other half were surface blasts. In this analysis, 1.15 billion fatalities and 1.1 billion injured were projected. Half of the world's population might become immediate victims if such predictions were borne out.

The initial medical problems resulting from nuclear war, in approximate temporal order, include flash burns, trauma, flame burns and smoke inhalation, acute radiation, fallout radiation, suffocation and heat prostration. In the longer-term, additional health problems will arise. In the post-attack period, enteric desease will be wide spread and will exact a heavy toll[37]. Vector-borne diseases (plague, epidemic typhus, mosquito-borne encephalitis, rabies and murine typhus), although less formidable than enteric disease, might cause hundreds of thousands of deaths and many more infected survivors[38]. Among the 35 million tuberculin positive individuals in the United States, a high incidence of conversion to clinical disease may be anticipated such as that observed in wartime and under circumstances of profound malnutrition[39, 40, 41].

There are numerous factors that point to increased risk of serious epidemics in the post-attack environment. Among them are the effects of radiation, malnutrition, and exposure on susceptibility; of unsanitary conditions, lenghty shelter stays, and insect population growth on the transmission of disease; and of depleted antibody stocks, physician shortages, laboratory destruction, and post-attack disorganization on the effectiveness of counter measures[42]. In the aggregate, deaths from communicable diseases among survivors may approach 20–25 %[43].

In a computer simulation of the effects of a single nuclear explosion nine miles south of New Orleans, it was calculated that 35 % of the survivors might die from infectious diseases in the first-year-post-attack, a far higher mortality than from heart disease and cancer[44].

Infection will pose a substantial threat to health and recovery for all those injured by blast, heat, and radiation. The resources to grapple with this threat will be inadequate.

Medical Resources

Any analysis of medical resource need versus availability following a nuclear war must be based on assumptions as to the megatonage involved and the destruction that follows. Using a model developed by the government, it is feasible to combine informed estimates and prior experience to arrive at acceptable approximations. Such figures – even if the projections are subject to some error – provide a perspective from which the magnitude of the disparities can readily be appreciated. It may be argued that this is a "worst case" analysis; if so, it would surely represent the most conservative approach to any problem in which death and disability loom so large.

The disparities are great: 273,000 available hospital beds compared to the 17.6 million needed; few burn beds, with 5.3 million needed; 15,000 intensive care beds, with 6.7 million required. Among essential personnel, 48,000 physicians may be confronted with the work of 1.3 million; or 150,000 registered nurses with that of 6.7 million; or 17,000 medical technologists with that of 450,000. If there are 14,000 units of whole blood available, for example, and 64 million units required, the problem of developing a credible medical response for the millions of surviving injured can readily be grasped[45].

The urgent questions about resource availability may well go beyond the forgoing estimates. Access to resources cannot be assured. In time of greatest need, beds, personnel, and supplies in outlying areas may be unavailable to the injured in populous centers of heavy destruction – not only because of the elimination of transportation systems, but also because of intolerably high radiation levels. In the end, disparities between need and resource availability may in fact be less important than superhighways, truck tonnage, drivers, freight cars, and fuel.

Concluding Comments

The accident at Chernobyl shattered the composure of hundreds of millions, particularly in the Northern Hemisphere. It demonstrated once more the destructive effects of uncontrolled radiation, and the degree to which national boundaries may be violated by events over which innocent bystanders have no control.

The importance of Chernobyl lies not alone in the immediate human tragedy of dead, injured, and evacuated, nor even in the potential long-term effects of cataracts, thyroid malfunction, and malignancy. Beyond the insult to cells, tissue and organism, it placed a major stress on the health resources of a major power.

The energy equivalent of the hydrogen explosion at Chernobyl was thought to be approximately that of a one-half kiloton bomb. In the perspective of the past, Hiroshima represented about twenty-five times that explosive yield, while the modern stockpiles are one million times as powerful as Hiroshima and twenty-five million times the explosive energy of Chernobyl.

Hopefully, this catastrophe is a warning about more than just nuclear power plants.

BIBLIOGRAPHY

1. Ilyin, L. 5/29/86. Personal communication at IPPNW Congress, Cologne, West Germany
2. Greenwald, J. 5/26/86. Grim lessons at Hospital No. 6. Time. p. 33.
3. New York Times. 5/1/86. Soviet statement on plant. p. A6.
4. Taubman, P. 5/15/86. U.S. doctors in Soviet face a "battlefield." New York Times. p. A8.
5. Schmemann, S. 5/19/86. Soviet mounts vast operation of men and machinery to combat disaster. New York Times. p. A6.
6. New York Times. 5/7/86. Nuclear accident in the Ukraine: The Soviet account. p. A18.
7. Lushbaugh, C. C., Hubner, K. F. and Fry, S. A. The Impact of Estimates of Human Radiation Tolerance Upon Radiation Emergency Management. In: *Control of Exposure of the Public to Ionizing Radiation in the Event of Accident or Attack.* National Council on Radiation Protection and Measurement. Washington, D.C., 1982. Topic 4, Session A, pp. 46-57.
8. Hemplemann, L. H., Lisco, H., and Hoffman, J. G. Feb.,1952. The acute radiation syndrome: A study of nine cases and a review of the problem. Annals of Internal Medicine, 36: 279–500.
9. Bond, V. P., Fliedner, T. M., and Archambeau, J. D. *Mammalian Radiation Lethality.* Academic Press, New York & London, 1965. p. 57.
10. Cronkite, E. P. The Effects of Dose, Dose Rate, and Depth Dose Upon Radiation Mortality. In: *Control of Exposure of the Public to Ionizing Radiation in the Event of Accident or Attack.* National Council on Radiation Protection and Measurement, 1982, Topic 1, Session A, pp. 21–27.
11. Mole, R. H. May, 1984. The LD 50 for uniform low LET irradiation of man. British Journal of Radiology, 57: 355–369.
12. Rodblat, J. Acute Radiation Mortality in a Nuclear War. Chapter 10, In: *The Medical Implications of Nuclear War.* Institute of Medicine – National Academy of Sciences, National Academy Press, Washington, D.C., 1986.
13. Baverstock, K. F. and Ash, P. F. Nov., 1983. A review of radiation accidents involving whole body exposure and the relevance to the LD 50 for man. British Journal of Radiology, 56: 837–844.
14. Gilbert, E. S. and O'Hara, J. L. Oct., 1984. An analysis of various aspects of atomic bomb dose estimation at RERF using data on acute radiation syndromes. Radiation Research, 100: 124–38.
15. Ohkita, T. Acute Medical Effects at Hiroshima and Nagasaki. Chapter 9, pp. 79-80, In: *Last Aid: The Medical Implications of Nuclear War.* W. H. Freemann and Company, San Francisco, 1981.
16. World Health Organization. *Effects of Nuclear War on Health and Health Services of the International Committee of Experts in Medical Sciences and Public Health Implement Resolution WHA34.38.* Geneva: World Health Organization, 1984, p. 79.
17. Gerstner, H. B. Mar., 1958. Acute radiation syndrome in man. U.S. Armed Forces Medical Journal, 9: 313–353.
18. *The Treatment of Radiation Injury: A report of the Subcommittee on the Treatment of Acute Radiation Injury of the Committee on Pathologic Effects of Atomic Radiation.* National Academy of Sciences, National Research Council (U.S.). Washington, D.C., 1963, p. 4.
19. Fajardo, L. F. *Pathology of Radiation Injury.* Masson Pub., New York, 1982, p. 270.
20. Greer, D. S. and Rifkin, L. S. The Immunological Impact of Nuclear Warfare. Chapter 15, In: *The Medical Implications of Nuclear War.* Institute of Medicine – National Academy of Sciences. National Academy Press, Washington, D.C., 1986.
21. Ibid., World Health Organization, p. 17.
22. Ibid., National Academy of Sciences, National Research Council (U.S.), p. 4.
23. *Hiroshima and Nagasaki: The Physical, Medical, and Social Effects of the Atomic Bombings.* Committee for the Compilation of Materials on Damage Caused by the Atomic Bombs in Hiroshima and Nagasaki. Basic Books, Inc., Publishers, New York, 1981. pp. 168–171.
24. Hasleton, P. S., Carr, N. and Schofield, P. F. May, 1985. Vascular changes in radiation bowel disease. Histopathology, 9 [5]: 517–34.
25. Ibid., Gerstner, p. 333.
26. Ibid., World Health Organization, p. 16.
27. WASH-1400 DRAFT, *An Assessment of Accidental Risks in U.S. Commercial Power Plants,* Appendix VI "Calculation of Reactor Accident Consequences." U.S. Nuclear Regulatory Commission, Washington, D.C., August, 1974, p. 37.
28. Ibid., Fajardo, p. 270.
29. Ibid., Committee for the Compilation of Materials on Damage Caused by the Atomic Bombs in Hiroshima and Nagasaki, p. 183–184.
30. Cronkite, E.P. Aug., 1956. Treatment of radiation injuries. Military Medicine, 118: 328–334.
31. Jammet, H. P. *Treatment of Victims of the Zero-Energy Reactor Accident at Vinca. Diagnosis and Treatment of Acute Radiation Injury.* World Health Organization, Geneva, 1961, p. 102.
32. Barlotta, F. M. The New Jersey Radiation Accidents of 1974 and 1977. In: Hubner, K. F. and Fry, S. A. (eds.) *The Medical Basis for Radiation Accident Preparedness.* Elsevier North Holland, Inc., 1980, pp. 151–160.
33. Taubmann. 5/15/86. New York Times, p. 8.
34. Abrams, H. L. and Von Kaenel, W. E. 1981. Medical problems of survivors of nuclear war: Infection and communicable disease. New England Journal of Medicine, 305: 1230–1231.

35. Haaland, C. M., Chester, C. V. and Wigner, E. P. June, 1976. Survival of the relocated population of the U.S. after a nuclear attack. ORNL-5014. Oak Ridge National Laboratory. Sponsored by Defense Civil Preparedness Agency. pp. 20–21.
36. Ibid., World Health Organization.
37. Johnston, D. R., Fogel, D. R., Moors, A. W. and Hill, E. L. Sept., 1969. Post attack prevention and control of enteric diseases. Contract DAFC20-68-0197. Office of Civil Defense, Washington, D.C.
38. Johnson, T. and Johnston, D. R. June, 1968. Vectorborne diseases and control. Contract N0022867CO689. Office of Civil Defense, Washington, D.C.
39. Mitchell, H. H. August, 1966. Survey of infectious disease problem as it relates to the post-attack environment. Memorandum RM5090, TAB. The Rand Corporation. Under contract to the Atomic Energy Commission.
40. Tuberculosis and Nutrition. Tubercle. 1948; 29: 20–21.
41. Scrimshaw, N. S., Taylor, C. E., Gorgon, J. E. 1968. Interactions of nutrition and infection. WHO Monograph Ser., 57: 61, 69–70, 88, 89.
42. Ibid., Abrams and Von Kaenel. p. 1231.
43. Hill, E. L. Voors, A. W., Lyday, R. O., et al. Nov., 1968. National emergency health preparedness study, including the development and testing of a total emergency health care system model. R-OU-332. Research Triangle Institute, Prepared for Office of Civil Defense, Office of the Secretary of the Army. pp. 3–10.
44. Ibid., Abrams and Von Kaenel. p. 1231.
45. Abrams, H. L. 1984. Medical resources after nuclear war: Availability vs. need. Journal of the American Medical Association, 252: 653–658.

THE CORE CURRICULUM

Zdenek Dienstbier, Czechoslovakia

Long-Term Medical Effects of Nuclear War

R adiobiology as a branch of science has come into existence shortly after the discovery of invisible x-rays by W. K. Roentgen in 1895. In the beginning of our century it was the German scientist H. Heinecke who studied the biological effects of x-rays. Already in 1903 he established that after exposure to acute radiation peripheral blood elements decreased as a consequence of damage to bone marrow hemopoiesis. Acute radiation has given rise to x-ray diagnostics and together with natural radioacitivity discovered by H. Becquerel and gamma-irradiation it found its full use in the tumor therapy. In addition to these two forms of ionizing radiation, broadly utilized in biology and industry, after the discovery of artificial radioactivity by Fréderic Joliot-Curie, his wife Irene and Enrico Fermi first works on diagnostical and therapeutical utilization of radioisotopes appeared.

The peaceful use of ionizing irradiation gave rise to many separate medical branches. x-ray diagnostics, radio-therapy and nuclear medicine came into existence. In professional workers of these branches harmful effects of low doses of the irradiation appearing with a great lapse of time were successfully determined. Thus, the first results of experiments in animals have been confirmed. The first case of death of a radiologist due to bone marrow suppression after 14 years of work without sufficient safety measures has been described by Gavazzeni and Minella in 1915. A similar cause of death in a pediatric radiologist following 12 years of work has been determined by Faber in 1923. Henshow and Hawkins published in 1944 a statistical retrospective study where they called attention to the fact that in male physicians having worked with x-rays only occasionally the incidence of leukemia appeared 1.7 times more frequently than in the normal male population. In the same year, March wrote in Radiology that leukemia was 10 times more frequent in radiologists than in physicians of other branches. In 1955, Brown and Ebatt have established in patients irradiated for Bechterev disease, the incidence of leukemia five to ten times more often than in nonirradiated patients with the same disease.

Also the genetic consequences following the effects of ionizing irradiation are to be found in the scientific literature of the fifties. In the first place there are warnings concerning the elevated number of malformations among the members of radiologists' families (Macht and Lawrence) that, nevertheless, were not confirmed neither by Crow nor by our working group that had followed up data in 3,700 physicians in the CSSR. Rugh in 1955 wrote that the primitive germ cells of the gonades are exposed to the danger of gene or chromosome changes during both local or whole-body irradiation. He concluded that after a dose higher than 0.8 Gy. genetic transformation took place.

It was nazism and racism in Hitler's Germany together with their fascist allies who started World War II, whereby the chain of peaceful discoveries of the utilization of ionizing radiation for man's benefit was interrupted. They caused the top scientists, e. g. A. Einstein, to initiate and collaborate on the first atomic bomb. Later on, most of them warned against its, from the military point of view already quite needless application. Nevertheless, mankind became acquainted with until that time unknown, i. e. with tremendous destructive power of the atomic nucleus during its splitting and the catastrophic consequences for hundred of thousands of affected individuals.

Not even 50 million victims in World War II were sufficient proof. The divided world of the subsequent allies stands now before the annihilation prepared by man himself.

The American atomic bombing of Hiroshima and Nagasaki has been a cruel radio-biological experiment. In the Japanese exposed to the effects of atom bombing, world science has gained the majority of data necessary for the presupposed consequence of long term effects in case of a nuclear war.

I had the occasion to work in Japan in 1977 in an international team led by Prof. Joseph Rotblat. We have analyzed some data for a document prepared for the International Congress Against Atomic Weapons having been held in the same year in Hiroshima. The incidence of leukemia and as its consequence the mortality among the survivors after atomic explosions rapidly increased. The peak of leukemia incidence began in 1955–1957. Although since that time a decrease appeared, the incidence remained higher against the mean values in the Japanese population.

There exists a direct relation between the mean yearly leukemia incidence and the radiation dose.

High incidence of leukemia after irradiation has been seen in the first place in children, relatively low in adolescence (10–20 years) and then it increased again with age. Between the irradiation and the incidence of leukemia at least 2–3 years have passed, most often 10–15 years dependant upon the age and the irradiation dose. There did not exist a difference between the incidence of individual kinds of leukemias. Nevertheless, one kind of leukemia (the chronic lymphatic one) did not show an increased incidence up to now.

In both towns, Hiroshima and Nagasaki, an increased incidence of cancer of the thyroid has been proven statistically in both sexes, in women it was breast cancer following the initial irradiation. Also death due to lung cancer was significantly higher.

Similarly, the incidence of other kinds of malignant tumors (of the salivary glands, stomach, bones, prostate and malignant lymphomas) in the surviving victims of the explosion is higher than in the nonexposed population.

Children born to women, pregnant at the time of bombing, surviving the atom explosions showed more frequent incidence of congenital development defects, partly smaller heads. This was connected with mental backwardness of these individuals. Moreover, their physical development was slower.

The mortality of children irradiated in utero was higher till the first year of their life and was dependent upon the irradiation dose. It was surprising that no other consequences did appear after the irradiation in utero, as for instance the elevation of leukemia counts in these children. This is in contrast with the findings in other countries where a marked increase of leukemia rate and other malignant diseases in children irradiated in utero has been described after roentgenological examinations. This is surprising even from that reason that many mothers-hibakusha, pregnant at the time of atom bombing, were irradiated with much higher doses than is so with roentgenological examinations. This gives evidence of different biological consequences of various kinds of irradiation and of different energy distribution in the irradiated object.

The gross noxious genetical postirradiation effect manifests itself in sterility, abortion, premature delivery, mental and physical retardation. The number of chromosomal aberrations in irradiated surviving children is still high – proportional to the received irradiation dose. Thus it might be presupposed that in children of such persons genetical disturbances will appear. Nevertheless, in the studied series of the first generation they have not been demonstrated.

In many children burned within the atom explosion keloids of different forms and extent appeared within 1–4 months after the healing of burns. The incidences of keloids in burns in Hiroshima reached 59 %, in Nagasaki 69 %. Later on the keloids were observed in the healed wounds again after injury. Most of the injured were young people between 10–20 years of age. After the peak in the years 1946–1947 the keloids began to decline spontaneously and the majority of them disappeared entirely within five years.

After the explosions traumatic injuries of the eyes, inflammation of the cornea, disorders of the bleeding of the retina and cataracts have been recorded. The incidence of cataracts is directly dependent upon the distance from the hypocentre – in Hiroshima up to 1.6 km, i.e. dose higher than 13.3 rad of gamma-irradiation and 5.6 rad of neutron irradiation. In Nagasaki it was approximately up to 1.8 km, i.e. dose higher than 37.6 rad of gamma-irradiation and 0.3 rad of neutron irradiation. Proportional to the distance from the hypocentre the number of eye cataracts increased.

Anemia has been determined more often in acutely irradiated persons. In 1955, markedly different lower values of red blood cells were measured in irradiated persons when compared to the control groups.

The decrease in white blood cells returned very slowly. Individual subjects continued to suffer from white blood cell insufficiency. Also by comparison of blood platelet counts there was no difference in the mean values in irradiated and control persons.

The bone marrow damage was not in relation to the distance and irradiation dose. Many of the involved persons died within some months. The subsequent hyperplasia of bone marrow cells appearing in some surviving persons led to leukemia in exceptional cases.

Besides these somatic changes the surviving victims have suffered and still suffer from psychological disorders. I myself could make sure about this in the course of their examinations 32 years after the explosions. In the best case they react inadequately when remembering the horrors experienced during the explosion and immediately after it. They become melancholic and sustain tearful states and hysteric shrieks. Nevertheless, many of them continue to be under psychiatric care.

The consequences of an atomic war would differ from the Japanese experiences in the amount of attacked countries, destruction of the organization of economical affairs and administrative systems of the attacked countries, complete setting aside of medical services, contamination of the life environment and in the consequences of a nuclear winter.

Persons who would survive the acute period of a nuclear war would look forward to a nonimaginable privation. This would also eventually carry over to the inhabitants of those countries not directly mixed up in a nuclear conflict.

Besides the insufficiency of food, people would consume contaminated water and food and gradually growing doses of external irradiation. That of the internal one would cause health injuries as observed in Japan. Due to the breakdown of immunological reactivity, the insufficiency of medication and medical security would give rise to a greater peril of infections and epidemics and the morbidity and mortality would rise. People would die without medical care, without possibilites of hospitalization, without psychopharmaceuticals, sedatives and opiates. The survivors would envy the dead. The adults would watch their suffering children unable to help them.

Besides by consequences of irradiation the surviving persons would also suffer in another way. Firestorms would cause the highest percentage of fatalities and in connection with them late consequences from burns (including the long term treatment) would exist in survivors. The total number of hospital beds in special burn treatment centres would be insufficient.

J. Rotblatt mentioned in Brussels the revised dosimetric data in Japan. An LD_{50} was 154 rad (1.54 Gy). This is three to four times lower than has been assumed up to now. In this connection, the increase of the rate of malignancies is considered in case of a direct effect of irradiation. In the case of coincidental attacks on nuclear installations in a nuclear war, the mean irradiation dose form global fall-out would be three times higher. The computerized studies show that cancerogenic risk factors would more than double. Higher would be the late mortality and morbidity due to the suppression of immune response. Besides ionizing irradiation the synergism of nocious factors in the survivors would include ultraviolet irradiation, polytrauma, burns, malnutrition and psychosocial stresses. The risks of summed mortality of two and more coincidental factors of the injury act simultaneously and the effect may be greatly enhanced by synergistic interactions.

Up till now it was supposed that global fall-out would reach the stratosphere where it would spread all over the globe. As the circulation in the atmosphere is very low, it takes months or years before the material is deposited on the ground. During this delay the external hazard from the penetrating gamma-rays would no longer be significant.

The radioactivity from smaller intercontinental ballistic missiles (in kilotons) is largely deposited in the troposphere. Radioactive fall-out from the troposphere is more rapid. We speak about "intermediate fall-out". Its consequence is increasing in severity due to the trend of the production of nuclear weapons containing large numbers of 200 kt warheads. There exists real danger of the rise of "hot-spots" under certain meteorological conditions which may cover a region for example of the size of Europe.

The intermediate fall-out would be to increase long-term effects – the induction of cancer and genetic defects in the first place.

The approximate risk of induction of radiation cancer can be (estimated by UNSCEAR) summarized in terms of the number of cases expected per million persons so exposed per rad of absorbed radiation dose. These estimations are very broad generalizations and for each tissue there are differing effects of such factors as sex, the kind of radiation, dose, dose rate, etc. For example, the pediatric population is more sensitive to thyroid cancer induction, female breast cancer is induced primarily by exposure during the early reproductive period, lung cancer is highest in males exposed at over 35 years of age, the induction of cancer in the fetus is distinctly elevated, estimated as 200 to 250 cases per million per rad.

The duration of the period at risk also varies with different tissues. The mean interval between exposure and leukemia development is in the region of ten years, for example, whereas the other malignancies typically appear in an exposed population with a mean of 25 years of latency. In a population exposure, the earlier appearing leukemia may serve as an indicator for the eventual total of all fetal malignancies, which ultimately may occur to six times as many individuals as those developing leukemia only.

The prognosis for the various delayed effects of radiation exposure is similar to that of the same pathology in the absence of such exposure. The ICRP derived the maximum risk rate from radiation-induced cancers as approximate numbers of fatal cases per million exposed per rad: female breast 50, leukemia 20, lung 20, thyroid 5, bone 5, all other organs together 50.

I stress these consideration also in connection with the program of strategic defense initiative prepared in the U.S.A.: "Low dose effects are of two kinds – carcinogenic and genetic – and in both cases the direct statistical evidence in human population is not large enough for an accurate construction of a dose-effect curve. An estimate of the dose commitment due to the delayed fallout had been made by a committee appointed by the U.S. National Academy of Sciences. These estimates were 8 μGy (0.8 mrad)/Mt in Northern and 2.5 μGy (0.25 mrad)/Mt in Southern latitudes. Assuring a population 2×10^9 in the north and 2.5×10^9 in the south, and applying ICRP risk factors (conservative estimate of 1.25×10^{-2} per man sievert for cancers in all sites and 8×10^3 per man sievert for genetic defects) one calculates a figure of 1.52×10^5 additional cancers spread over a period of 20 to 30 years, and of about 8×10^4 genetic defects in all later generations, incurred by the explosion of 545 Mt until the year of 1980."

Therefore, let the physicians solve these inevitable consequences of contemporary contamination of the life environment and mankind and let us try with yet greater intensity to achieve a ban on nuclear weapons. Nuclear energetics will sufficiently engage us – specialists to make it more safe.

Let us prevent mankind to have to look forward again to a Adam and Eve creation, let us prefer to solve the problems of risk factors such as e. g. obesity and smoking. Nuclear war would threaten the very existence of mankind.

BIBLIOGRAPHY

1. Biochemical Indicators of Radiation Injury in Man. Vienna, IAEA 1971.
2. Cassel, Ch., McCally, M., Abrams, H.: Nuclear Weapons and Nuclear War. New York, Praeger 1984.
3. Dalrymple, G. V., Gaulden, M. E., Kollmorgen, G. M., Vogel, H. H.: Medical Radiation Biology. Philadelphia, W. B. Saunders Co. 1973.
4. Dienstbier, Z.: Hiroshima – Conscience of the Mankind (in Czech). Praha, Avicenum 1979.
5. Dienstbier, Z., Arient, M., Kofránek, V.: Radiation Sickness (in Czech). Praha, State Medical Publishing House 1957.
6. Effects of Ionizing Radiations on the Haematopoietic Tissue. Vienna, IAEA 1967.
7. Effects of Nuclear War on Health and Health Services. WHO, A 36/12 1983.
8. Hiroshima and Nagasaki. The Physical, Medical, and Social Effects of the Atomic Bombings. Tokyo, Iwanami Shoten 1979.
9. Radiation Damage and Sulfhydryl Compounds. Vienna, IAEA 1969.

THE CORE CURRICULUM

Wilfrid Bach, Federal Republic of Germany

Climatic Consequences of Nuclear War

Military and commercial use of atomic energy: changing perspectives and prospects

In the old perspective emphasis was on the effects of blast, heat, and ionizing radiation in the immediate vicinity of the burst as well as on global radioactive fallout from bomb tests and the destruction of the stratopheric ozone layer (NAS, 1975; ACDA, 1979; OTA, 1979; UN, 1980). It was only four years ago that Crutzen and Birks' (1982) pioneering work opened a new perspective by drawing attention to the potential effects that massive emissions of smoke, soot and dust from urban and forest fires might exert on the atmosphere, and hence the weather and the climate.

Until then it had simply been overlooked that emissions of huge masses of smoke could effectively block the earth from receiving sunlight, an event appropriately dubbed "nuclear night". Based on Crutzen and Birks' work and their own experience with duststorms on Mars Turco et al. (1983), from their first letters known as the TTAPS group, calculated that the global mean temperature would drop by several tens of degrees below zero, for which they introduced the universally adopted term "nuclear winter". To put this in perspective, the seventeenth century "Little Ice Age" was caused by only a 1° C drop below the mean ambient temperature, and peak-to-trough changes between major glacial and interglacial periods may have only been 10–15° C (McNaughton et al., 1986).

The recent nuclear reactor catastrophe at Chernobyl has added a further dimension to the new perspective. Until that incident we had all pushed out of our minds the fact huge amounts of long-lived radionuclides exist in reactor cores, spent fuel rods, fuel processing plants, and waste storage facilities. Even the most recent and most comprehensive SCOPE-Report (Pittock et al., 1985) deals with radioacitivity from civilian reactors only as an afterthought in a short appendix, because the "targeting with nuclear warheads of nuclear fuel cycle facilities" ... is "considered highly improbable". It can be argued, however, that with the several hundred civilian and military nuclear reactors accumulated in Europe alone, in a nuclear war it would be practically impossible not to hit and damage such reactors. The gamma radiation dose rate from a 1 Mt weapon detonated on a commercial reactor would be higher from the nuclear weapon in the first few days, but beyond about a year the gamma radiation of the reactor would greatly dominate that of the weapon. Moreover, to give but one example, the inventory of one of the most deadly poisons, namely, strontium 90, in a single 1000 MW nuclear reactor and its spent fuel pond is more than that produced in a 1000 Mt nuclear war.

Atomic bombs together with nuclear reactors thus constitute a danger potential that is a major threat to all the peoples of the world. The Chernobyl catastrophe has shown that the radioactive fallout from even a single reactor can affect food production on a continent-wide scale. Food production would even be more severely crippled in a nuclear war. Man might be able to survive on a radioactively-poisoned diet for some time. But Man cannot survive the effects of a nuclear winter, because the changed climate effectively eliminates the basis for food production. The prospects of the nuclear age are mass starvation.

The following review is restricted to an update on recent developments in nuclear winter research. For a more comprehensive treatment the reader is referred, among others, to Turco et al. (1983), Ehrlich et al. (1983), Ehrlich et al. (1984), Harwell (1984), NAS (1985), Pittock et al. (1985), Harwell and Hutchinson (1985), and Bach (1986 a, b).

Fires and smoke

Many military installations and industries are in or near cities. Therefore, it would seem plausible to expect that a nuclear war would produce large city fires with the concomitant release of huge quantities of smoke. The resulting climatic effects depend on the types of fuels consumed by the fires, the amounts and injection heights of the smoke, microphysical processes, and the optical properties of the smoke.

Amounts of smoke   The estimation of smoke emission requires the development of nuclear war scenarios. Table 1 lists the results of the 4590 Mt scenario by Crutzen et al. (CGB, 1984) which targets 800 Mt on cities, and the 6500 Mt baseline scenario of the NAS (1985) which reserves 1000 Mt for a city attack. Multiplying the individual factors results in a total urban smoke emission estimate of 80 million tons by CGB and 150 million tons by NAS. A similar assessment for forest fires results in 60 and 30 million tons, giving a total smoke emission of 140 and 180 million tons obtained by CGB and NAS, respectively. The NAS has also attempted to assess the plausible ranges. The resulting "excursions" (see Table 1) extend from 20 to 450 million tons for city fires and from 0 to 200 million tons for forest fires. City fires have a greater effect on climate than forest fires because of their greater quantities of smoke emission and due to their greater share of highly absorbing soot particles.

Washout of smoke   Residence times of the smoke aerosols in the atmosphere and washout processes determine the smoke's effectiveness on climate. These, in turn, depend on the emission height of the smoke and on microphysical processes. The two major microphysical processes are coagulation and scavenging. Coagulation implies smoke particles colliding and adhering thereby forming larger particles which results in a reduced optical efficiency and hence a smaller impact on climate. During the scavenging process the smoke particles interact with water vapor, condensed water, ice, and snow, thereby removing them from the atmosphere. Thus, scavenging is an important process in determining the lifetime of the smoke and hence its potential to absorb and scatter solar radiation.

To study the various processes involved Malone et al. (1986) have used a three-dimensional (3 D) global model which allows for localized injection of smoke, its transport by the model-simulated winds, its absorption of solar radiation, and its removal by the model-simulated precipitation. The experiment is based on an NAS nuclear war scenario which injects 170

URBAN FIRES $(2.5 \times 10^5 \, km^2)$ Factor	STUDIES CGB (1984)	NAS (1985) Baseline	NAS (1985) Excursions
Explosive yield over burnable areas, Y (Mt)	0.8×10^3	10^3	10^3
Area ignited by Mt of yield, A (m²/Mt)	3.125×10^8	2.5×10^8	$1.25 \times 10^8 - 3.75 \times 10^8$
Loading of flammable materials, m(g/m²)	4×10^4	4×10^4	$2 \times 10^4 - 4 \times 10^4$
Fraction of fuel burned, f	0.40	0.75	0.75
Smoke emission factor, ε(g of smoke / g of material burned)	0.02	0.02	0.01 – 0.04
Smoke emission $E(g) = Y \cdot A \cdot m \cdot f \cdot \varepsilon$	80×10^{12}	150×10^{12}	$20 \times 10^{12} - 450 \times 10^{12}$
FOREST FIRES $(2.5 \times 10^5 \, km^2)$ Factor			
Explosive yield over burnable areas, Y (Mt)	10^3	10^3	10^3
Area ignited by Mt of yield, A (m²/Mt)	2.5×10^8	2.5×10^8	1×10^9
Loading of flammable materials, m(g/m²)	2×10^4	2×10^4	2×10^4
Fraction of fuel burned, f	0.20	0.20	0.20
Smoke emission factor, ε(g of smoke / g of material burned)	0.06	0.03	0.05
Smoke emission $E(g) = Y \cdot A \cdot m \cdot f \cdot \varepsilon$	60×10^{12}	30×10^{12}	$0 - 200 \times 10^{12}$
TOTAL	140×10^{12}	180×10^{12}	$20 \times 10^{12} - 650 \times 10^{12}$

Table 1:
Estimation of smoke emissions from urban and forest fires ignited by a nuclear war
Extracted from: Crutzen, Galbally and Brühl (CGB, 1984) and NAS (1985)

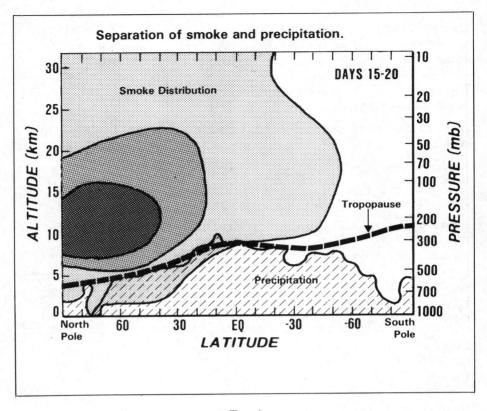

Figure 1
The relative positions of the modified tropopause (heavy dashed line) and the precipitaion distribution (cross-hatched region below the tropopause), both averaged over days 15-20, and the smoke distribution at day 20 (stippled area above the tropopause) for the 170 million tons of smoke "NAS" scenario. – Source: Malone et al. (1986)

million tons of smoke over Europe, the western U.S.S.R. and the U.S.A., into a July model atmosphere. Fig. 1 shows the smoke distribution from the north pole to the south pole up to a height of 30 km. Solar heating lifts the smoke above the tropopause. This has important consequences: The tropopause reforms below the heated smoke layer separating it effectively from precipitation and thus preventing it from being washed out. During summer conditions about one third of the heated smoke is lofted above the tropopause prolonging the nuclear winter effects and leading to marked surface temperature reductions. A winter war could result in less solar heating, faster smoke removal, and hence less significant temperature changes.

Optical properties of smoke   Depending upon their optical properties the emitted aerosols can significantly influence the radiation budget of the earth-atmosphere system. The optical properties can vary greatly depending on three important physical characteristics: The composition, the size distribution, and the shape of the particles. As we have seen above smoke from urban fires contains substantial quantities of elemental carbon or soot which absorbs solar radiation very efficiently. Scattering of solar radiation occurs mainly with mineral dust produced from targeting missile sites. Solar radiation is also much more strongly absorbed by soot particles than is radiation. The intensity of solar radiation reaching the ground decreases exponentially with the amount of absorbing aerosols in the atmosphere. In contrast, the amount of infrared radiation reaching the earth's surface is not so much a function of the aerosol quantity but rather one of air temperatures. Consequently, a large quantity of sooty particles translates into a substantial cooling of the earth's surface (Turco et al., 1984).

The calculation of the reduction of solar radiation requires information on the vertical aerosol distribution and the solar absorption coefficient. If we assume the NAS smoke quantity of 180 million tons (see Table 1) to be uniformly distributed between latitude 30 to 70° N over an area of 1.1×10^{14} cm^2, then we obtain a smoke quantity of 1.6 g/m^2 considered to be representative of an air column reaching to an altitude of 8 km. With Thompson et al. (1984) we assume a wavelength-independent solar absorption coefficient of 1.8 m^2/g. The product of the two results is an optical depth of 3. Optical depth is related to I_0, the intensity of sunlight at the top of the atmosphere, and I, the intensity at the earth's surface, through Beer/Bouguer/Lambert's law $I = I_0 \exp(-\bar{i})$. With an optical depth of $\bar{i} = 3$ and the sun overhead (i. e. the solar zenith angle is zero) only about 5 % (exp(–3)) of the sunlight reaches the ground. For a more typical zenith angle of 60°, and hence a longer path of the solar beam through the atmosphere, $\bar{i}$ becomes $3 \times \sec(60°) = 6$ implying that only exp(–6) = 0.25 % of the sunlight reaches the surface (nuclear night). Uncertainties in the estimation of $\bar{i}$ are not very critical for the calculation of the temperature reduction as long as only a fraction of the normal sunlight reaches the ground. Compared to smoke, dust is generally considered to be a minor factor influencing climate (NAS, 1985; Ramaswamy and Kiehl, 1985).

Climatic consequences

Since the real experiment would entice the demise of mankind, it is necessary to rely on theoretical model simulations to assess the climatic effects of nuclear war. While there has been much improvement since 1982, when nuclear winter research began, there is still a good deal of uncertainty. As research proceeds there is a good chance that many of the uncertainties, especially regarding the smaller-scale details of the smoke properties can be removed, but there will always remain some uncertainty, especially due to the uncertain nature of any nuclear war scenario. It is, however, important that such model simulations be done so that politicians can appraise the consequences of a nuclear war on man's life support system. In the following sections I shall highlight the progress in nuclear winter research with recent results.

Three generations of studies   The first generation models include simple analytical studies and 1 D radiative-convective models (RCMs) (e.g. Turco et al., 1983; MacCracken, 1983; Crutzen et al., 1984; Ramaswamy and Kiehl, 1985; Golitsyn and Ginsburg, 1985; Vupputuri, 1986). These studies have been used to gain some more insight on the sequence of events indicated in area 1 of Fig. 2. The second generation models made use of 2 D (MacCracken, 1983) and 3 D climate models (e. g. Alexandrow and Stenchikov, 1983; Thompson et al., 1984; Covey et al., 1984; Covey, 1985; Cess et al., 1985 a, b). While smoke and dust, in some cases even varying with time, formed the radiatively-active model input, they were still treated in a passive manner, i. e. they were not being moved around by the model-generated circulation. This added the two boxes in area 2 of Fig. 2, but the lack of feedback between the changed circulation and the vertical, as well as the horizontal distribution of smoke and dust still limited the realism of the results. A third generation of studies now utilizes a fully interactive aerosol scheme in 2 D (Haberle et al., 1985) and 3 D models (e. g. MacCracken

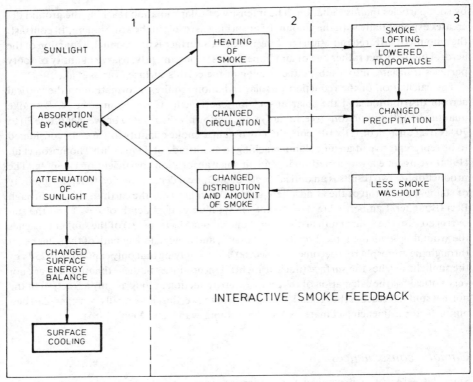

Figure 2
Schematic diagram of smoke-weather/climatic effects. The area labelled 1 shows interactions included in first generation models. Second generation models added calculations of effects in area 2. Third generation, or fully interactive models, complete the feedback loops as shown in area 3. Changed weather/climate effects are indicated by thicker lines. – Source: Pittock et al. (1985)

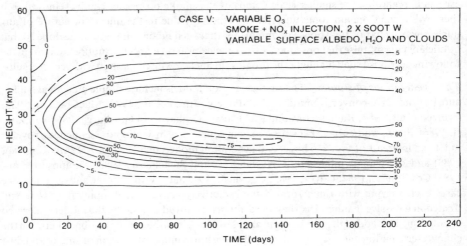

Figure 3
Altitude-time cross-section of calculated ozone concentration changes (%). – Source: Vupputuri (1986)

and Walton, 1984; MacCracken, 1985; Stenchikov, 1985; Thompson, 1985; Malone et al., 1986). In these models (see area 3 in Fig. 2) the tropospheric smoke is heated and lofted by solar radiation, which changes the atmospheric circulation, the vertical and horizontal distribution of the smoke as well as the precipitation patterns, which, in turn, affect the smoke remaining in the atmosphere and hence its ability to absorb solar energy and to change the climate. It is important to realize that this hierarchy of models has different limitations so that their results are not strictly equivalent.

Results from simple models   The effect of a smoke layer on equilibrium planetary temperatures can be studied qualitatively using simple analytical models. Golitsyn and Ginsburg (1985) used a model which considers the radiative energy balance at the top of the atmosphere and at the surface, and absorption and scattering of the smoke within the atmosphere, for globally averaged conditions. They find that the main changes in the mean atmospheric temperature and mean surface temperature occur when the optical depth for solar radiation is smaller than one, and that these temperatures are fairly insensitive to optical depths greater than two or three.

These simple analytical models are limited in their vertical resolution and spectral detail. For more realistic studies, 1 D radiative-convective models (RCMs) have been used which average all horizontal variations and consider quantities such as temperature only as a function of height. These models are well suited to do detailed sensitivity studies on the modification of solar and infrared radiation by smoke and dust, and on microphysical processes. Surface temperatures usually calculated for a land-only planet typically drop to -20 to $-40°$ C depending upon the nuclear scenario. In the real world the oceans, due to their large heat storage capacity, do, of course, mitigate the land surface cooling. The criticism is justified that 1 D RCMs overestimate somewhat land surface cooling. Turco et al. (1983) have done the most extensive sensitivity studies with this model type, and since they have been widely reviewed, the results are not repeated here.

Instead, I report on some new findings by Vupputuri (1986) who coupled a 1 D time-dependent RCM with a photochemical-diffusion model to study the effects of smoke and NO_x on the vertical temperature and O_3 structure and on surface climate. On the one hand, the stratospheric temperature increase, due to the absorption of sunlight by the emitted smoke, decreases O_3 production, because temperature and O_3 are inversely correlated through temperature-dependent reaction rate coefficients of chemical reactions. On the other hand, NO_x injection decreases O_3, which leads to a temperature reduction, which in turn increases the O_3 concentration. These complicated ozone-temperature interactions were considered for an injection of 280 million tons of smoke and 0.5×10^{32} NO molecules per Mt in case V as shown in Fig. 3. The altitude-time cross-section shows that the O_3 reduction (%) develops slowly (due to the slow transport of NO_x to higher levels where it can catalytically destroy O_3 more effectively), reaching a maximum of 75 % after 100 days. It is of particular importance that more than half the total O_3 reduction can be expected by the smoke injection alone.

Fig. 4 shows that, for the above specifications, surface temperatures would drop as much as 45° C within the first 30 days, and that a smoke injection reduced by one half would still lead to a cooling of more than 30° C (dashed-dotted line). Comparison of the solid and dashed lines shows that the effect of stratospheric O_3 reduction on the surface climate is small amounting to an additional cooling of only about 2.5° C. Finally, it is shown that the thick smoke layer decreases the UV-B radiation at the surface by almost 100 %. When the

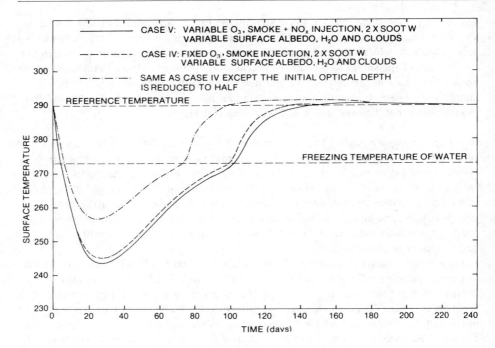

Figure 4
Comparison of the time evolution of the calculated surface temperature changes (K) for the specified experiments.
Source: Vupputuri (1986)

smoke is removed, the stratospheric O_3 depletions would permit the biologically deleterious UV-B radiation to increase at the surface by more than 160%.

Results from advanced models with non-interactive smoke This generation of studies makes use of 2 D and 3 D models in which the smoke is spread instantaneously throughout the entire northern hemispheric atmosphere but remains passive or fixed during the whole simulation. Two examples are presented in this category, one is to demonstrate how quickly the frost would spread after a nuclear war, and another one is to investigate to what extent the southern hemisphere could become involved.

In the first example the National Center for Atmospheric Research (NCAR) 3 D GCM is used which has nine vertical layers reaching to an altitude of about 30 km, and a horizontal resolution of about 4.5° latitude by 7.5° longitude (Covey et al., 1984). Sea surface temperature, sea ice, snow cover, and solar insolation are all prescribed for the time of the year to be simulated. The specification of a non-interacting ocean in particular implies that reasonable results can only be expected for simulations up to a few weeks. The experiments are based on the NAS baseline 6500 Mt nuclear war scenario generating ca. 200 million tons of smoke which is evenly distributed between an altitude of 1 to 10 km and between latitude 30° to 70° N.

Three simulations were run each over a period of 20 days starting on June 30 "summer"), December 27 ("winter"), and March 22 ("spring") with initial conditions taken from an unperturbed long-term seasonal cycle simulation. A summertime perturbation is shown here

t = 0

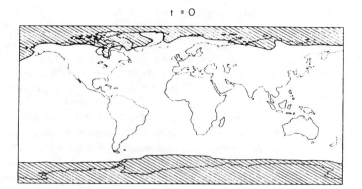

t = 2 days

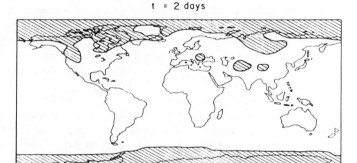

t = 10 days

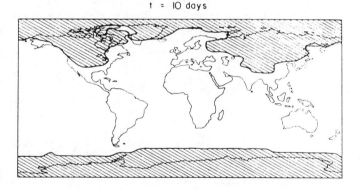

Figure 5
Surface temperature at three selected instants of time. T = 0 is the time just before
smoke is added to the atmosphere in the "summer" case. Areas of temperatures of
less than 270 K (i.e. below freezing) are hatched. – Source: Covey et al. (1986)

because it is likely to give the greatest response since more solar radiation is available for
absorption by the smoke. Fig. 5 shows surface temperature "snapshots" just before smoke
injection (t = 0) and two subsequent times. It is noteworthy that even at early times (t = 2
days after the war) substantical subfreezing temperatures are occurring underneath dense

smoke patches. By t = 10 days large areas in Eurasia and North America experience freezing temperatures. Only coastal areas and western parts of continents escape the stark continental cooling due to the influence of air masses from the warmer oceans. These and other simulations showed that even a few days of dense smoke could lead to a transient "quick freeze" which would be transported by the lottery of winds (a sort of "weather roulette") to almost any place (Schneider, 1985). This has, of course, very serious implications for food production, especially at the more climate-sensitive southern latitudes.

In the second example the Computing Center of the U.S.S.R. Academy of Sciences (CCAS) 3 D GCM is used to study the perturbation of the atmospheric circulation through smoke injection caused by a nuclear war (Alexandrov and Stenchikov, 1983). The model has a rather coarse horizontal resolution of 12° latitude by 15° longitude with two layers for the troposphere up to a height of ca. 12 km. The atmospheric model is coupled to a thermodynamic model of the upper ocean thereby allowing to assess the change in sea surface temperatures. Unlike the NCAR model, the CCAS model may thus also be used to simulate the longer-term climatic effects, i.e. for a period of several months or even years. While the NCAR model can simulate individual seasons, the CCAS model can only generate annual mean conditions. The CCAS simulations are based on a 10,000 Mt nuclear war scenario whose smoke and dust is instantly injected and uniformly distributed into the model atmosphere between 12 and 90° N.

Fig. 6 shows the meridianal circulation pattern simulated by the CCAS model before smoke injection (day 0) and on day 35 after a nuclear war. The unperturbed circulation system shows the typical cellular structure with one cell north and one south of the equator and rising air masses over the intertropical convergence zone and sinking air masses over the subtropical high pressure belts on either hemisphere. The intense heating of the smoke between 30 and 70° N completely reverses the circulation system. Now the air rises over the northern hemispheric subtropics carrying with it the smoke toward the southern hemisphere within the newly-established large single cell system. Such a situation would have severe impacts on the low-latitude and southern hemispheric food production and the natural ecosystems.

Figure 6
The zonally averaged atmospheric circulation shown as a mass streamfunction in the latitude-height plane. Arrows indicate the direction of meridional and vertical motion (units: 10^{10} kg/s). Day 0 refers to the time just before which smoke is added to the model. The meridional circulation is completely altered by day 35 of the simulation, with solar heating of the smoke driving a single, large, interhemispheric circulation cell. – Source: Thompson et al. (1984)

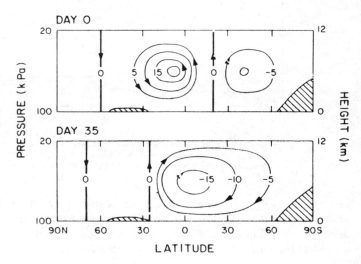

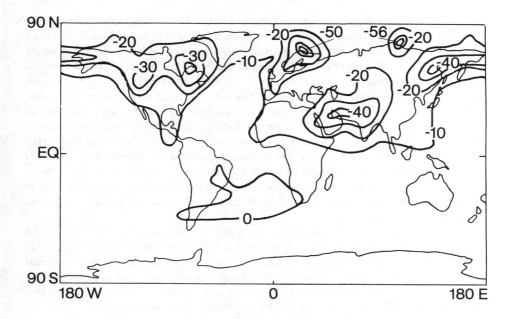

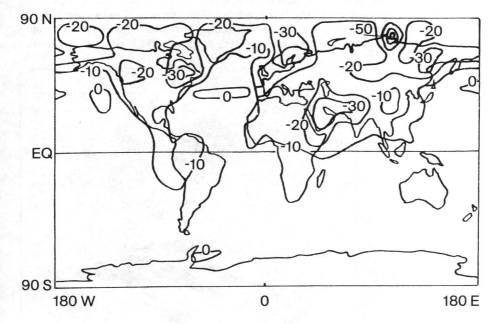

Figure 7 a, b
Change in the geographic distribution of the annual mean surface temperature 40 days after a nuclear war for the
non-interactive smoke case (a) and the interactive smoke case (b).
Sources: Alexandrov and Stenchikov (1983), Stenchikov (1985)

Results from advanced models with interactive smoke   In the latest quest to make the simulations more realistic, the smoke is injected over the most likely target areas to be moved around with the circulation altered by the heated smoke. A few examples may demonstrate this new approach. Stenchikov (1985) has modified the CCAS model discussed above to account for the transport of smoke and dust in the atmosphere by horizontal and vertical motion. Both the non-interactive and interactive cases were run with the smoke and dust uniformly spread between 12 and 90° N, with an initial optical depth of 3, and by considering scavenging processes. Comparison of the global annual average surface temperature changes of the non-interactive case in Fig. 7a with those of the interactive case in Fig. 7 b for day 40 after a nuclear war shows that due to the more uniform smoke spread the cooling is somewhat reduced in the interactive case, but at the same time it is extended to more southerly regions (see e. g. the 10°-isotherm over Central and South America in Fig. 7b). It appears that also nations far away from the immediate target areas are forced to suffer the aftermaths of a nuclear war.

To study the effects of interactive transport and scavenging of smoke MacCracken and Walton (1984) have coupled the two-layer Oregon State University 3 D GCM to the 3 D GRANTOUR trace species transport model developed at the Lawrence Livermore National Laboratory. The latter uses transport (wind field) and precipitation data calculated by the 3 D GCM to spread the smoke around the globe and to scavenge it by rain and snow. GRANTOUR divides the troposphere from the surface to 11 km into some 10,000 parcels of equal air mass spread evenly throughout the atmosphere. The climatic effects are calculated for two interactive smoke cases. The first involves 150 million tons of smoke produced by fires over the eastern and western U.S., Europe and western Asia. In the second case only 15 million tons of smoke from city fires over North America and Eurasia are considered.

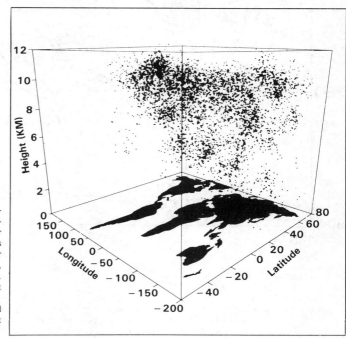

Figure 8
Three-dimensional representation of the smoke distribution 30 days after a summer injection of 150 million tons of smoke in four regions over the eastern and western U.S., Europe, and western Asia. Each dot represents about 5000 tons of smoke.
Source: MacCracken and Walton (1984) cit. Pittock et al. (1985)

Fig. 8 shows a three-dimensional view of an observer in the South Pacific looking north-west from a position of 60° S latitude and 160° W longitude at 150 million tons of injected smoke for day 30 after a summer injection. Each dot in the picture represents ca. 5000 tons of smoke particles of a size larger than 1 μm. Within the first few days the smoke distribution was rather patchy with extinction optical depths of ten and greater. After the first few weeks the smoke had spread nearly uniformly over the Northern Hemisphere and also over much of the equatorial and sub-tropical regions of the Southern Hemisphere exhibiting optical depths of about 2.

The above smoke specifications are used as input to calculate the temperature changes in a comparison of the non-interactive or uniform smoke case with the interactive or moving smoke case. Starting with a perpetual July atmospheric condition, Fig. 9 a shows the model-calculated temperature changes over the first 30 days after a nuclear war for a grid point in the central U.S. This region is representative of the dry mid-western bread basket in summer. The temperature variations of the control simulation (solid line) show both the large diurnal cycles (about 15° C) which are typical of continental areas, and the fluctuations between warmer and colder periods due to the different synoptic disturbances which pass over that area. In the uniform smoke case with an optical depth of $\bar{\tau} = 2.4$ (the dashed line) there is still a diurnal cycle – albeit with a reduced amplitude. Apparently there is still some sunlight reaching the surface presumably due to forward scattering by the smoke particles. The simulation with moving smoke (the dotted line) exhibits a completely different picture. In the first few days there is a very sharp temperature drop of about 35° C and a virtual disappearance of the diurnal cycle. This means that practically no sunlight reaches the ground. After about a week the temperature recovers temporarily to very near the control levels as clean Pacific air drifts in to replace the initial smoke-filled air mass.

Fig. 9 b shows the temperature changes for the area around Moscow. Noteworthy for the uniform smoke case is the pronounced temperature reduction with the marked diurnal cycle. One plausible explanation for the persistence of the diurnal cycle may be that under the strong temperature inversion the latent and sensible heat losses from the surface are reduced so that this heat is available to drive the diurnal cycle of the surface temperature. The moving smoke simulation shows a very drastic temperature drop of about 35 to 45° C persisting for two weeks. The diurnal temperature cycle has completely disappeared, signifying that practically no sunlight reached the surface. In some instances the summer temperature drops even below freezing killing most food-producing plants. In addition, radioactive fallout and the trapping of toxic pollutants within the stable surface inversion layer will further aggravate the situation.

Summary of modeling effort

MAJOR ADVANCES

- The use of a fully interactive aerosol scheme in 3-D GCMs in which the heated tropo-spheric smoke changes the temperature structure and the circulation and, in turn, is dispersed by the altered circulation.
- The simulation of smoke dispersion from plausible separate target regions rather than assuming an instantaneous and uniform smoke distribution.
- The consideration of cleansing processes determined by the model-generated precipitation.

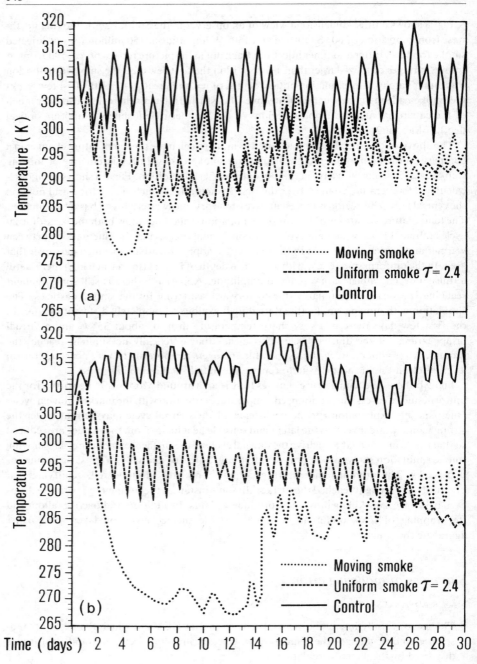

Figure 9 a, b
Thirty-day temperature record at various grid points for the control (solid line), fixed uniformly-spread smoke with an
average optical depth of 2.4 (dashed line), and 150 million tons moving smoke simulations (dot-dashed line).
(a) Midwestern U.S.; (b) Western continental Asia. – Source: MacCracken and Walton (1984)

MAJOR UNCERTAINTIES
- The number, locations, heights, and yields of weapons explosions. Assumptions on these are bound to remain unknowable.
- The injected amount, distribution, and time evolution of atmoshperic smoke and dust. Direct measurements of the characteristics of smoke emissions from fires of the appropriate fuel loading could shed further light on this using laboratory and field experiments.
- Radiative transfer calculations. The scattering of smoke and dust other than water clouds need to be incorporated in the model simulations. Better infrared radiative transfer algorithms are required since they play a key role with respect to a smoke-induced climatic change.
- Surface and boundary layer parameterizations. For example, the present NCAR model has only a crude zero heat capacity land surface and includes no planetary boundary layer parameterization. Heat flow into the surface and local stability-dependent vertical transport should also be included. All of this and a better simulation of low-level cloud and radiation fog formation would be important for the calculation of rapid transients in surface temperature.
- Subgrid-scale vertical convection. Its inclusion in the very unstable parts of the solar-heated smoke layer could lead to a lofting of smoke that is greater than that obtained by the large-scale direct thermal circulation alone. Most GCMs have a simple moist convective adjustment that allows only for movement of moist static energy. For the simulation of convective-scale transport of smoke a scheme for the explicit inclusion of vertical mass flux is required.
- Aerosol transport and removal. The three-dimensional interactive transport in and removal from the atmosphere of smoke and dust is a prerequisite for the comprehensive simulation of the climatic effects of a nuclear war. This involves difficult microphysical and physico-chemical processes such as transformation, coagulation, sedimentation, scavenging, oxidation, and photochemical reactions which will have to be studied for their effects on the time-dependent optical properties of the evolving aerosols. Events in the first hours and days following a nuclear war are decisive in determining the amount, composition and height of smoke and dust injection into the atmosphere, and the initial degree of removal.
- Static stability and precipitation. The formation of a strong inversion below the smoke-heated layer increases the static stability which greatly reduces precipitation, and which, in turn, suppresses the cleansing processes. The combined positive feedbacks lead to greatly increased lifetimes of the overall effects. There are still great uncertainties in modeling the various aspects of these feedbacks.
- Accumulation of chemicals. The stable layer near the ground is conducive to the accumulation of a constantly changing mixture of radioactive materials, pyrotoxins, and trace gases. The synergistic effects of tropospheric chemistry need to be investigated.
- Modeling smaller-scale effects. The assessment of the nuclear war climate problem requires the use of a hierarchy of atmospheric models. For example, smoke amount and distribution to be suitable for input in GCMs depend critically on microphysical and plume-cloud interactions which can be best modeled by smoke plume and mesoscale atmospheric models.
- Modeling longer-term effects. Seasonal and yearly simulations of the climatic consequences of a nuclear war are required. In particular, in order to assess the world food situation, the impacts for the second summer season after a nuclear war are needed.

MAJOR RESULTS

Climate models are the only means to simulate the world-wide atmospheric effects of nuclear war. The results obtained from the most advanced 3-D GCMs with a fully interactive smoke scheme and the inferences drawn therefrom can be summarized as follows:

a. Northern Hemisphere (NH)

– In a winter war the solar heating of the injected smoke is too small to appreciably loft it so that it can be removed from the atmosphere relatively rapidly by the scavenging processes. The resulting surface temperature decrease is therefore relatively small.

– In a spring and summer war solar heating is sufficient to loft the smoke to high altitudes. This has several major implications. The aerosol lofting to upper tropospheric and lower stratospheric levels and the increased stability in the lower troposphere (which reduces precipitation) effectively separates the smoke from the cleansing processes. Moreover, the lifetime of the smoke is considerably increased so that it can become more widely dispersed throughout the atmosphere. The initial effect is a substantial decrease of the high- and mid-latitude continental surface temperatures. The most drastic decrease is experienced within the first few days below the densest smoke patches. With the continuing smoke spread also subtropical and tropical regions come under the influence of damaging temperature reductions. Low-latitude ecosystems are particularly vulnerable to even slight temperature reductions.

b. Southern Hemisphere (SH)

– The intense smoke heating over the NH alters the circulation pattern with the result that the two Hadley cells on either side of the equator merge into one large cell. In a complete reversal of the normal situation, now the air masses rise over the NH subtropics and transport large masses or smoke to the SH causing also there a temperature reduction.

– In the SH the most severe effects will not come from a temperature decrease but rather from a precipitation reduction. The smoke spread to the SH will reduce the heating of the continental land surfaces which drives the monsoons that bring the rainfall to south-east Asia and Africa. The rainfall over Australia is expected to decrease, initially because of the strengthening of the descending branch of the Hadley cell over the SH subtropics, and later because of the general decrease of the hydrological cycle.

c. General

– In the recent interactive smoke simulations for summer the surface temperatures in mid-latitude continental areas rarely exceed freezing. But the temperature decrease occurs in consecutive cold pulses with rapid temperature drops of 20 to 40° C. Some plants may recover a single or a double loss of leaves, but most plants are likely to deplete their food reserves and perish.

– The latest findings that there may be a situation less than continued deep freeze and that there may be rather a drastic cooling occurring in irregular pulses does not make the situation less serious, especially in those areas randomly hit.

– The potential reduction of precipitation in NH low-latitude and SH regions whose livelihood critical depends on it, is a very serious problem. Precipitation changes are very difficult to model and require therefore special attention.

Temperature effect scenarios The SCOPE-group (Pittock et al., 1985) have felt that despite the many existing uncertainties some guidance was needed to evaluate the potential effects from a nuclear war. They have therefore developed some provisional temperature

REGION	TIME INTERVALS AFTER A NUCLEAR WAR		
	Acute 1st few weeks	Intermediate 1 to 6 months	Chronic** one to few years
N mid-latitude continental interiors	−15 to −35 when under dense smoke*	−5 to −30	0 to −10
N Hem sea surface* (ice free)	0 to −1	01 to −3 plus local anomalies	0 to −4 and local anomalies
tropical continental interiors	0 to −15	0 to −15	0 to −5
coastal areas*	very variable 0 to −5 unless off-shore wind when −15 to −35	very variable −1 to −5 unless off-shore wind when −5 to −30	variable 0 to −5
N Hem and tropics small islands**	0 to −5	−0 to −5	0 to −5
S mid-latitude continental interiors	initial 0 to +5 then 0 to −10 in patches	0 to −15	0 to −5
S Hem sea surface** (ice free)	0	0 to −2	0 to −4
S mid-latitude coastal areas	0	0 to −15 in off-shore winds	0 to −5
S Hem small islands	0	0 to −5	0 to −5

* "dense smoke" refers to smoke clouds of absorption optical depth of the order of 2 or greater, staying overhead for several days.
** These figures are climatological average estimates. Local anomalis may exceed these limits, especially due to changes in oceanic behavior such as upwelling or El Nino-type anomalous situations.

Table 2:
Temperature anomalies (°C) for smoke injections (180 million tons between 0–9 km) in the Northern Hemisphere spring/summer using the NAS (1985) baseline case of nuclear war. Source: Pittock et al. (1985)
– This table should only be read in the context of the discussion. –

effect scenarious for those studying the biological impacts. These scenarios are contingent upon the assumed input including the total amount, injection height, initial distribution, and the season in which the smoke injection occurs, plus a host of other factors. The derived temperature changes refer to general types of regions and are subject to wide ranges of uncertainty. They are not predictions but rather plausible estimates based on the presently

REGION	TIME INTERVALS AFTER A NUCLEAR WAR		
	Acute 1st few weeks	Intermediate 1 to 6 months	Chronic** one to few years
N mid-latitude continental interiors	0 to –20 when under dense smoke*	– to –15	0 to –5
N Hem sea surface* (ice free)	0	0 to –2 plus local anomalies	0 to –3 and local anomalis
tropical continental interiors	0 to –15	0 to –5	0 to –3
coastal areas*	very variable 0 to –5 unless off-shore wind when 0 to –20	very variable 0 to –5 unless off-shore wind when –0 to –15	0 to –5 0 to –3
N Hem and tropics small islands**	0 to –5	–1 to –5	0 to –5
S mid-latitude continental interiors	0	0 to –10	0 to –5
S Hem sea surface** (ice free)	0	0 to –1	0 to –1
S mid-latitude coastal areas	0	0 to –10 in off-shore winds	0 to –5
S Hem small islands	0	0 to –5	0 to –5

* "dense smoke" refers to smoke clouds of absorption optical depth of the order of 2 or greater, staying overhead for several days.
** These figures are climatological average estimates. Local anomalis may exceed these limits, especially due to changes in oceanic behavior such as upwelling or El Nino-type anomalous situations.

Table 3:
Temperature anomalies (°C) for smoke injections (180 million tons between 0–9 km) in the Northern Hemisphere winter using the NAS (1985) baseline case of nuclear war. Source: Pittock et al. (1985)
– This table should only be read in the context of the discussion. –

best available evidence. They should only be quoted in full recognition of their qualified and tentative nature.

The scenario specifications are as follows. Three plausible smoke injections are considered, namely 60, 180 and 540 million tons. The 180 million tons case corresponds to the U.S. NAS (1985) "baseline" scenario with an average absorption cross-section of about 2 m^2/g

and an extinction coefficient of about 5.5 m²/g. Three injection profiles are considered, namely "low" (0–5 km), "middle" (constant smoke density between 0 and 9 km), and "high" (a major proportion of the elemental carbon is injected into the stratosphere). Two seasonal cases are considered, i. e. a northern spring and summer injection, and a northern winter injection.

Two examples have been worked out in detail, one for a Northern Hemisphere spring/summer smoke in injection (Table 2), and another one for a northern winter injection (Table 3). The ranges of estimates are given in terms of surface air temperature departures from the respective seasonal normals. Both examples are based on the 180 million tons and "middle" height profile cases. The estimates are for three time intervals: "acute" (the first few weeks after smoke injection with emphasis on the most extreme effects); "intermediate" (referring to the first 1 to 6 months); and "chronic" (meaning 1 to several years after the holocaust). Comparison of the figures in Tables 2 and 3 reveals that in the Northern Hemisphere for both the summer and winter injections the severity of the cooling decreases, as one would expect, from "acute" to "chronic". This is the case for all regions except the sea surface, which, because of the higher heat capacity, reaches the lowest temperatures after years. The situation is quite different for the Southern Hemisphere regions which are initially hardly affected showing the greatest impact during the "intermediate" phase. Of importance is also that a northern winter nuclear war results in less severe cooling in both Northern and Southern Hemispheric regions, especially in the short run. For longer-term effects both the summer and the winter injections produce similar coolings for Southern Hemisphere regions. The subjective temperature estimates shown here are confidence limits, meaning that there are 2 chances in 3 that the temperatures could fall within these limits when averaged over the given regions.

For the 60 million tons smoke scenario, not shown here, winter injections would have only small effects in the acute stage which would quickly disappear. A summer injection would produce shorter and more patchy effects in the acute stage and chronic effects that would be quite small. The 540 million tons smoke scenario would lead to greater effects than the 180 million tons scenario, but it would not lead to proportional increases in either the magnitude or duration of the effects. This is because a higher particle concentration would lead to a higher coagulation rate which, in turn, would reduce the optical effects. Moreover, a greater amount of smoke would be shielded from the incoming solar radiation by the dense smoke in the upper layers, leading to less efficient lofting due to the reduction of solar absorption, and hence to a reduced overall residence time of the smoke.

Due to the great uncertainties the SCOPE-group felt unable to develop similar tables for the precipitation effects. In general, modeling results indicate a rainfall reduction in the "acute" and "intermediate" phases, but also some local and perhaps transient increases would be possible.

Conclusions and implications

Climate is an essential part of our environment. An unperturbed climate is needed to produce sufficient food for the growing world population. Man's "peaceful" activities already constitute a serious encroachment upon the climate-environment-food production systems. Nuclear war, the ultimate insult on climate and environment, would also be Man's final activity. Nuclear winter and mass starvation could very well end Man's ignominious interlude on planet earth.

The gist of the latest nuclear winter research is that, barring some mitigating effects that may have been overlooked, there is a distinct possibility that large land areas of the Northern Hemisphere would be exposed to drastic temperature reductions (especially if the war occurred in summer) lasting for weeks, or to subnormal temperatures persisting for months or more. Additionally, the perturbed circulation system could lead to transient "quick freezes" in tropical areas and to reduced rainfall in the subtropics and tropics on either hemisphere. All of this would have severe impacts on the surviving population and on the ecosystem that is needed to support the survivors. There is now a consensus that the climatic effects of a nuclear winter and the resulting lack of food aggravated by the destroyed infrastructure could have a greater overall impact on the global population than the immediate effects of the nuclear explosions. The evidence is growing that in a post-war nuclear world Homo Sapiens will not have an ecological niche to which he could flee. It is apparent that life everywhere on this planet would be threatened.

The doctrine of deterrence has now aquired a new political and ethical dimension. Before nuclear winter there existed some basic mutual hostage arrangement between the opposing superpowers. Now the whole world, and with it all of human civilization, is held hostage. Apparently, the vertiginous pace of scientific and technological development has overtaken that of understanding the social and ethical implications. Scientists and engineers now face these complex ethical problems that, to a certain extent, are of their making. They must realize that much of mankind's destiny lies in their hands. They are in a key position to help reverse the trend.

The results from nuclear winter research have clearly shown that nuclear weapons cannot serve any military or political purpose. The more weapons are accumulated, and the more accurate they are, the less secure this world becomes. They are just good for a mutual assured suicide.

The stakes are very high, so everybody is called upon to help prevent the highest level of human madness. Now is a truly historic opportunity because the findings from nuclear winter research provide the world's leaders with strong arguments to halt the spiralling arms race. A freeze on the development of new nuclear weapons systems and an annual quota decrease of the existing warhead inventories would be a first step in the right direction.

BIBLIOGRAPHY

ACDA (Arms Control and Disarmament Ageny) (1979): The effects of nuclear war, Washington, D.C.

Alexandrov, V. V. and Stenchikov, G. L. (1983): On the modeling of the climatic consequences of the nuclear war, The Proceeding of Appl. Mathematics, The Computing Center of the AS U.S.S.R., Moscow, 21p.

Bach, W. (1986 a): Nuclear war: The effects of smoke and dust on weather and climate. Progress in Phys. Geography (in press)

Bach, W. (1986 b): Kann die Menschheit einen Atomkrieg überleben? In: R. Goltermann et al (eds.) Katastrophenmedizin – Hilfe oder Gefahr, Jungjohann Verlagsgesellschaft, Neckarsulm (in press)

Cess, R. D., G. L. Potter and Gates, W.L. (1985 a): The climatic impact of a nuclear exchange: Sensitivity studies using a general circulation model. Third Conf. on Climate Variations and Symp. on Contemporary Climate: 1850–2100, 4–5, Amer. Met. Soc., Boston.

Cess, R. D., G. L. Potter, S. J. Ghan, and Gates, W. L. (1985 b): The climatic effects of large injections of atmospheric smoke and dust: A study of climatic feedback mechanisms with one- and three-dimensional climate models, Preprint UCRL-92 504, Lawrence Livermore Nat. Lab., Livermore.

Covey, C. (1985): Climatic effects of nuclear war, BioScience 35 (9), 563–569.

Covey, C., S. H. Schneider and Thompson, S. L. (1984): Global atmospheric effects of massive smoke injections from a nuclear war: Results from general circulation model simulations, Nature 308, 21–25.

Covey, C., S. L. Thompson and Schneider, S. H. (1985): Nuclear winter: A diagnosis of atmospheric general circulation model simulations, J.G.R. 90 (D3), 5615–5628.

Crutzen, P. J. and Birks, J. W. (1982): The atmosphere after a nuclear war: Twilight at noon, Ambio 11, 114–125.

Crutzen, P. J., I. E. Galbally and Brühle, C. (1984): Atmospheric effects from postnuclear fires, Climatic Change 6, 323–364.

Ehrlich, P. R. et al. (1983): Long-term biological consequences of nuclear war, Science 222, 1293–1300.

Ehrlich, P. R., C. Sagan, D. Kennedy and Roberts, W. D. (1984): The Cold and the Dark: The World after Nuclear War, W. W. Norton & Co., New York.

Harwell, M. A. (1984): Nuclear Winter: The Human and Environmental Consequences of Nuclear War. Springer, New York.

Harwell, M. A. and Hutchinson, T. C. (1985): The Environmental Consequences of Nuclear War. Vol. II, Ecological and Agricultural Effects, SCOPE 28, J. Wiley & Sons, New York.

MacCracken, M. C. (1983): Nuclear War: Preliminary estimates of the climatic effects of a nuclear exchange, Lawrence Livermore Nat. Lab. Rept. UCRL-89 770, Livermore.

MacCracken, M. C. (1985): Global atmospheric effects of nuclear war. Energy and Technol. Rev., Lawrence Livermore Nat. Lab., May, 10–35.

MacCracken, M. C. and Walton, J. J. (1984): The effects of interactive transport and scavenging of smoke on the calculated temperature change from large amounts of smoke. Preprint UCRL-91 446, Lawrence Livermore Nat. Lab., Livermore.

Malone, R. C., L. H. Auer, G. A. Glatzmaier, M. C. Wood, and Toon, O. B. (1986): Nuclear winter: Three-dimensional simulations including interactive transport, scavenging and solar heating of smoke, J. Geophys. Res. 91 (D1), 1039–1053.

McNaughton, S. J., R. W. Ruess and M. B. Coughenor (1986): Ecological consequences of nuclear war, Nature 321, 483–487.

NAS (National Academy of Sciences) (1975): Long-term worldwide effects of multiple nuclear weapons detonations, Nat. Acad. Press, Washington, D.C.

NAS (1985): The effects on the atmosphere of a major nuclear exchange, Nat. Acad. Press, Washington, D.C.

OTA (Office of Technology Assessment) (1979): The effects of nuclear war, Congress of the US, No. OTA-NS-89, Washington, D.C.

Pittock, A. B., T. P. Ackerman, P. J. Crutzen, C. S. Shapiro, R. P. Turco and MacCracken, M. C. (1985): The Environmental Consequences of Nuclear War. Vol I Phys. and Atmos. Effects, SCOPE 28, J. Wiley & Sons, New York.

Ramaswamy, V. and Kiehl, J. T. (1985): Sensitivities of the radiative forcing due to large loadings of smoke and dust. J. Geophys. Res. 90 (D3), 5597–5613.

Schneider, S. H. (1985): Large-scale three-dimensional modeling aspects of "Nuclear Winter". Third Conference on Climate Variations and Symposium on Contemporary Climate: 1850–2100, 8–9, Amer. Meteorol. Soc., Boston.

Stenchikov, G. L. (1985): Mathematical modelling of the influence of the atmospheric pollution on climate and nature. The Prcdgs. on Appl. Mathem. The Computing Centre of the AS USSR, Moscow.

Thompson, S. L., V. V. Alexandrov, G. L. Stenchikov, S. H. Schneider, C. Covey and Chervin, R. M. (1984): Global climatic consequences of nuclear war: Simulations with three dimensional models. Ambio 13 (4), 236–243.

Thompson, S. L. (1985): Global interactive transport simulations of nuclear war smoke, Nature, 317, 35–39.

Turco, R. P., O. B. Toon, T. P. Ackerman, J. B. Pollack and Sagan, C. (1983): Global atmospheric consequences of nuclear war. Science 222, 1283–1292.

Turco, R. P., O. B. Toon, T. P. Ackerman, J.B. Pollack and Sagan, C. (1984): The climatic effects of nuclear war. Scientific American 251 (2), 23–33.

U.N. (United Nations) (1980): Comprehensive study on nuclear weapons. New York.

Vupputuri, R.K.R. (1986): The effect of ozone photochemistry on atmospheric and surface temperature changes due to large atmospheric injections of smoke and NO_x by a large-scale nuclear war. Atmosph. Environment 20 (4), 665–680.

THE CORE CURRICULUM

Victor Sidel, U.S.A.

Socio-Economic Effects of Nuclear War

It is a privilege to be at this Congress as President-elect of the United States Physicians for Social Responsibility and also as Immediate Past President and official representative of the American Public Health Association. Relevant to my theme is the fact that in 1961 I was one of the founding members of Physicians for Social Responsibility and was one of the authors of its first series of articles on the medical consequences of nuclear war in *The New England Journal of Medicine.* For the almost 25 years since that auspicious beginning my colleagues in PSR and I have been addressing – in articles, books, lectures, and films – the medical consequences of the use of nuclear weapons and the consequent responsibility of physicians: since doctors can do almost nothing to deal with the medical problems once the bombs have fallen, they must, by analogy with other non-treatable medical problems, work actively for their prevention.

As many of you know, over the past three years I have been traveling throughout the United States speaking on a different but closely-related topic: "Destruction Before Detonation: The Impact of the Arms Race on Health and Health Care". In these presentations I discuss the consequences of the production of weapons to the health and well-being of people even if the arms themselves are never used to kill and maim. In my speeches in the United States, I usually concentrate on arms expenditures by the United States and their impact on health and well-being of our people, because I believe that to be the special responsibility of United States health workers. At this session I want to concentrate instead on arms expenditures over the entire world and on what I believe to be the responsibility of health workers in *every* nation – rich and poor, aligned and non-aligned – to protest what is being spent in their nation on arms and their responsibility to bring to those in power in their society knowledge of the ways in which these resources can be used to strengthen health and health services in their own country and throughout the world.

Since the start of this Congress two days ago, 80,000 children have died of preventable illness. As James Grant, Executive Director of UNICEF, reminded us in Budapest last year, the number of children who die preventable deaths every three days is greater than the number of people killed by the nuclear bombing of Hiroshima and Nagasaki. So it is with a great sense of urgency, not only about forebodings of the future but also about problems of the present, that I address you today.

It has been said that "statistics are people with the tears washed off." One way to put the tears back on is to show pictures of the victims, as I will using slides during the course of this lecture. Another way to illustrate the magnitude of the tragedy is through the use of a metronome, which I carry with me for my lectures in the United States, set to beat once each second. [Metronome placed on podium and started.] With every other beat – once every two seconds – a child dies of a preventable disease, a disease that could have been prevented by immunization, safe water supply, or basic adequate food supply. With each intervening beat – also once every two seconds – a child is permanently disabled, either physically or mentally, by a preventable illness and is destined to live the rest of his or her life with that severe disability. In sum, with each beat of the metronome a child is killed or maimed by preventable disease.

At the same time that this appalling needless sacrifice of human lives is taking place, the world is spending each second – with each beat of the metronome – the equivalent of 25,000 dollars on arms. The calculation is a very simple one. During 1985 the nations of the world spent an amount equal to about 900 billion dollars on arms. That is two-and-one-half billion dollars each day, one hundred million dollars each hour, 1.5 million dollars each minute, or 25,000 dollars each second.

The total expenditure – 900 billion dollars – is an extraordinary sum of money. It is equivalent to the total gross national products of all of the countries in which the poorest one-half of the world's population live. To make the point clear, if we list all of the countries of the world in order of gross national product per capita and begin to count up from the bottom, adding total gross national products until we reach a total of 900 billion dollars, we will have counted up the countries of the world in which two billion people live. Stated another way, these expenditures exceed the combined gross national products of China, India, and the African countries south of the Sahara.

As another comparison, this one-year expenditure on arms is equivalent to the entire debt that the poor nations of the world owe the rich nations. This is the debt whose interest payments are strangling many of the world's poor countries and which, if not rescheduled or repaid, is said to threaten much of the world's banking system. If ten percent of the money spent on arms annually were used instead to reduce this debt, the debt would be wiped out in less than twenty years. Would this conversion make the nations of the world – rich or poor – less secure or more secure?

Not only money is being spent. Many of the world's most productive scientists and engineers are working on arms rather than on methods to improve the quality of life and the health of the world's people. Estimates of the number of the world's scientists and engineers working on arms ranges from one in every five to two of every five. Expenditures on weapons research exceed the combined spending on developing new energy technologies, improving human health, raising agriculture productivity and controlling pollutants.

Furthermore, this extraordinary waste of the world's resources is increasing at a rapid rate. In 1960, world military expenditures totaled approximately 400 billion dollars (in terms of 1984 dollars), 4.7 percent of world economic output; the expenditures of 900 billion dollars in 1985 amounted to over 6 percent of world output.

This unforgivable waste of human and material resources takes place in a world that cannot stand by and permit it to continue. In the world's least developed countries, the gross national product per capita in 1980 was $ 170; in the most developed countries, $ 6,230, 35 times as great. The annual public expenditures on health per capita in the least developed countries was $ 1.70; in the most developed countries $ 244.00, 140 times as great.

Over 300 million children in the developing countries are reported to be chronically hungry. There are 26 countries whose people on the average eat 10 percent or more below their estimated caloric requirements.

Two billion of the world's people do not have access to a dependable and sanitary supply of water; in some countries fewer than five percent of the population have access to safe water. Literacy in the poor countries of the world is at a far lower level than in the rich ones. In a number of the poorest countries fewer than 10 percent of the adult women are literate.

In some poor countries, health services are almost nonexistent. There are fewer than 10 physicians per 100,000 population in a number of areas, compared to 100 or more per 100,000 in most developed countries. It is believed that only about three percent of babies in the least developed countries are born with the help of a trained midwife or doctor. Infant mortality rates are almost ten times as high in the least developed countries as in the most developed ones. Life expectancy at birth in the least developed countries is almost 30 years shorter than in the most developed countries.

As is well known, the rich countries of the world with a few exceptions such as the Scandinavian countries, transfer far less than the 0.7 percent of the gross national product that the United Nations has formally asked to transfer annually in economic aid to the poor countries. The rapidly rising military expenditures by the developed countries have far exceeded the slight rise in their foreign economic aid since 1960. The developed countries on the average now spend 5.4 percent of their GNP for military purposes and 0.3 percent for development assistance to poorer countries.

Compounding this tragedy is the fact that even small conversions of the funds being spent on arms into spending on health could produce enormous benefits.

- The cost of one hour of world arms spending is equivalent to the entire cost of the successful twenty-year effort to eradicate smallpox from the Earth.
- The cost of three hours of world arms spending would pay for all of the World Health Organization's 260 million dollar annual budget.
- The cost of one half-day of world arms spending annually could pay for the full immunization of all the children in the world against the common infectious diseases.
- The cost of four days of world arms spending would pay for a five-year malaria control program, dealing with what is probably the world's greatest cause of morbidity.
- The cost of six months of world arms spending would pay for a twenty-year program providing essential food and health needs in all the developing countries.

A series of self-help measures proposed by UNICEF would save 20,000 children a day from preventable death, cutting the rate of the beating of the metronome in half, and would cost a tiny fraction of the amounts being spent on arms:

- Growth monitoring – With the help of a 10-cent growth chart and basic advice on weaning, most mothers could maintain their child's healthy growth and prevent most child malnutrition before it begins – even within their limited resources.
- Oral rehydration – Simple materials could save most of the more than 4 million young children who now die each year from diarrheal dehydration.
- Breast-feeding – Maintenance of this practice can ensure that infants have the best possible food and a considerable degree of immunity from common infections during the first six months of life.
- Immunization – A 5-dollar course of immunization can protect a child against measles, diphteria, whooping cough, tetanus, tuberculosis, and polio; at present, these diseases kill an estimated 3.5 million young children a year, leave 3.5 million more disabled, and are a major cause of child malnutrition.

In order not to forget the primary continuing message of the International Physicians for the Prevention of Nuclear War, we can also use the beating metronome in another way. The world now has stockpiles of nuclear weapons equivalent to about 16 billion tons of TNT, approximately 4 tons for every human being on the planet. If each metronome beat represents a ton of TNT, it would have to beat at this rate for 500 years to count up the tonnage of the world's nuclear weapons.

Pablo Picasso created a moving painting about fifty years ago. It was inspired by the wanton bombing, by Fascist bombers, of the small Basque town of Guernica. In that raid a few tons of bombs were used and a few hundred people were killed. Within several years, during World War II, single bombing raids with thousands of tons of TNT each killed tens of thousands of people. In Hiroshima and Nagasaki, single bombs equal in destructive power to over ten thousand tons of TNT killed over a hundred thousand people. Now we have bombs with the power of millions of tons of TNT, a single one of which can kill over a million people. This change, representing an increase of six orders of magnitude in destructive power, occurred in less than thirty years. As Einstein put it, "The unleashed power of the atom has changed everything except our way of thinking, and thus we drift toward unparalleled catastrophe. We shall require a substantially new manner of thinking if mankind is to survive."

In finding this new manner of thinking, we in IPPNW must avoid two pitfalls. On the one hand, as we work for international cooperation in health work, we must not forget the fundamental objective around which we have come together: the reduction and eventual elimination of nuclear weapons in the world and the prevention of nuclear war. On the other hand, as we strive for "short-range", inexpensive methods, such as immunization, to improve the health of the children of the world, we must not forget the importance of working for "middle-range" methods, such as the development of universally-accessible, high-quality primary health care services in every country, and – most important – working for the only "long-range" solution to these problems, a "new international economic order" that would end the continuing exploitation of the poor nations by the rich nations.

The health workers of the world cannot ignore the enormous threat to health that the arms race poses, certainly if the weapons are used, but in addition even before they are used or even if they are never used. Health workers must be the leaders in developing the new manner of thinking that Einstein called for. In the Italian city of Venice, one is shown masks representing the Dottore della Peste, the Plague Doctor. The mask has a large nose, representing a place for perfume so the doctor cannot smell the stench of the victims of the plague; the mask has eyeglasses, representing the doctor's shielding his or her eyes from the sight of the victims of the plague. We cannot afford any longer to shield our eyes, to avoid the stench, of what is happening around us. As health workers we have a special responsibility to take action.

This responsibility extends throughout the world. A statue of a worker beating a sword into a ploughshare was a gift by the Soviet Union to the United Nations fourty years ago. It stands on soil within the United States. The metronome used in this presentation came from Germany. Chinese doctors originally prescribed gunpowder as a treatment for "ringworm sores, eczema, and pestilence." We must, figuratively if not literally, turn the weapons of war to peaceful and health-giving use. The health workers of every nation must make a contribution to ending the destructive arms race by urging that their nation immediately initiate action to convert funds from arms to human services.

There are some examples around the world that give us hope. Costa Rica has consistently over the past three decades spent extremely little on arms, with consequent additional re-

reserves to spend on, and marked improvement in, health and social conditions. The People's Republic of China began systematically in the mid-1970's to reduce its military expenditures; they have fallen from 15 percent of GNP, one of the world's highest percentages of spending on arms, to 7.5 percent in 1985. China has announced a plan to cut its armed services from 4.2 million in 1985 to 3.2 million in 1987, a drop of 24 percent; it will invest $ 360 million over two years to retrain these one million service people for return to civilian life. Argentina is also reducing its military expenditures; by 1984 arms spending had been cut to half the peak level of 1980.

This conference comes at a very important moment. Last year was the 40th anniversary of the atomic bombing of Hiroshima and Nagasaki and of the establishment of the United Nations. The number 40 has played a very important role in many of the world's religions and cultures, representing a period of waiting, of expectation. Noah and his companions remained on the ark during a flood that lasted 40 days and 40 nights before disembarking on dry land. Moses and his followers wandered for 40 years in the wilderness and he then waited 40 days on a mountain before receiving the Ten Commandments. Jesus fasted for 40 days, a time now commemorated by the period of Lent. In 1377, Ragusa, on the Dalmatian coast of the Adriatic Sea, detained all travelers from an infected area at a point distant from the city for 40 days (quarantina); Marseilles and Venice soon adopted the same policy, which led of course to our word "quarantine". When the U.S. in the last century wanted to induce settlers to come to its western territory it provided them with 40 acres of land and a mule. The number 40 has come to represent not only waiting, but a promise of better things to come. Let us view these past 40 years as a time of preparation for the enormous work that all of us must do to ensure the prevention of nuclear war and the conversion of the resources now being spent for arms to productive use for the health and well-being of all people.

Olof Palme, to whose memory this Congress is dedicated, stated the goal well for everyone: "Between now and the year 2000 it should be possible to eliminate hunger and what is called absolute poverty in the world. It is a matter of drive and political will ... There is no other action that would be more important in our times for the defence of peace in the world." And Dr. Ian Munro, editor of the *Lancet*, summarized the task that we specifically have as health workers: "The medical profession must never neglect its responsibility to protest the grim paradox between the world's enormous and mounting military expenditures and the comparatively meager efforts devoted to the relief of poverty, malnutrition and disease.

BIBLIOGRAPHY

Brown, L. R. (1986) Redefining national security. *State of the world 1986*. New York: Norton.
Department of Political and Security Council Affairs, United Nations Center for Disarmament (1978) *Economic and social consequences of the arms race and of military expenditure*. New York: United Nations.
Grant, J. P. (1986) *The State of the World's Children 1986*. Oxford: Oxford University Press.
Independent Commission on International Development Issues (Brandt Commission) (1980) *North-south: A program for survival*. Cambridge, MA: MIT Press.
Sidel, V. W. (1985) Destruction before detonation: The impact of the arms race on health and health care. *Lancet, 2* (7 December), 1287,
Sidel, V. W. (1985) "... With Each Beat of the Metronome ... " *IPPNW Report 3*, No. 2 (October), 11–14.
Sivard, R. L. (1985) *World military and social expenditures, 1985*. Leesburg, VA: World Priotities, Inc.
Stockholm International Peace Research Institute (1985) *World armaments and disarmament; SPIRI yearbook 1985*. Philadelphia: Taylor and Francis.
Threat of nuclear war. (1980) *Lancet, 2* (15 November), 1061

THE CORE CURRICULUM

James Thompson, Great Britain

Psychological Effects of Nuclear War

It is an honour to give this talk in Cologne, a city which knows better than most the full horror of modern warfare. The great cathedral, whose twin spires tower over the city, survived the bombing to stand as a memorial to the past. But in a modern nuclear war, both the present and the past would be consumed. We would lose both our cathedrals and our modern buildings. We would lose our past music and Bach, we would lose our modern pop music, we would lose our total culture. Those problems of the danger and the power of war were foreshadowed by Freud, who said, "Man has gained control over the forces of nature to such an extent that there will be no difficulty in exterminating one another to the last human being. We know this and hence comes a large part of our current unrest, our unhappiness and our mood of anxiety."

What I should like to do in the first half of the talk is to take Freud's words as my text and to consider some of the costs in psychological terms of having a nuclear threat hanging over us. Could the nuclear threat explain some aspects of our current condition? The rise perhaps in terrorism, in drug abuse and in crime? Or could it be, that we are capable of living in a society which can totally destroy itself in less time than it will take us to have lunch today and yet not show effects, live, as if that danger was not present? What I should like to do is to first of all go through some of the data which have been collected on these issues and then to look at some of the consequences of dealing with that mood of anxiety.

First of all, we should consider the psychology of the development of human fears. Very briefly, if one looks at the change of fears in childhood, what one finds is, that some things become less feared by children whilst others increase. And if one considers our species, then certain things such as a decrease in a fear of sudden noises, decreases in pain, decreases in specific fears take place up until the 71st month of life. If one then looks at the fears which increase, you will see that they are largely things which are due to social influence and to the power of imagination. So, for example, taking the fears which arise most strongly, there are the fears of ridicule, robbers, dreams and death. It seems therefore that our capacity to be anxious becomes, as we mature, more linked to social factors and to factors of the imagination. It is our capacity as a species to imagine which serves us as our warning system. Now, there are many models of anxiety; the simplest one I wish to look at is one proposed by Lazarus. And in this one would say, that when an event occurs we have a sudden primary appraisal of the threat. That is what we call our startle response – our capacity to suddenly jolt and to notice something has changed. We then turn to secondary appraisal, which is to decide what is the nature of the threat, what can we do about it. We then turn to our coping mechanisms, our capacity to deal with danger and hazard, and we go one of two directions, either to direct action or to some palliative action. And now I would like to think about nuclear war and to realise: the big debate which faces us all is whether we take the turn towards direct action or whether we persist in secondary forms of palliative action. The other thing, of course, I ask you to consider is that since we are creatures capable of imagination, our capacity to fear and to deal with fears depends on our ability to appraise the situation and to understand it. So, for our species a lot of fear is based on knowledge.

Now, what is our background knowledge about disasters? We are here today, because we wish to prevent a disaster, the disaster of a modern thermonuclear war. When you look at the frequency of disasters and their casualty rates, you find that the most frequent disasters have rather small casualty rates. So car-, marine-, railway- and air-accidents, explosions and fires generally have casualty rates lower than a hundred persons. It takes hurricans or earthquakes or tidal waves to get us casualty rates which are in the twenty- to thirty-thousand level. Consider now the case of nuclear war; in the case of a mass exchange we are talking about casualty levels which might run into one hundred-, two hundred-, even one thousand million people, figures hardly conceivable. So our database and our knowledgebase in dealing with threat and disaster is pitifully deficient. We have difficulty in imagining the extent of the threat, because it is so far from our ordinary experience. We argue by very weak analogies. Now, one might try to understand the situation. Those who are highly optimistic on the lower part of the scale think that they can increase in opportunity considerably with only a small amount of increase in risk. Whereas you consider, for example, the case of an anxious and depressed patient to whom it seems that every little attempt to get out into the world and to reap those opportunities causes a massive increase in risk. And amongst this hall we will have people with different views about the balance between risk and opportunity, but certainly out in the public we will have massive differences in outlook and we must remember that, when we take our knowledge-based message to the general public.

Now, how sensitive are human beings to warnings of disaster? There is a lot of literature on this and I only wish to give one example: [Slide] This is a town in America which was being approached by a large wall of water coming down a river. They had seen the wave coming from the top, and they had about two hours or three hours of warning. So what they did was, they started on television telling people that a flood was coming, and you will see that when they were saying some areas are flooding or evacuating, 36 % of the population continued with their routine activities, 38 % tried to confirm the news and only 26 % of the population bothered to evacuate. Now let us go to the final part where the two hours had worn out and police cars were travelling through the area, announcing that people should leave. All the media were saying the flood is coming, you must get out. Notice, 22 % of the sane and sensible citizens are continuing their routine activities, we have a 60 % who have evacuated, but there are 18 % who are still trying to confirm the news. So I believe, and there is a lot of data to support this, that we should not be too surprised, that people do not heed our warnings of nuclear war, because as a species we tend to be insensitive to warnings. Warnings disrupt our behaviour, they have a behavioural cost and so we tend not to bother to follow them. Those of us who have heeded warnings are probably rather different from the general population.

I should now like to summarise quite large sections of work, which is published elsewhere. I will give the general outlines, so we can understand something about the costs in psychological terms of nuclear threat. The work which comes out on children's attitudes on nuclear threat, based largely on Western studies, but one Western-inspired Russian study, studies in

Australasia as well, show that most people aren't well informed, youngsters are not well informed about nuclear war, but they are afraid of it and that is between one third and one half of our young people say, that they expect a catastrophic nuclear war to occur in their lifetime. That is an astounding figure. It means that our new generation expects that nuclear war will be part of their history, indeed, that that will be the end of their history. The majority, of course, do not expect to survive such a war, and many do not expect mankind as a whole to survive the war. The youngsters in America are slightly more optimistic about survival than in other countries, whereas youngsters in Russia see a nuclear war slightly less likely than do youngsters in other countries. Now, 25 % of young people worry frequently or intensely about nuclear war or regard it as their main anxiety. Now that again is astounding, because the most common fears of people of that age are the death of their parents or worries about school work. Yet we have ranked either for some children as one or some number one worry or for other children as number three worry the fear of a catastrophic war. In the United Kingdom, because of our special difficulties, our children worry more about unemployment, which is the everyday thing which they face, the Scandinavians more about war, girls in general worry more about war than boys, and the younger adolescents more than the older adolescents. Now what is interesting is, that those who worry about nuclear war are not especially neurotic or anxious. They are children who tend to have environment concerns and whose parents share those concerns. There are about 35 references and a growing literature on this topic, much of it since about 1979. Now what about adults? People think of nuclear war as somewhat unlikely in adulthood in the general public. They imagine mainly complete material destruction with themselves definitely not surviving. People worry seldom that they overwhelmingly favour mutual nuclear freeze on nuclear weapons. In terms of actions, and as a behavioural psychologist, I find this interesting, most people do nothing. If one takes anti-nuclear activists and survivalists, those are people who believe in bomb-shelters and in laying in large stocks of food, they think a lot about nuclear war, and they believe that in their different ways they can do something about it. The public as a whole feels ineffective and the issue is not salient for them most of the time. Their most salient worries are things about the family, about employment, about their living circumstances, not about the threat of war. But when people do think about nuclear war it does cause worry, fear and sadness. The solution proposed by Susan Fisk is that one has to find some way of increasing the sense of hope through action. Remember the Lazarus model of anxiety in which we talked about direct action and palliative action. It seems that the key in psychological terms lies in direct action. The other thing, and this is important, is that one must put together fear-arousing communications with possible action solutions. And if there is a criticism I think we should make of much of the peace movement and include ourselves, it is that we have given a message of fear without the additional message of hope.

What we will have to do, and I shall return to this, is to produce something which would be perceived as being politically effective, and something which the ordinary citizen is capable of doing. So, let us think about some of the things which the capable citizen is capable of doing and let me show you now some current British data. As an example of the paradox, the paradox which we heard so elegantly in the last lecture: if you ask British people what is their priority for extra public expenditure, overwhelmingly health is given the top of the bill, followed by education and then help for industry. To find defense, you must go right down the list and it is 3 % of people in Britain in 1985 who want to spend more money on defense. So their heart is with us and they strive for health and for education. So where do our problems lie? Well, the first problem is that most people do not regard themselves as particularly politically effective. They feel they cannot change things in their life. If you ask people in Britain, what would you do if there was a harmful or unjust law considered by parliament, you find that some people take personal actions, that is they say they would, and some people say they would take collective action. The most common thing, you see, is to contact the member of parliament or perhaps to talk to the media. In terms of collective action the thing overwhelmingly which people will do is, they will sign a petition, 57 %. Then ask them, what do you consider to be the most effective? You see that they regard contacting their MP as reasonably effective, 43 %. But when one comes down to collective action, although 57 % will sign a petition, only 12 % see that as the most effective thing to do. So we have a difficulty in producing a product from the peace movement which is seen by the public as effective. How agitated are people about the defense issue as a whole? Well ask them, in what circumstances would you be willing to break the law? And notice, it is the protection of familiy and the protection of existing rights which gets the priority. Defense's use animates only 4 % of the population. This leads me to propose what I will call "Thompson's law of apathy". 90 % of the people 90 % of the time mind their own business. And we must understand that we are perhaps an unrepresentative section and that our work must be to get that passive majority to join us, at least some of the time, in order to make changes. It is the question of how to do that, that must tax us and must make us think now. How powerful are governments? Well, most people feel that one third of them are rather powerless. It tends to be the middle classes that see governments powerful and the rich that see governments powerful, because they have more of a personal history of effectiveness.

Although Britain has been for 40 years a partner in the NATO Alliance, an astounding 54 % of the British public think that both Russia and America are equally great threats to world peace. It seems that the public is aware that possession of nuclear weapons is itself the threat and the nature of the alliance and even the cultural similarity between Britain and America is not an overwhelming factor. Some more data recently collected from London on 1005 people in the middle of 1985: people were asked how likely is nuclear war? And we have a grading scale from zero, certain it will not happen, to ten, certain that it will happen. And notice, that if you ask them what is the likelihood of Britain coming under nuclear attack in the next five years, a full 50 % of the public are absolutely certain that it will not happen. I do not know on what grounds one can be absolutely certain but that is their measure of risk. However, if you say, well if war does happen, how likely or unlikely is it that you would live through the attack, there is only a valiant 2 % who think it is very likely that they would live through this attack. This includes a friend of ours, who believes the safest place in nuclear war will be to stay in London, because all the scenario say that London will be attacked and as he does not trust the military planners, he thinks that London will not be attacked. And now a question which is interesting psychologically: do you hope that you would survive such an attack? Or do you hope that you would be among those who do not survive? And you see that 70 % of the public hope not to survive. So, although they see war as unlikely, they know that if it happens, they are likely to die and the circumstances will be so bad that they will wish to die. So that is one of the paradoxes which people are carrying in their heads. Finally, how much do members of the ordinary public think or talk or worry about a nuclear attack? And I'm afraid, as quickly as I can, I will just give some data which I obtained myself from 20 year old students, in which I asked them to rate the possibilities of various types of health hazard, and you will see that the third ranked fear was nuclear war, so we have confirmation again of these results. I cannot, in the time available to me, go through this.

The last thing I will talk about is the difference between activists and the public and to make a suggestion. It seems that the massive difference between people who are activists and people who are just members of the public is in the extent to which they believe that nuclear war is survivable, The other main difference is the extent to which poeple believe that they can make difference in political terms. What I would propose in my final comments is that we go back to the idea of direct action and we understand that what we should do, as a movement, is to get out of the partitionary mode. We must stop asking other people to do things and we must start doing things ourselves. And those things we must do are things which are in the capacity of the ordinary citizen which support internationalism and which have something to do with the shifting of resources. I think governments are not worried by people who sign petitions and go on demonstrations and then go back home and pay their taxes. A final comment now to end: Einstein asked Freud, with whom we began, "Is there any way of delivering mankind from the menace of war?" Freud replied "All that brings out the significant resemblances between men and causes interplay of feelings of community and identification must serve us as war's antidote".

THE CORE CURRICULUM

Nikolai Trapeznikov, U.S.S.R.

The Physicians Role in the Prevention
of Nuclear Holocaust

Now that the unwinding rounds of the arms race push the world closer to a nuclear abyss, not a single honest person can be a passive observer of what is going on around. Antiwar movement that stimulated our planet to action in recent years, has united millions of people adhering to entirely different political views and representing various professions. People do not put up with an absurd idea imposed on them concerning the fatality of nuclear war.

It is no mere chance that medical professionals are in the vanguard of the public coming out for the alternative peaceful way of human development. Human life and health have always been the primary concern of physicians. Those who solemnly took the Hippocratic oath remember the words of what kind of person a physician should be: "Let him be nice and kind in spirit, and, as such, full of worth and good will".

André Maurois delivering a speech at the congress of French physicians said that mercy was not an indispensable feature of a physicist or chemist but it was obligatory for a physician. Yes, it is quite true that humaneness and mercy determine physician's everyday life and activities. Can he forget about them in the face of a threat of annihilation of millions of human lives, in the face of distress and sufferings of the whole mankind?

The Hippocratic oath is one of the most generous human documents. Following this oath, physicians take care of the health of people, save their lives. We remember the words of the oath: "Whatever house I enter, it will be for the patient's benefit". So every physician will treat the patient, help the weak, save the dying man. We have not combated all diseases so far, but progress in medical science helps us to fight them. Diseases, premature aging and death are retreating more and more.

For this purpose we need but one condition, that is peace. We can follow the Hippocratic oath only if we are alive, our hands are working, our hospitals and instruments functioning and drugs are available.

However we must admit that in the event of nuclear war which would be a global disaster, we will be unable to follow the Hippocratic oath. A physician can visit each patient's house till this house exists, he will be able to treat a patient till he is alive himself.

Nuclear war is a new dimension of disaster. It would bring not only death, pain and wound but it would also annihilate all oppotunities of rendering assistance to millions of the wounded, irradiated, burnt and injured people. Therefore entering the houses of our patients and they are people of all countries, we cannot conceal the truth of impending danger to their health and life.

Physicians have a profound understanding of the nature and magnitude of the biomedical effects of nuclear weapons, they know better than anybody else the meaning of death and human sufferings, all these points being of paramount importance in moulding the civic attitude of this category of professionals. When a call "Man overboard!" is heard on a ship on the high seas the engines come to a stop, boats are descended, scores and hundreds of people save one drowning person. The call "Human life is in danger!" cannot leave physicians indifferent. Each of us knows what it means to save a man. Sometimes scores of physicians and nurses struggle for one human life not thinking of fatigue, difficulties, giving all their knowledge and strength to save a man. And today we are talking about the rescue of mankind as a whole.

Can we forget that the ghost of Hiroshima is still haunting the Earth? The power of the world's nuclear arsenals exceeds 5,000 times all the explosive force used in World War II which resulted in the loss of approximately 50 million human lives.

Can we forget that in the event of an all-out nuclear war one billion people would be burnt in its fire and one more billion would be affected by injuries, burns, radiation disease and would slowly die as no effective medical response would be possible? Can American and Soviet physicians forget that according to some estimates an all-out nuclear war would result in death to approximately 100 million Americans and 100 million Soviet people?

I would like to draw your attention to one more source of nuclear danger that has recently appeared. I mean militarization of outer space. Attempts to transfer the arms race to space and the building up of a large-scale antimissile system are aimed in fact at enhancing the nuclear first-strike potential of the country which is building it up. Work at the development of such a shield can only increase the arms race making the problem of strategic arms limitation and reduction difficult.

No doubt that nuclear weapons are weapons of genocide, and nuclear war could become not only a catastrophe for mankind and human civilization but also wipe out all life on earth.

Knowing all this, has a physician a moral right to keep silence when there is danger to his patient's health and life? We must stir the indifference of some of our colleagues, to raise their professional responsibility and to protect our patients from nuclear death.

I believe that one of the most important achievements of the International Physicians for the Prevention of Nuclear War is the breakthrough in a psychological wall separating us from understanding the magnitude of a nuclear catastrophe.

We, physicians, must be fully aware of the fact that many of our patients do not quite realize the actual danger of nuclear war. This may be due to the fact that with joys and sorrows of everyday life they forget the horrors of Hiroshima. The results of the 1945 nuclear bombing have become some kind of abstraction devoid of any concrete content. Our reason and heart cannot accept such notions as "one million Hiroshima" or "the death of hundreds of millions of people". We turn away in horror and take up petty problems that we can personally control or solve. Fewer and fewer people who fought in World War II have remained – 3 per cent only have survived as of today.

Such is the psychological mechanism of underestimating the threat of unleashing nuclear war and the magnitude of its effects. Therefore it is necessary to shake up people, and to motivate them to vigorous actions to prevent a nuclear catastrophe. After all, it is not a question of another war but of the survival of human civilization.

Owing to their research and educational acitivities International Physicians for the Prevention of Nuclear War have brought the true scope of nuclear threat to the awareness of the public at large. Having honestly admitted that no effective medical response would be possible in the event of nuclear explosions, they have shown every sensible person that the abstract world problem has a direct personal dimension.

Physicians committed professionally to protect health and life on earth must not forget about one more aspect of the nuclear arms race. It detracts resources from the struggle against poverty, starvation and diseases. Today in developing countries 450 million people are undernourished, 11 million children under one year die every year, 120 million children are deprived of the opportunity to attend school.

Sometimes we do not realize how extravagant the war machine is as compared to expenditures on public health. Here are a few examples showing how military spendings or, to be more exact, their small part might be used:

– 2 billion inhabitants of our planet drink contaminated water resulting in 80 % of all their diseases. The cost of the WHO program on safe drinking water for this part of the Earth population would require a mere 18-day world military spending annually for 10 years.

– A need for 300 million dollars, i. e. the amount spent in the world on military purposes in 5 hours, would be enough for complete liquidation of measles.

– Over 5 million children die annually of diphtheria, whooping-cough, tetanus, measles, poliomyelitis and tuberculosis. Vaccination of all infants on the Earth costs a mere 260 million dollars. At the same time 800 billion dollars are spent in world annually on armaments, i.e. 2.2 billion dollars every day!

Can one put up with the fact that one of 350 people in the world is a soldier and only one of 3700 is a physician; an average of 16,000 dollars is spent annually on the instruction and maintenance of a soldier and 260 dollars only on the education of a child. These are illustrative figures. One can hardly imagine a more dangerous "disease" than the arms race, especially the nuclear arms race. Apart from the threat of these armaments to our civilization it is becoming more evident now that the madness of the arms race requires excessive costs from mankind without enhancing its security and depriving it of an opportunity to spend on the essentials of socioeconomic development.

That is why we want our voice, the voice of professionals to whom the patients entrust the most precious – their health and life – to sound louder, there should be no indifference among physicians whom people believe and whose opinion they consider. At our third International Congress we proceeded from these ideas and put foreward a proposal concerning an addition in the Hippocratic oath.

Taking into account the wishes of the medical public at large an addition was introduced into the official text of the Physician's oath adopted in the U.S.S.R. It reads: "Realizing the danger of nuclear weapons we must pursue a tireless struggle for peace to prevent nuclear war". Soviet physicians most of whom suffered the tragedy of war, are well aware of its effects, therefore they are active supporters of the ideas of the International Phyisicans for the Prevention of Nuclear War movement: refusal to use nuclear arms in any conflict, freezing tests, production and deployment of nuclear weapons and means of their delivery including outer space, a comprehensive nuclear test ban and, finally, the reduction and complete destruction of the nuclear arsenals.

In the period of only six months over one million Soviet physicians signed the Call of the Amsterdam Congress of our movement to put an end to the nuclear arms race and to prevent unleashing a nuclear war.

We, physicians, who take care of human life from birth to death know that man possesses courage and is capable of controlling his actions. We believe in human reason! We believe that physicians and their patients can do much to preserve peace on earth. Life must triumph. It is the purpose of our activities, our moral and professional duty!

Scientific Programme

SCIENTIFIC PROGRAMME

Inga Thorsson, Sweden

The Disarmament-Development Relationship: The Current Situation

The idea of a disarmament-development relationship is continuously gaining ground – in spite of possible temporary damage done to it by the French Government's inexplicable way of doing UN business on behalf of the United States by forcing the postponement of the summer 1986 U.N. Conference on the issue. Let me recall the three main conclusions arrived at in 1981 by the U.N. Group of Governmental Experts:

1. The world finds itself at a cross-roads. It can either continue to pursue the arms race or it can move towards a more sustainable economic and political order. It cannot do both.
2. Irrespective of economic systems and level of economic development all countries would benefit economically from an effective disarmament process. They would thus have a mutual enlightened self-interest in disarmament.
3. In a disarmament situation governments would face certain conversion problems. If solutions to these problems were well planned and prepared, they would cause no serious technical and economic difficulties.

In approving the Group's report, including its recommendations the General Assembly in 1982 urged Governments of Member States:

1. to reconsider their present policies of secrecy concerning the real costs, economic, social and human, inherent in military resource use,
2. to start to plan and prepare for a conversion process which could be implemented in a disarmament situation.

Like so many economists, I believe firmly that the economic factor – at least over the longer run – quite decisively works for disarmament. In my view, the reason why this argument has not come more forcibly to the fore is the extra-ordinary short-sighted and unimaginative policies of the political leaders of the major powers who appear to believe that the task entrusted to them by their voters is to promote peace through military strength, indeed if possible military superiority. These are dangerously outdated concepts of national security in the 41st year of the nuclear age and in an increasingly interdependent world.

Thus I do not believe that the failure so far of the political leaders of the dominant powers to recognize that an intensified arms race will ultimately bring economic ruin is due to gaps or inconsistencies in U.N. or other studies. The facts are available, in the case of the particular

U.N. study through a research progamme involving more than a hundred economists around the world. The analyses are available as well as the conclusions and recommendations. The time should indeed be ripe for decisions and action.

But the required decisions and actions would of course have as a prerequisite rather drastic changes in the behaviour of political leaders everywhere, and particularly those of the dominant military powers. The U.N. Governmental Expert Group was aware of this. But it was also painfully aware that it was not within its mandate, nor within its competence to suggest the necessary means by which these decisions could be reached. To achieve this, to create a worldwide political constituency for disarmament and conversion would require a political process at the national level, something to which a Governmental Group within the U.N. cannot contribute.

Meanwhile, the arms race just continues and intensifies. The latest available figures indicate military expenditures in excess of 900 billion dollars per year. This represents well over five per cent of total world output and more than twenty-fivetimes all official development assistance to developing countries.

Increasing annually at a rate either higher or similar to the annual rate of increase in world's gross national product, the continuing military expenditures include a growing allocation for military use of technology. By 1985, global expenditure on military research and development was approximately one quarter of all research and development. Real expenditure on military research and development is estimated to have increased annually by under one per cent from 1974 to 1980, from five to eight per cent between 1980 and 1983 and to more than ten per cent from 1983 to 1984. As this last figure is higher than the rise in military expenditure as a whole, military research and development as a proportion of total military expenditure has risen.

There are, however, some reasons why the international system can to some extent be blamed for the present deadlock. In my view, there is not enough understanding of the interlinkages between the numerous global crises of our times, including the arms race. To isolate this particular problem from other main problems, such as the world economic crisis with all its components – the debt burden, the inflation process, the mass unemployment, the problems of international trade, commodity prices and monetary instability – together with resource scarcities, the environmental degradation and the polarization of wealth and poverty within and among nations, is to disregard some of the fundamental reasons for the social and political unrest now liable to emerge at both national and international levels, with increasingly dangerous repercussions.

This becomes painfully evident when one looks at the way in which the countries in the so-called Third World have been affected by the arms race and the international trade in weapons. First, there is the need to recall the wellknown fact that almost all of the numerous armed conflicts in the world since 1945 have occurred in the Third World. One of the many reasons for this tragic situation seems to be the links between the East-West conflict and the almost complete lack of progress in the North-South dialogue. These links have several dimensions. Here are, in my view, some of them:

– Political: The major powers, through being so absorbed by the East-West conflict, fail to react to the polarization between rich countries in the North and poor countries in the developing South.

– Economic:By continuing and intensifying the arms race, the parties to the East-West conflict worsen the world-wide economic crisis, the costs of which tend to be imposed on peoples in the South much more than in the North.

– Military:The parties to the East-West conflict, especially the superpowers, make it more difficult to solve conflicts between countries in the South, by tying developing countries, or groups of developing countries, to their respective military blocs, in order to serve their own purposes and to strengthen their own power positions.

No wonder then, that the superpowers, but also other major military powers, consider themselves entitled to intervene, more or less openly, in conflicts in the Third World. A Hungarian researcher, Istvan Kende, has estimated that out of 120 armed conflicts between 1945 and 1975, in 70 – well over half – there was outside intervention from the North. The same interventionist approach is reflected in their maintenance of a global network of military facilities and bases, with over 1,800,000 soldiers currently stationed on foreign territory, including that of around seventy developing countries, as well as in the flow of arms from the industrialized to the developing world, entailing a rapidly increasing militarization.

Arms deliveries to developing countries (according to figures of the Arms Control and Disarmament Agency of the U.S.) have increased from $ 14.4 billion (in constant 1981 U.S.-dollars) in 1972 to $ 28.2 billion in 1982. Agreements rose even more steeply, from $ 10.5 billion in 1973 to $ 46.2 billion in 1980. Industrialized countries in the North have been only too eager to play the supplier. Indeed, during the world economic crisis the arms industries in the North have been among the few sectors that have continued to flourish. In 1984, according to a report released by the U.S. Census Bureau in April 1985, ten of the largest U.S. arms industries realized on average a 25 % return on equity, compared to an average return of 12.8 % for other manufacturers.

What, then, are the economic effects of arms imports on the economies of the South? A number of the forty-odd research reports submitted to the UN for our study on the disarmament-development relationship show, that increased military spending tends to be related to lower investment, to greater tax burdens, to cuts in consumption and social welfare spending and to inflation. In recent years another factor has come into prominence: the addition to the debt burden. In a study that I recently undertook for the Swedish Government it was found that arms imports are responsible for around twenty-five per cent of the debt burden of countries in the South. Another estimate, reported in the U.N. 1985 Report on the World Social Situation, indicates that in at least four of the twenty countries with the largest foreign debt in 1983, the value of arms imports amounted to forty per cent or more of the rise in debt between 1976 and 1980.

The negative effects in social and human terms are also considerable. In a report to the U.N. Group, the American economists Bruce Russett and David Sylvan estimated various social opportunity costs of arms purchases, examining their potential relationship to health and literacy. They found that for an average developing country, with a population of 8.5 million and a GNP per capita of around $ 350 (in 1970 dollars), the first $ 200 million of arms imports would add approximately 20 additional infant deaths per 1000 live births, decrease average life expectancy by 3 to 4 years, and result in 13 to 14 fewer literate adults out of every 100.

It can reasonably be assumed that such a deterioration of conditions of human life would also result in increased social tensions and political unrest. And in the unfortunately numerous developing countries ruled by military or authoritarian regimes this could well be another reason for the use of military force to keep internal tensions and unrest under control.

However, in the 1980s there has occured a rather remarkable shift in the pattern ot the international arms trade, most markedly in terms of the total volume of sales. According to a fairly recent U.S. Congressional Research Service report, both arms transfers and arms deliveries have been substantially reduced. Agreements plunged from a record high of $ 46.8

billion in 1982 to $ 24.7 billion in 1983, a drop of 47 %. In its 1985 Yearbook SIPRI notes a similar decline in arms deliveries. This decline follows directly from the worldwide economic crisis and the closely related debt problems faced by so many countries in the Third World. The fact is that the hard currency earnings needed to purchase arms are no longer there and, because of the international debt crisis, credits to buy them are not there either. Recently published figures for 1985 show the same downward trend in arms sales to developing countries.

Some might think that I have dealt unduly much with the military situation in countries in the South. However, I happen to believe that that situation not only causes serious political, economic, social and human problems in Third World countries themselves, important enough as such, but could also be decisive for the future of the rest ot the world. In spite of the terrifying arms race between the superpowers, the disarmament-development debate takes on ominous proportions when looked at from a Third World perspective.

The arms race and world military expenditures are due to a way of priority-setting which seems to be extremely hazardous. This is particularly so when we look at the alarming political instability resulting from the neglect of economic, social and human development. Let me elaborate this fairly briefly, by quoting some concrete examples from Ruth Leger Sivard: "World Military and Social Expenditures" and other sources:

– There is one soldier per 43 people in the world, one physician per 1,030 people.
– Every minute 30 children die from hunger, starvation and diseases, every minute the world spends U.S.$ 2 million for military purposes.
– The U.S. and the U.S.S.R., first in military power, rank 14 and 51 respectively among all nations in their infant mortality rates.
– When we consider the relative change 1945–1985 in the quality of weapons and the quality of life in developing countries respectively, what we find is the following: Quality of weapons: the range has increased 262 times; the area of destruction has increased 250 times; lethality has increased 199 times; speed has increased 42 times. Quality of life in developing countries: school enrolment has increased 4 times; GNP per capita has increased 2 times; literacy has increased 2 times; life expectancy has increased 0.3 times.

A fairly eloquent report on priority-setting, isn't it? I shall now ask the question: how and in what form could disarmament and development be put effectively on the international agenda? The question is particularly justified considering the way in which the French Government, using a number of artificial arguments, has served the United States interest in calling off the special U.N. Conference on the subject, to have been convened, on the invitation of the French Government, in Paris in July to August 1986. My hope is that neither the French nor the U.S. Government can keep the 41st session of the U.N. General Assembly from deciding on the date in 1987 and the venue of the Conference. And the fact is that the preparations for the special U.N. Conference have stimulated favourable reactions and a great amount of interest around the world, not least among influential groups of non-governmental organizations, which, to a number of more than 300, have announced their intention to attend the Conference.

But, one may ask, what happens in the real world? Not very much. Evidence of this is the fact that in spring 1985 and facing the debate on the issue at the 40th session of the General Assembly, Governments were asked to answer a questionnaire from the Secretary-General: what had they done to implement the decision of 1982? Out of a total U.N. Membership of 159 States, from 12 of them did the Secretary-General receive answers. Of these 12 governments nine hadn't anything to say on the issue of doing something at the national level. One government reported on the beginning of a reduction in the number of soldiers and the start of a retraining programme for those who were demobilized. One government said that it had taken a decision in principle to appoint a national commission to look into the matter. One government, finally, reported the conclusion of a national study, having it translated into English and transmitted to the United Nations.

Why this obvious lack of interest in and commitment to an Assembly resolution on the part of government? One reason is, as I have already stated, the myopic and outdated security concepts of so many of today's dominant political leaders; leading them to neglect the extent of mutual enlightened self-interest among nations in an increasingly interdepend-ent world. But the realities of this world, including the increasing interdependence of issues, will continue to impose themselves on political events. Above all, the arms race has become a major factor in the world economic crisis, influencing economies all over the world. The sharp decline in Third World arms purchases is an early warning. Purchases may not remain at their present record low level, but specialists in the international arms trade seem to believe that they will never again reach the peak of 1982.

However, the economic effects of the arms race are not confined to the countries of the South. And the U.S.S.R. is not the only major power which will be forced to discover the need for its own disarmament-development strategy. Whatever President Reagan says, and whatever the indications of economic recovery in the United States – and the indicators point sometimes in different directions – it is likely that the difficulties apparent in U.S. civilian in-dustry will remain and the competitiveness of American products will continue to decline, unless U.S. military expenditures are brought to a standstill and then reduced. No trade war with Japan or Europe will rescue an economy whose GNP growth has mainly depended on an absurd military build-up and which devotes around forty per cent of its total R and D – more than seventy per cent of federal R and D funds – to military purposes, denying civil in-dustries the resources badly needed for innovation, modernization and productivity growth. The continued effects of soaring military expenditures on one hand, and budget, trade and (for the first time this century) balance of payments deficit on the other, have made the richest economy in the world a net debtor to the outside world in 1985, in the magnitude of about U.S.\$ 100 billion.

It is generally acknowledged that the only really safe basis for national security is a strong and sound economy. The time will come, perhaps in the late eighties or early nineties, when not only the U.S. but also other major military powers will be compelled by economic circumstances to change their present course, to reduce their military spending, and to convert their available and productive resources to civilian production.

Many people working in the disarmament-development field, including myself, have pointed out that if major weapon-producing countries were to publicise detailed plans for converting their armaments industries to the manufacture of other products, when dis-armament agreements are being negotiated, confidence in the sincerity of their negotiating would be greatly enhanced. The reason: this would show their willingness to face and solve the conversion problems once successful disarmament agreements were arrived at. As a matter of fact, an American economist specializing in this field said some time ago: "If you want to disarm, first plan for conversion". Such unilateral steps would be a major con-fidence-building measure, improving the international atmosphere without incurring any risk at all. Against this background, it is a pity that governments have not adhered to the General Assembly resolution in 1982, according to which governments were urged to undertake national follow-up studies to look into preparation for conversion.

A few minutes ago I referred to the fact that, one year ago, one government reported to the U.N. on such a national follow up study. That was my own government of Sweden. In September 1983 the Swedish Government asked me to undertake, as a special expert, a study examining how a country like Sweden could, in the context of a broader process of disarmament in Europe, reduce its defence spending and convert resources needed for military purposes into constructive civilian use.

My report was transmitted to the government in August 1984, followed by a second part with more detailed case studies and analyses in the autumn of 1985.

This is not the place to go into details of my findings and conclusions. Let me only state that if there were to take place a gradual reduction of troops and weapon systems in Europe, with particular emphasis on offensive systems, this would allow for an equally gradual reduction of Swedish defence expenditures, making possible a process of conversion. Considering the size of the Swedish defence establishment and the Swedish defence industries within the Swedish economy, this would not cause major macroeconomic problems. But it would create microeconomic problems, both regionally and in human terms. These would have to be looked into very carefully, particularly at the local level, where local communities can be highly defence-dependent. Disarmament is a positive and, by its very nature, inevitably a political process, its consequences occurring as the result of political decisions. It is of utmost importance that no single human being and no single family need have to experience it as a threat to their own economic security and their own future. This is all the more reason why conversion must be the subject of the most careful advance preparation and planning.

Although the Swedish study does not necessarily establish a model that can be replicated in detail by studies in other countries, it does show that the recommendations made in the U.N. report can in principle be put into effect. The next question is of course how to convince governments that they ought to be implemented.

Again, however, as is so often the case, governments are only likely to respond positively if they are obliged to, as a consequence of constructive political action from their own citizens. And, as a matter of fact, interest in the disarmament-development issue is increasing in many parts of the world. Conferences and seminars are organized, study groups are formed, public meetings are held. I hope that this augurs well for the special U.N. Conference to be convened in 1987.

As is usually the case, this Conference is preceded by a thorough preparatory process. I should like to conclude this article with a few words on an event which, as one part of the preparations, took place in April 1986 at U.N. Headquarters.

The Secretary-General of the Conference had been authorized by the General Assembly to convene what in the U.N. language is called a panel of eminent personalities to work out a declaration which was aimed to serve as a point of reference for the Conference. The composition of the panel justified the term "eminent": there were former Heads of States and Governments, former Foreign Ministers, retired U.N. Heads, Nobel Prize Laureates etc. They were not selected and instructed by any government. They, or rather we, as I was a member of the panel, did speak for ourselves and for ourselves only.

As I was elected moderator of the panel, I am very pleased that the outcome of three days of deliberations was a unanimously adopted declaration which, by agreement of the group, constitutes a message to the peoples of the world.

The document contains a strong request for a radical change in the setting of priorities for the use of finite resources in the world. The members of the panel agreed, very firmly, that particular emphasis should be given to security needs of peoples and nations, security being taken in that much broader context than is usually the case, to which I have already referred. Very special attention is here given to the prevailing situation in most of the developing world, looked at in conjunction with the situation and the policies of the industrial countries.

As a synthesis they point out that "harsh economic conditions, hunger, poverty, and political instability are natural allies. Not to grasp the wider implications of these issues may well amount to a central misperception of our times".

But, I should like to add, efforts towards disarmament and efforts towards justice, economic, social and human development are also natural allies.

I want to quote the final paragraph of the declaration: "Our small planet is getting endangered: by the arsenals of weapons which could blow it up; by the burden of military expenditures which could sink it under, and by the unfulfilled basic needs of two-thirds of its population which subsists on less than one-third of its resources. We belong to a near universal constituency which believes that we are borrowing this earth from our children as much as we have inherited it from our forefathers. The carrying capacity of this earth is not infinite, nor are its resources. The needs of national security are legitimate and must be met. But must we stand by as helpless witnesses of a drift towards greater insecurity at higher costs?"

The answer to this rhetorical question is of course a firm no. If governments fail to change values, attitudes, priority-setting and directions, then the public opinion, the public will must speak.

SCIENTIFIC PROGRAMME

Herbert Abrams, U.S.A.

The Problem of Accidential or Inadvertent Nuclear War

The following Lecture was given on September 18, 1998 at 2:00 p.m. to undergraduates studying history at the University of Buenos Aires. – This course in Northern Hemisphere History, Professor Cordoba said, will deal selectively with the last decade from our modern perspective of 1998. Living and working at this University in Buenos Aires, we had the chance to watch the dangers of the nuclear age unfold. From the time he came to power in September 1969, Colonel Qaddafi made no secret of his desire to secure nuclear weapons. Technical assistance and the promise of a small research reactor were two of the subjects discussed during the visit of Premier Kosygin to Libya in 1975. An agreement on nuclear cooperation was signed, calling for the construction of an atomic research center, the provisioning of a small, ten-megawatt reactor, and training of the team that would run the complex. The partnership was further strengthened by the two countries' training arrangement. An estimated 700–800 Libyan students were sent to the Soviet Union to study nuclear engineering in 1980. This figure was many times the number that could be realistically absorbed by a civilian program.

Over the prior decade, the Libyan Government had intervened forcefully in Chad – attempting to seize control of the uranium-rich Aozou Strip. At various times, the Libyan military had controlled as much as one-third of Northern Chad. In December, 1980, Libya went so far as to launch a full-scale but unsuccessful invasion of Chad, with the stated aim of "throwing open the borders and unifying the two countries."

In February, 1985, Qaddafi moved again to seize control of Chad. Rather than launch an invasion, he tried to blow up Chadian President Habre and his entire Cabinet. The objective was to bring a pro-Qaddafi rebel fraction to power in Chad, and to maintain unimpeded access to Chad's uranium-rich Aozou regions. Despite Qaddafi's failure to seize complete control, Libya continued to occupy 200,000 square miles of Chadian territory in September of 1985.

In late 1985 and early 1986, a number of terrorist acts took place in Europe and the Mediterranean in which American lives were lost – an Egyptian cruise ship, a TWA passenger plane, a German night club, and others. On April 9, 1986, President Reagan called Qaddafi the "mad dog of the Middle East" and said the United States was now weighing moves to strike militarily against Libya. Two aircraft carriers were stationed near Tripoli. On April 11th, the Libyan radio announced that Libya might call on the Soviet Bloc for assistance against the Americans, and Qaddafi stated that Libya would indiscriminately attack targets in Southern Europe following an American assault. American intelligence sources then learned that 10,000 Libyan troops had been mobilized by Qaddafi. There were reports that a squadron of fighter planes in the Libyan Air Force were preparing for combat.

On April 14th, a squadron of American fighter planes attacked and destroyed a number of Libyan targets and bases, in spite of cautionary comments by Craxi of Italy, Kohl of Germany and Mitterand of France. The attacks were devastating.

Qaddafi had long considered the prospect of a world without superpowers. Since developing a crude nuclear device in mid-1985, he had thought that he might one day use it in a confrontation with a major power. Now he perceived a special opportunity. He waited until twelve months after the American attack, while he developed his plans. He calculated that U.S. leaders would interpret a nuclear strike on Washington as Soviet-inspired – if not orchestrated – as long as the President believed that Moscow and Tripoli were allied.

When the Libyan missile exploded on Washington at 6:00 a.m. on April 23, 1987, the United States was stunned. NORAD picked up the incoming missile on its radars in time to get word to the President to leave Washington. Despite Reagan's escape, the U.S. Capitol was annihilated. The vast majority of the President's civilian advisors was killed. The President immediately gave the word to the Strategic Air Command to prepare for a counterattack. The Commander of NORAD informed the President that the missile had come from Libya. Because Reagan was aware of Moscow's support for Libya's nuclear program and of the shipment of fighter aircraft, he was convinced that Qaddafi had acted with the support of the Kremlin.

On April 25, 1987, President Reagan, outraged that the United States could be so violated, ordered the firing of 1,000 Minuteman ballistic missiles at Libya and the Soviet Union. Across the Atlantic, Soviet leaders had been trying to contact American officials to vindicate their claim of noninvolvement, but the Hot Line had been rendered inoperative. When the Soviet general staff realized an American strike was imminent, Soviet leaders made the decision to launch on warning. The American and Soviet homelands were annihilated within minutes of each other. Libya was reduced to rubble, in spite of Qaddafi's plans. The first Minuteman to explode devasted Tripoli and Tobruk and most of the Sahara Desert. Radioactive debris spread through the atmosphere, as fires swept the subcontinents. The sky darkened, and the temperature began to drop. By week's end the survivors focused on a burning question: Who was more fortunate, the dead or the living?

And so, as things happened in the last decade, many of the elements that thinking people had considered potential triggers of inadvertent nuclear war while the arms race intensified became a reality. No single factor – but many in sygnergy – could be defined.
– Regional conflict.
– Proliferation of nuclear weapons.
– An irrational, fanatical leader.
– State nuclear terrorism practiced by Qaddafi.
– A vulnerable communications system: The Hot Line down.
– Misinterpretation and misconception: The U.S. thought the U.S.S.R. had sanctioned the strike.
– Shortening the decision time – Soviet leaders could not deflect the U.S. decision to launch.
– Launch on warning by the Soviets – to make sure the weapons in silos were usable.
How lucky we were in Argentina – said Professor Cordoba – never to have nuclear weapons.

* * *

L et us move back from 1998 and Argentina to 1986 and Cologne. Why has the concern about unintentional or accidental nuclear war heightened within the past decade? It seems clear that neither of the leaders of the great powers – either Mr. Reagan or Mr. Gorbachev – would intentionally initiate a nuclear war because of their knowledge of the annihilatory effects of the huge stockpiles. This assumes rationality in leadership. An irrational leader might choose to employ nuclear weapons in the belief that he could prevail over an adversary without self-destruction. But it is far more likely that nuclear war will come through misunderstanding, miscalculation, misinterpretation or accident.

What do the terms mean? Accidental nuclear war is undesigned and unforeseen, occurs by chance, is unintended, unexpected, unpremeditated. An accidental launch of a missile at Washington or Moscow is interpreted as an aggressive act; or, in crisis, with the country on launch-on-warning, a false alert is perceived as a true alert, and the ICBMs are launched.

Inadvertent nuclear war occurs because of inattention, oversight, misperception, mis-understanding, or failure to respond appropriately when no nuclear conflict was anticipated or desired. It is not initiated by either party with the intention of achieving specific and well defined national goals beyond the destruction of an adversary. It begins in a crisis despite the fact that neither side desires it and that both sides are following programs designed to avoid a nuclear war.

Among the potential triggers of inadvertent nuclear war, nuclear weapons accidents require consideration if only because they assume far more significance in times of inter-national stress than in peacetime.

Nuclear weapons accidents

Broken Arrows and Bent Spears are the military code names used to indicate major accidents and less severe incidents involving nuclear weapons. A broken arrow has been officially de-fined as: "Any unexpected event involving nuclear weapons resulting in accidental or un-authorized launching, fire or use which could create the risk of out-break of war; or nuclear detonation; or burning of a nuclear weapon; radioactive contamination; and seizure, theft, or loss of a nuclear weapon". Bent Spear, less severe, covers: "Any unexpected event involving nuclear weapons or components which results in damage to a nuclear weapon." [1]

Because of the secrecy surrounding weapons accidents, their exact number is a matter of conjecture. The D.O.D. officially lists 32 U.S. Broken Arrows between 1950 and 1980. [2] The most comprehensive estimate appears to be that of the Stockholm International Peace Research Institute (SIPRI), which documents 125 nuclear accidents, major and minor combined, between 1945 and 1976, about one every 2½ months. Included in this figure are twenty-two publicly known Soviet accidents, eight British, and four French. [1] The public figures represent a minimum number.

If the U.S. stresses non-disclosure, other countries with nuclear armaments do the same, to an even greater degree. The D.O.D. list of Broken Arrows largely involves long-range bomber aircrafts (B-52s). Since nuclear weapons are carried in many other types of aircraft, as well as in frigates, destroyers, and submarines, it would be naive to assume accidents have never occured on these other delivery systems.

In 1977 it was disclosed that nine U.S. nuclear-bomber accidents had occurred between 1950 and 1960, over Canada or Canadian territorial water. There have been at least nine occasions in which U.S. submarines have collided with foreign, apparently Soviet, vessels. Some of these were armed with nuclear weapons.

One well described accident occurred on January 17, 1966 over Palomares, Spain. A B-52 carrying nuclear weapons collided with a KC-135 aerial tanker during a refueling operation. The B-52 dropped four nuclear bombs. High explosives in two bombs detonated, spewing plutonium over a wide agricultural area. The cost of clean-up amounted to fifty million dollars, and 5,000 barrels of contaminated topsoil were shipped to a nuclear waste burial site in North Carolina.[3] An aviator misjudged, and a terrible accident followed. At least ten nuclear bombs have never been recovered from accidents.

Hazards of Nuclear Weapons Accidents

No nuclear weapon accident has ever caused a nuclear detonation. While it may occur, its likelihood is slim. This is because the safeguards built into weapons design have a great deal of redundancy.[4] The weapons will withstand tremendous physical impacts as well. Accidental jettisoning from great heights, earthquakes, and explosions of the material surrounding a nuclear core will almost certainly not trigger a detonation.

There are others dangers. Nuclear submarine accidents in peacetime may be reviewed carefully and their causes determined. In time of crisis, the sinking of a submarine may be interpreted as a deliberate act of provocation. In June 1981 a nuclear-powered Soviet submarine with about ninety people aboard sank in the Northern Pacific. A previous sinking of a Soviet submarine had occurred in 1970. Two U.S. nuclear submarines have sunk in accidents, one at Cape Cod with 129 aboard, one in the mid-Atlantic with a crew of 99. On March 23, 1982, a Turkish merchant vessel collided with a nuclear submarine off the Virginia Coast.

Accidental launches may be a far greater threat. The explosion of a nuclear weapon on an adversary's territory is the worst case, but accidental launching of nuclear-capable missiles in a time of crisis would constitute a grave threat. The time for verifying the non-nuclear character of the missile or the accidental character of its launch might not be available.

There have been five reported instances of U.S. nuclear-capable missiles flying over or crashing into or near the territory of other nations. These include a Mace Missile overflight of Cuba, and a crash of a Matador Missile into the straits of Taiwan after an aberrant flight toward China.[5]

In October 1984, the U.S.S. Iowa was moored in Brooklyn to the accompaniment of accusations that the retrofitted ship – which could now carry nuclear weapons – might expose New York to a nuclear accident. The Iowa was the same ship that carried President Roosevelt to meet Stalin and Churchill in Cairo and Teheran to plan the second front against Hitler. It left on November 13, 1943. On the second day out the ship's speakers announced that a torpedo was moving toward the Iowa. A furious effort to detonate the Torpedo ensued, with continous firing of the Iowa's guns. It failed. As the Torpedo closed in, the Army Chief of Staff, White House Chief of Staff, and many other high military figures watched it in horrified silence – then cheered as it missed its target.

What a daring German mission to attempt to destroy American command. Or was it? The President was almost the victim of one of his own Naval destroyer's drills. It was an accident: The torpedo was not supposed to fire, but someone had attached the primer. In spite of present safeguards, the increasing number of weapons implies an increase in the absolute number of accidents. As systems become increasingly complex, the possibility of malfunction rises.

Perhaps most significantly, more nations are in the process of acquiring nuclear weapons. Developing nations may rely more on "man-guided delivery systems," and they may lack the technologically advanced safety features of the more industrialized countries.

Human instability

On May 26, 1981, the day after Memorial Day, an EA-6B Prowler jet crashed into the flight deck of the nuclear aircraft carrier Nimitz off the southern coast of Georgia. The plane burst into flames in a tragedy in which fourteen young men lost their lives and forty-four others were injured. In addition, the crash destroyed four fighter aircraft and damaged sixty others, at a cost of more than two hundred million dollars. It was the worst accident in the history of U.S. peacetime naval aviation.

Three weeks later, New York's Democratic congressman Joseph P. Addabbo, who chaired the House Appropriations Subcommittee on Defense, informed the press that many of the marines and sailors killed had had traces of drugs in their systems. In a letter to Navy Secretary John F. Lehman, the congressman wrote, "If any of the air operations personnel on board the Nimitz were under the influence of drugs at the time the Marine EA-6B made its final approach, it would be tantamount to a death sentence for those in the aircraft as well as those on the flight deck." The Navy replied that Addabbo's information was inaccurate. "I can categorically state," Secretary Lehman said, "that drug use or abuse did not contribute to this tragic crash." Only two days later, however, the Navy conceded that six of the fourteen men who died on the Nimitz had been marijuana users, and that at least three of them had smoked it heavily or shortly before the crash. Nevertheless, Lehman said the crew's use of marijuana in no way established "that any of these men were impaired in the performance of their duty"; he insisted instead that the crash had been caused by "pilot error."

Ironically, he may have been right. An autopsy revealed that, at the time of the crash, the pilot of the EA-6B had six to eleven times the recommended level of the antihistamine brompheniramine in his system. He had been taking the prescription drug without the military's approval. A congressional committee looking into the accident concluded that the effects of the medication – which, at such a level, can cause sedation, dizziness, double vision, and tremors – together with other stress factors, probably precipitated the pilot error that caused the crash. The investigation also revealed that, among naval personnel in general, twenty-eight percent habitually used amphetamines.

The extent of drug use uncovered in the investigation would be alarming even if it were exceptional. But several government studies have found drug abuse to be widespread throughout the armed forces. This situation assumes special importance in light of a 1982 report by an investigative arm of the House Appropriations Committee indicating that many of the military's drug incidents and arrests have involved personnel responsible for controlling and maintaining nuclear weapons. Indeed, numerous investigations, surveys, and anecdotal accounts suggest that personnel charged with handling the nuclear weapons of both the United States and Soviet Union – individuals whose stability and reliability we depend on – frequently suffer from drug or alcohol abuse or psychiatric problems.

About one hundred and twelve thousand individuals are involved in handling America's nuclear arms. Most are responsible for strategic nuclear weapons – long-range weapons for a war waged on Soviet and American territory – including the air force's land-based intercontinental ballistic missiles and nuclear bombers and the navy's submarine-launched ballistic missiles. In addition, about fourteen thousand five hundred army personnel work with tactical or theater nuclear weapons – shorter-range weapons for a war that might be fought on the battlefields of Europe. Widely deployed on the Continent, these weapons include the Pershing 1a missile, the defensive Nike-Hercules surface-to-air missile, and nuclear land mines known as atomic demolition munitions.

The U.S. military is deeply concerned about ensuring the psychological stability of its nuclear weapons personnel and takes special precautions in appointing them. The heart of the effort is the Personnel Reliability Program, designed to select competent and reliable persons to manage and control the nation's nuclear arms. The program screens candidates both for "critical" jobs (commanders of nuclear weapons delivery units, pilots and crews of delivery aircraft, and delivery unit personnel with access to and technical knowledge of nuclear weapons) and for less autonomous, "controlled" positions (security guards, storage and supply personnel, and launch personnel in nuclear missile silos).

The Personnel Reliability Program selects only individuals thought to meet a variety of qualifications, such as physical competence, mental alertness, and technical proficiency; dependability and flexibility in adjusting to changing work environments; social adjustment and emotional stability; the ability to exercise sound judgment in an emergency; and a positive attitude toward nuclear weapons duty. The initial screening procedure includes a security clearance and a background investigation into the individual's personal and professional activities and affiliations, including a check of police records, former teachers, employers, and personal references. Then the candidate's personnel files are reviewed, and he receives a medical evaluation. He is also briefed on the workings of the Personnel Reliability Program.

More telling than what is included in the screening process, however, are the omissions. No psychiatric interview or psychological testing is required, and if up-to-date medical records are available, the candidate need not have a physical examination. Further, because of the secrecy that surrounds many assignments, even when a review of the records suggests that a medical examination is essential, the examining physicians may have little knowledge about the position for which they are screening the candidate. The medical records of the candidate's family – which might contain information about psychiatric problems, alcoholism, or a history of drug abuse – are not reviewed.

Once a candidate is appointed, no one from the Personnel Reliability Program follows up to ascertain that he is carrying out his job adequately. Instead, the appointee's superiors are relied upon to report any unusual behavior, and co-workers are expected to evaluate one another. Needless to say, inertia, camaraderie, peer pressure, and personnel shortages (which create a need for extra hands, however unstable) may hinder honest evaluations.

Independent evaluations of the Personnel Reliability Program are not available; it is not even clear whether the military has conducted such studies. One indirect measure of the program's effectiveness in screening out undesirable candidates, however, is the number of persons appointed through the program who are later decertified – removed from their positions. Program regulations dictate that individuals should be decertified if they are found guilty of negligence, serious civil infractions, repeated alcohol or drug abuse (though an isolated instance of marijuana or hashish use need not be grounds for dismissal), or other aberrant behavior that might lead to unreliable performance. According to Defense Department figures, from 1975 to 1984, some fifty-one thousand individuals were decertified – an average of more than five thousand a year. Given that approximately one hundred and twelve thousand people were appointed to fill nuclear weapons jobs during each of these years, if their average length of service was one year, then five percent of all appointees were ultimately decertified; if service ran two to four years, then anywhere from nine to eighteen percent of personnel were removed from their jobs.[6]

No one can argue, of course, with the wisdom of removing individuals discovered to be unstable. But the high rate of decertification is disturbing because it suggests that there are inherent weaknesses in the Personnel Reliability Program as a screen for stability. Even though the rate seems to be on the decline, more than three thousand personnel were decertified during 1985 alone. So at any given time, thousands of potentially unstable individuals have day-to-day responsibility for handling nuclear weapons.

Since the Personnel Reliability Program appears to be an imperfect tool for excluding undesirable job applicants, it would at least be encouraging to know that the pool of people from which candidates are drawn is basically fit. But the military population in general suffers from high rates of drug and alcohol abuse and psychiatric disturbances.

In a 1980 Defense Department survey of fifteen thousand randomly selected military personnel, thirty-six percent admitted to using illegal drugs. Forty percent of the respondents between the ages of eighteen and twenty-five had used marijuana during the preceding month, ten percent had taken amphetamines, seven percent cocaine, five percent hallucinogens, and one percent heroin. In the Navy, more than a quarter of respondents under twenty-five admitted they had been "high while working" during the preceding year – half of them on more than forty days. And a 1981 survey of U.S. peronnel at military installations in Italy and West Germany found that drugs were used *on duty* by forty-three percent of army personnel, seventeen percent of air force personnel, thirty-five percent of marines, and forty-nine percent of navy personnel. A full sixty percent of the crew of the aircraft carrier U.S.S. Forrestal used drugs on duty.

Alcohol abuse has also been widely reported. According to the U.S. Naval Safety Center, in Norfolk, Virginia, the effects of alcohol and hangovers played a role in fifteen to twenty percent of major naval aircraft accidents in 1979. Defense Department officials testified before Congress in 1982 that an estimated twenty-eight percent of Army personnel and twenty-one percent of Naval personnel drank while on duty. The highest prevalence of drinking was reported among senior officers.

Any drug- or alcohol-induced instability in the people chosen to handle nuclear weapons is likely to be exacerbated by the character of the work itself. The isolation aboard nuclear submarines and in nuclear missiles silos, unnatural work shifts, and, in times of emergency, the extreme stress of being responsible for nuclear weapons are all likely to affect job performance.

A large body of psychological research has established the severe emotional consequences of prolonged isolation. Don A. Rockwell, a psychologist at the University of California's Davis campus, found in a 1976 study that men subjected to one hundred and five days of social isolation in a special laboratory suffered from abnormally high levels of depression, irritability, and hostility. And psychologist Irwin Altman and others have reported increased territoriality among socially isolated groups and greater withdrawal from interaction among members of the groups.

Consider the psychological changes that might occur among crews on extended submarine patrols, who face the pressures of leaving family members behind for two or three months at a time, or among members of an ICBM launch crew, who, over a normal four-year tour of duty, serve hundreds of shifts of up to twenty-four hours inside launch control centers. Life in these underground bunkers, with its isolation and inactivity, may induce anxiety and alienation.

Unnatural work schedules cause additional stresses for some military personnel. The routine duties of the navy's nuclear submarine crews are organized around an eighteen-hour cycle, composed of three six-hour shifts. Crew members work one shift, then take twelve hours off before working another. The schedule is not in keeping with the body's biological clock – the internal mechanism that coordinates the hourly release of hormones, sleep-wake cycles, and other physiological processes that follow twenty-four- to twenty-five-hour cycles. Thus, adjusting daily to a six-hour change in work shift is humanly impossible; the feeling is one of perpetual jet lag.

Many investigators have reported high rates of emotional disturbance and impaired coordination among military personnel and civilian employees forced to work when their circadian rhythms dictate they should be asleep. Harvard physiologist Martin Moore-Ede has noted that, in industries with constantly changing round-the-clock work shifts, accidents and errors increase between the hours of three and five in the morning, when normal circadian rhythms are at an ebb. [7] Pilots flying in aircraft simulators make more errors at this time, and the incidence of truck accidents is eight times higher than at other times of day.

The reliability problems posed by violating circadian rhythms would be compounded during a prolonged nuclear alert, with missile crews working double shifts, bomber pilots on sustained airborne alerts, and submarine personnel on duty for extended stretches. Moreover, research on pilot performance suggests that the chances of human error rise sharply during crises.

Similar on-the-job stresses probably are faced by the personnel who handle the Soviet Union's fourteen hundred intercontinental ballistic missiles, six hundred intermediate- and medium-range ballistic missiles, one thousand submarine-launched ballistic missiles, and hundreds of bombers. Although reliable information about the stability of Soviet military personnel is scarce, a few generalizations seem valid.

Abuse of hard drugs appears not to be a major problem in the Soviet Union. The annual death rates from opiates are much lower than in the United States. On the other hand, many soldiers returning from Afghanistan are said to have used hashish and to have brought the habit home with them.

More significant, alcoholism is a problem of epidemic proportions in the Soviet Union. About forty-five thousand Soviets died in 1976 from acute alcohol poisoning – one hundred times the number of victims that year in the United States. Robert B. Davis, a psychologist at the U.S. Army Foreign Science and Technology Center in Charlottesville, Virginia, reports that per capita consumption of alcohol in the Soviet Union has more than doubled in the past twenty years. Alcohol abuse among the Soviet military, Davis says, is even more common than among the population at large. According to one estimate, a third of Soviet Union military personnel are alcohol dependent, and heavy drinking is said to be especially common among officers.

There seems little doubt that a Soviet counterpart to the Personnel Reliability Program exists, though details about it are kept secret. Soviet officials are clearly aware of the stress to which nuclear weapons personnel are subject, and attempt to select these people carefully. A 1984 article in the Soviet *Military Medical Journal* emphasized the importance of psychological testing in selecting individuals who are intellectually and emotionally able to handle complex and demanding military technology. The current selection process for pilots, for instance, involves examination of an individual's analytic abilities, motivation, capacity to communicate, stability, and many other factors. Those who score high on the psychological tests are much more successful in completing flight training than those with lower scores, and such tests have been used for many years in the Soviet Union.

Still, the Soviet military appears to be afflicted with many of the same staffing problems faced by the U.S. armed forces.

* * *

Even if it is true that rank-and-file nuclear weapons personnel of both superpowers are sometimes undependable, does it matter? After all, there are safeguards to prevent unauthorized launching of nuclear weapons. Wouldn't any launch have to be approved by a top-ranking officer?

In the Soviet military, strategic nuclear forces are commanded by the General Staff, which receives orders on the use of nuclear weapons from the Defense Council and the Politburo. If the General Staff granted release authority, tactical nuclear weapons would fall under the control of the theater command, or directly under the FRONT Command, and both commands would have considerable flexibility in deciding whether and when to use these weapons. A top Soviet military authority observed in 1971 that the "transfer of nuclear weapons to the disposal of strategic, operational, and tactical command echelons gives each great independence and enables them to choose for themselves the means and methods of military operations within the zones of their responsibility and within the bounds of their authority." Although there is strong evidence that most Soviet strategic and tactical nuclear weapons have been fitted with electronic locks to guard against unauthorized launching, the devolution of authority over tactical weapons in the field in times of crisis makes the issue of human instability of paramount importance.

In the United States, as in the Soviet Union, tactical nuclear weapons cannot be as tightly controlled as strategic arms during periods of international tension. Thus, tactical weapons are more vulnerable to misuse by unstable personnel. In crisis, commanders might find it essential to give subordinates the authorization codes needed to launch tactical weapons, to avoid delay if the order to fire were issued. Such devolution of control could put hundreds of people in a position to fire such weapons as artillery projectiles and short-range ballistic missiles.

It is true that there are many safeguards in place to prevent the unauthorized use of U.S. nuclear weapons. Most are fitted with "permissive action links" that inhibit the weapons until the proper combination, supplied by the National Command Authority (the president and the secretary of defense), is entered electronically. In addition, before an intercontinental ballistic missile can be fired, a total of four officers at two launch control sites, or capsules, connected to the missile silo must decide individually to launch the weapon. And even after the launch has been ordered, officers in other launch control capsules can issue an inhibit command.

Controls over the firing of submarine-launched ballistic missiles are less stringent. The Navy maintains no permissive action links on SLBMs; it argues that, in times of crisis, it cannot be dependent on authorization codes transmitted from Washington because communications could easily be disrupted by, say, the electromagnetic pulse triggered by an atomic explosion. (Critics assert that the Navy's refusal to use permissive action links is just a stubborn show of independence.) The captain and crew of a nuclear submarine are supposed to receive higher authorization before firing a missile, but if they should decide to act independently, there are no technical safeguards to prevent them from launching the weapon. Similarly, the crew of a Soviet submarine is supposed to receive approval from both a top military officer and a KGB officer for any missile launch, but no electronic locks or other technical safeguards appear to be in place to prevent an unauthorized launch.

Still, in peacetime, the inadvertent firing of even a submarine-based missile is unlikely, because numerous crew members would have to approve of, and participate in, the launch. The problem arises during crisis, when measures to guard against inadvertent launches tend to undermine launch readiness. To ensure that their forces are able to respond rapidly to an attack, commanders on both sides might loosen safeguards – issuing advance authorizations, reducing the number of people necessary for a launch, or partially "enabling" weapons so they could be fired quickly. In doing so, they might open the way for unstable personnel to exert control over nuclear weapons.

Systems Fallibility

What about faulty warnings in the nation's missile alert system? These occur when an odd movement or an infrared signature is detected by satellite guards, signalling the possibility that an SLBM or ICBM has been launched. Between January, 1979 and June, 1980, 3,703 minor alerts or "routine missile display conferences" were called to evaluate ambiguous sensory data in the warning system.[8]

False warnings can also be caused by computer malfunction. A NORAD spokesman indicated that failures in computer or communications systems may happen two to three times a year. Random technical errors within the communication codes and computer software are inherent in missile alert systems.

During an eighteen months time span in 1979 and 1980, NORAD reported 147 warnings that were serious enough to invoke threat evaluations. An additional five major false alarms occurred as well, for which the appropriate military units and various top officials were called to a preliminary state of alert.

- On October 3, 1979, an SLBM radar picked up a low orbit rocket body that was close to decay and generated a false launch and impact report.
- On November 9, 1979, false indications of a mass raid were caused by inadvertent introduction of simulated data into the NORAD computer systems.
- On March 15, 1980, four Soviet SLBMs were launched from the Kuril Islands as part of a training program, one of which generated an unusual threat signal.
- One June 3 and June 6, 1980, false alerts were caused by a bad computer chip.

The most serious aspect of false alarms is the decreasing time span we are allowing ourselves for efficient checking of errors. The shorter the delivery time of new weapons, the more likely we or the Soviets are to move to launch-on-warning policies. This dependence, coupled with shorter checking time, clearly implies the greater likelihood of a launch-on-false warning. The New York Times said it clearly: "If the world is ever blown up by mistake it will be because men are recklessly shortening the time they should have to detect it."[9]

Other aspects of the more wide-spread communications system have shown themselves prone to mishap and error. The Hot Line, set up to facilitate speedy and direct communication between the two national leaders during a crisis, has had a series of false interruptions.[5] Furthermore, no special measures have been taken to protect if from nuclear explosions.[10]

A topic of great concern is the reliability of complex systems in general. A well-known computer failure was the synchronization problem between back-up computers that delayed the first launch of the space shuttle. There is a large computer communications network in the United States called the ARPA-NET, which links together quite a number of machines and is intended to be very redundant and reliable. The network collapsed completely in October 1980 because of a kind of grid-lock, in which some routing tables became mixed up and different communications computers kept exchanging messages trying to get the situation straightened out.

Why should computers malfunction? There are may reasons, some inherent in the software, some in the hardware, many in the operator.

Every piece of hardware is the composite of a host of parts. Parts failure can be labeled as early fallout, stress-related, and wear-out. Early failures are often limited to design and manufacturing flaws or to reliability screen test escapes. Normal operating stresses cause most failures that occur after the early ones. Wear-out failures are linked to aging and deterioration.

The high early failure rate is caused by built-in flaws or faulty workmanship, inferior materials, inadequate process controls, transportation and assembly damage, and installation and test errors.

Stress-related failures for most electronic devices focus on excessive temperature and voltage. Humidity, vibration, thermal or mechanical shock are other factors.

Wear-our failures have an increasing hazard rate, with mechanical fractures, corrosion, oxidation, insulation breakdown or leakage, and frictional wear and fatigue. The space shuttle explosion of January 28, 1986 is an example of both human failure and component failure that was catastrophic.

Charles Perrow suggests that major accidents may be inevitable within complex technological systems. Simply put, these systems are usually composed of many distinct parts, and these parts interact in many different ways. To this "interactive complexity" we must add tightly coupled processes. These happen very quickly within the systems, and once in motion, cannot be stopped at any precise point because the interactions are so closely linked. In a tightly coupled system, the entire system responds to a small, technical stimulus located in one part.

When failures arise, they have the potential of becoming common-mode or whole-system failures. Three Mile Island represents just such an occurrence, where a series of small, independent failures within a tightly coupled and complex system, led to a major catastrophe.

High-risk systems can be characterized by the rarity of serious accidents coupled with the unacceptable level of damage if one does occur. When the consequences for mishap are so high, the systems cannot afford to learn from their mistakes; they simply cannot make mistakes. They must therefore be run on a trial-without-error basis. All eventualities must be accounted for beforehand, and all controls, prearranged.

Time after time, control systems, imposed in the name of error prevention, result only in the elimination of search procedures, the curtailment of the freedom to analyze, and a general inability to detect and correct error. [12]

Here, the dichotomy becomes clear: The high-risk military system is far too dangerous not to control, yet too complex to control completely. The very controls which are so necessary and integral a part of this system may ultimately lead to its failure – error in one part will bring the whole system down. In this nuclear age, the whole system is comprised of the American and Soviet nuclear forces, for they are tightly coupled together. [13]

Security of Nuclear Weapons and Materials

The security of nuclear materials, both weapons and weapons-grade plutonium and uranium, offers a major area of concern.

In 1974, the Cyprus crisis between Turkey and Greece brought the security of nuclear weapons into sharper focus. U.S. tactical nuclear weapons were stored in both Turkey and Greece at this time despite the instability of the relationships between the two countries.

According to one report at the time, "Only a U.S. custodial unit, normally a handful of men with police dogs on an airbase, plus a complicated arming device, stood in the way of an unauthorized use of the weapons."[14]

In 1984, in Orlando, Florida, eight nuclear weapons protesters broke into a Pershing 2 missile plant, and wandered around the complex for nearly an hour. The group's purpose was to reveal "an appalling lack of security of one of the most dangerous weapons in the world." One member stated that had the group been terrorists, they "could have blown-up, destroyed, or removed one of the weapons and taken it with us."[15]

The control of nuclear fuel is a major problem. At the Department of Energy's Savannah River Reprocessing Plant, between fiscal years 1955 and 1978, the plant had a net shortage or MUF of 145.5 kilograms of plutonium-239.[16] The Department of Energy assumes that none of this lost material was diverted. They attribute the overall shortage to basic measurement inaccuracies and normal operating losses. The General Accounting Office stated that there is "no valid basis for this assumption" and that there is no definitive assurance that plutonium has not been diverted.[16]

In short, the inherent uncertainty in the accountancy of nuclear fuels means that the protection and detection of possible diversions may not be reliable. In October, 1965, a nuclear reprocessing plant in Apollo, Pennsylvania announced a shortage of 178 kilograms of U-235 over the previous eight years. In the following six months, the plant reported an additional loss of 36 kilograms of U-235. The losses at Oak Ridge bring the total unaccounted for enriched uranium in the U.S. to 4,500 kilograms since 1950, enough for 225 Hiroshima size bombs.[11]

Theft by the Non-state Adversary

Given that it is possible to obtain nuclear material, would there be an individual or group willing to take such high risks? Growing concern about non-state nuclear adversaries is based on a number of factors. Recent terrorist acts reveal a developing sophistication in the use of technology, intelligence and communications systems, as well as a growing interdependence and networking among terrorist groups in different parts of the world. Another cause for increasing concern is the realization that reasonably intelligent people may be able to design and build a nuclear explosive.

How likely is a serious act of nuclear violence? The record of threats and acts of violence against nuclear facilities in the U.S. totals 288 incidents between 1969 and 1975.[18]

240 Bomb Threats
  14 Bombings or attempted bombings.
  22 Incidents of arson, attempted arson, or suspicious fires.
  12 Forced entry or other breach of security.
   1 Possible diversion of a small amount of plutonium.

What will the next attempt at nuclear extortion bring? Potentially, a terrorist group with a nuclear device could render their opponent ineffective and remain anonymous and/or unlocatable. The opponent could not threaten to retaliate against an unknown adversary. Furthermore, a terrorist group could deliberately misidentify themselves in order to provoke hostilities. If a group had more than one explosive, their position would be even stronger. The terrorist group need not have an actual second device after a successful first threat; they could bluff their way into additional gains.[19]

Proliferation

Proliferation is clearly a major concern and the amount of available fuel is steadily increasing. There are many countries with a short term capability and others with a longer term capability of making nuclear weapons. The increasing potential for production of nuclear weapons and for new nuclear power suggests that regional conflicts between countries that do not at the present time have nuclear weapons may ultimately become a potential catalyst of nuclear war.

Conclusion

It may be said that accidental or unintentional war is in fact an event of low likelihood. But the magnitude of such an event – no matter how unlikely – is so great that we must understand the elements involved.

We know that it is impossible for a space shuttle with a school teacher on board to blow up seconds after launch. We know that it is impossible in the modern era for a 747 commercial airliner packed with passengers on route to a major city to be shot down by a military fighter plane. We know that nuclear power is a clean, safe energy source and that the occurrence of a Chernobyl disaster is a one in a million possibility. So when these impossible events occurred, they proved once more the central lesson of the century – that the impossible is always possible.

The resolution of conflict among the great powers is a 30–50 year affair; the preservation of nuclear peace is the indispensable prerequisite.

For each potential inciting factor to inadvertent nuclear war, there is a series of steps that the nuclear nations might undertake. Some of these are short range, some intermediate, some long.

- A more multipolar international order.
- Strengthening the non-proliferation treaty.
- Controlling nuclear fuels, and preventing thefts.
- A joint U.S.–U.S.S.R. accident prevention commission.
- Exchanging information about nuclear safety devices and safeguards.
- Increasing the authority of the standing consultative commission.
- Establishing better crisis prevention and management procedures.

The list could go on and on.

The law of cumulative probability illustrates that we are living with a finite probability of nuclear conflict – accidental or otherwise. If this relatively low likelihood event is projected over a sufficient time-span, the likelihood may then begin to approach certainty.

So we must grapple with this problem, and understand it, and do everything in our power to cut the risk.

There may be less time than we think.

BIBLIOGRAPHY

1. Leitenberg, Milton. Accidents of Nuclear Weapons Systems. In: Stockholm International Peace Research Institute, Ed. SIPRI Yearbook of World Armaments and Disarmament, 1977. Cambridge, MA: MIT Press. p. 53.
2. Halloran, Richard. U.S. discloses 5 accidents involving nuclear weapons. New York Times. May 26, 1981
3. Talbot, Stephan. The H-bomb next door. The Nation. Feb. 7, 1981. p. 147.
4. Frei, Daniel. Risks of Unintentional Nuclear War. Totowa, NJ: Rowman and Allenheld. 1983.
5. Dumas, Lloyd. National insecurity in the nuclear age. Bulletin of the Atomic Scientists. May, 1976.
6. Abrams, H. L. Who's minding the missiles? The Sciences. 26: 22–28, July–August, 1986.
7. Moore-Ede, Martin. The Body's Inner Clocks. In: Health and Medical Horizons. New York: MacMillan Education Co. 1984.
8. U.S. Congress. Recent False Alerts From the Nation's Missile Attack Warning System. Report to the Committee on Armed Services, U.S. Senate by Senators Barry Goldwater and Gary Hart. Oct. 9, 1980. p. 4, 5.
9. New York Times. June 30, 1980.
10. Ball, Desmond. Can nuclear war be controlled? Adelphi Paper No. 169. The Institute for Strategic Studies. 1981. p. 38.
11. Perrow, Charles. Normal Accidents: Living with High Risk Technologies. New York: Basic Books, Inc. 1984.
12. Landau, Martin and Stout, Russel. To Manage is Not to Control: Or the Folly of Type II Errors. Public Administration Review. March/April 1979. p. 148–156.
13. Bracken, Paul. The Command and Control of Nuclear Forces. New Haven: Yale University Press. 1983.
14. Pincus, Walter. Congress and tactical nukes. New Republic. Oct. 12, 1974. p. 19-20.
15. Demonstrators criticize security at missile plant. New York Times. April 24, 1984.
16. U.S. General Accounting Office. Report to Congress. Nuclear Fuel Reprocessing and the Problems of Safeguarding Against the Spread of Nuclear Weapons. March 18, 1980.
17. Torrey, Lee. Searching for missing Uranium. New Scientist. Feb. 9, 1984.
18. U.S. Congress. Office of Technology Assessment. Nuclear Proliferation and Safeguards. Praeger Pub., New York, 1977.
19. Kreiger, David. What happens if ...? Terrorists, revolutionaries, and nuclear weapons. Annals, AAPSS, 430. March 1977, p. 50.

SCIENTIFIC PROGRAMME

Oleg Atkov, U.S.S.R.

Medical Co-operation and Space Technology

T he subject of my talk is medical cooperation and space technology. I would like to deal with a number of achievements and to dwell upon problems I am concerned with as a physician and a cosmonaut. There is nothing more urgent and pressing today than to realize the eternal dream of mankind for peace among nations. And there can be no bystanders here: neither states, nor political parties, public organizations nor individuals.

The most important thing I believe is to respect and accept the ways of life of the neighbouring states. The variety of genofond and the national diversity of mankind are the features and the condition of life stability, both biological and cultural. And isn't it better to be different in all the rest during the life-time than to become similar at the moment of death?

Everything, everything should be mobilized – arguments, patience, tenacity not to miss the chance, not to lose time we are short of. And we have no right to shift off the terrible burden of nuclear threat to the coming generations who will face even more difficult problems if the development of antihumane technology is not discontinued.

We wish it so much to believe that our partners, our allies in the struggle to survive and preserve life on the planet will respond and the cause of peace will not be strangled or restrained by the reasons of prestige, who and when was the first to put forward this or that peace initiative. All this is so shallow in comparison with the main value – the need to safeguard peace. And as to differences among peoples, let them decide their own fate without the outside pressure and coercion.

The appeal of the First International Congress of the Association for Space Flight Participants held last year in France to the General Secretary of the CPSU M. Gorbachev and the President of the U.S.A. Reagan read: "We have got together to unite the efforts of people who had a unique opportunity of seeing our planet Earth from space in the struggle to use space engineering and technology exclusively for the benefit of all the peoples living on the Earth. And we shall strive for the achievement of this goal." And I am one of them.

With every passing year the progress on the exploration of space for peaceful purposes is more and more widely used for the solution of pressing earthly problems. Numerous well equipped orbital space systems help to cope with such important issues as the assessment of natural resources of the Earth, environmental control, safe and prompt communication and navigation, meteorological surveillance, phototopography, etc. The world's oceans are being successfully studied from space; the state and distribution of its biological mass and mineral resources are analysed and the direction of weak and strong currents and temperature zones are recorded.

The progress in space technology ensuring scientific and applied activities outside the Earth atmosphere has stimulated the development of new scientific fields – space biology and medicine, space studies of land and materials, etc. Each of them opens new vistas for the humanity. Future industrialization of circumterrestrial space will permit the production of various products and materials in conditions of weightlessness and high vacuum. It is quite obvious that further exploration of space for peaceful purposes and the benefit of mankind will require joint efforts of many countries. The international cooperation could certainly facilitate the realization of vast potentials associated with the exploration of space and contribute to the effective solution of many global problems (ecological, mineral, raw material, power generating), the elevation of the living standard, and eradication of cultural backwardness, disease, hunger, poverty.

Being an active proponent of extensive international cooperation on earth, the Soviet Union from its first steps in space has been true to its principles in this new sphere of human activities and has taken an acitve part in the fruitful cooperation in the field of space exploration. The U.S.S.R.'s loyalty to these principles was once again emphasized in the Programme of the CPSU, adopted at the 27th Congress of our party. "The exploration of space should be carried out only for peaceful purposes, for the development of science and technology in accordance with the needs of humanity. The U.S.S.R. is for collective efforts in the solution of these problems and will take an active part in the international cooperation to this effect", the document reads. And the Soviet Union has confirmed this by concrete practical steps.

An obviously human position of the Soviet Union has manifested itself in a successful implementation of a unique multipurpose international project "Vega" ("Venus – Halley's comet"). The complex of scientific equipment of Soviet automatic interplanetary stations "Vega-1"and "-2" was created by scientists and specialists from the U.S.S.R., Austria, Bulgaria, Hungary, GDR, Poland, France, FRG and Czechoslovakia. The scientific project "Venus – Halley's comet" was coordinated with the analogous studies performed by European space agency, U.S.A. and Japan. It won't be an exaggeration to estimate the flight of two Soviet automatic stations "Vega" and foreign space systems to Halley's comet as an outstanding contribution into the study of the universe. The joint work has also strengthened the ties of friendship between the scientists and specialists from different countries united by a common goal, the learning of an objective truth.

At present international space systems of satellite communication and navigation "Intersputnik", "Intelsat", "Inmarsat" successfully operate. An international system "KOSPAS-SARSAT" meant for saving people who had land and sea accidents has proved equally successful. It comprises a network of surveillance and communication satellites and receiving land stations in the U.S.S.R., U.S.A., France, Canada and other countries. During only the first four years of work hundreds of people, victims of 137 accidents have been saved.

The Soviet Union implements a comprehensive scientific programme on specialized biological satellites of the "Kosmos" series. Seven such biosatellites have been recently launched. The main goal of these studies is the expansion of our knowledge on the effect of space flight factors on the living organism. Scientists from socialist countries, U.S.A. and France take part in the investigations. The results of joint scientific studies help to answer numerous questions related to many problems of space exploration and the role of gravitation in the origin and evolution of life on earth.

Joint space flights of Soviet cosmonauts with spacemen from socialist countries, France and India on Soviet space ships and orbital space laboratories "Salyut" according to "Interkosmos" programme are a convincing example of fruitful international cooperation. At present two candidate cosmonauts from Syria are being trained in the Soviet Union. An agreement has been achieved on the second joint Soviet-French flight scheduled for 1988.

In the course of joint international flights the crews have been implementing a comprehensive programme of scientific and applied studies and performing the experiments on the equipment manufactured in the member-states. Namely, over fifty pieces have been devised specially for medical and biological studies. The application of new equipment and techniques has considerably expanded and intensified studies of cardiovascular and respiratory systems, vestibular and locomotor systems, made it possible to obtain new data on the functioning of various body systems in weightlessness. It should be noted that each space flight of an international crew was a step forward, supplementing and enriching the previous scientific results. The results of each flight have become known to all the participants of the programme.

I believe it important that some instruments were successfully used not only during space flights of international crews, but also during long-term expeditions of Soviet cosmonauts. Thus, during my 237-day flight together with Leonid Kizim and Vladimir Solovyov we happened to work on "Balaton", a device made in Hungary, assessing the effect of space flight factors on the operator skills and psychic working capacity of cosmonauts, on blood separator "Plasma", made in Czekoslovakia, French "Echograph" and Indian "Vector-cardiograph" for the studies of the cardiovascular system. Photographs of the earth surface and world oceans were taken with multifunctional photocamera, made in GDR.

It is common knowledge that the costs spent on the exploration of space are extremely high, however they are being repaid now. For instance, the information obtained from space gives a yearly profit of up to 40 billion roubles for geologists, 30 billion roubles for specialists in topography and over 100 billion roubles for oil and gas production. Prophetic words of our great compatriot, the founder of cosmonautics, Konstantin Tsiolkovsky, have come true. He believed that the exploration of space would reward people with "heaps of bread and infinite might".

As a physician, I can most clearly see vast potentials of cosmonautics that can be successfully applied in medicine on earth. The techniques and medical equipment devised specially for space flights are now widely used in the clinical practice.

I will try to demonstrate the potentials of space medicine in relation to the prevention of cardiovascular diseases, as they can be indeed called the ailment of the 20th century.

As circulatory changes observed during space flights were less marked than those recorded in sick people, it was necessary to develop a number of new techniques, instruments and methods of information analysis capable of detecting and controlling slight functional changes induced mainly by regulatory mechanisms. Timely detection of the first functional changes makes it possible to predict untoward shifts and perform adequate preventive procedures.

This experience seems useful for the prevention of cardiovascular diseases, as the functional changes associated with ischemic heart disease, essential hypertension and other circulatory disorders are never sudden. They develop gradually and are caused by the so-called risk factors. Functional tests used in space medicine, mathematical analysis of heart rhythm, dynamic electrocardiography, other noninvasive procedures permit the detection of adverse trends in the health status by minimal deviations that remain within the limits of "Expanded norm" and allow the adequate prevention of the disease. Nowadays it is quite often that one can see in the clinics the equipment devised specially for space flights. It is characterized by compactness, easy handling, high reliability. Many pieces have been created in the framework of the international cooperation programme. For example, "Oxymeter", a device made in Czechoslovakia for the assessment of changes in tissue oxygen supply during space flights, is now used in some clinics for diagnostic purposes. "Balaton", a device made in Hungary is used for the assessment of operator proficiency. "Argument" proved very useful in space for the ultrasound location of the heart and major vessels. This portable instrument is at present successfully used in our clinics and will soon be installed in ambulances, which will considerably broaden the possibilities of express diagnosis of cardiovascular diseases. The list is far from being complete, but the main thing is that an active international cooperation in this field is going on.

The preparation of highly purified biologically active compounds (hormones, enzymes, vaccines, antibiotics) in the unique conditions of space for their subsequent use on earth seems quite promising.

The first biotechnological experiments employing electrophoresis technique were performed on "Tavria" at the orbital space probe "Salyut-7". The cosmonauts have compared various technological processes employing different eletrophoresis techniques both for biological compounds and blood cells. A higher degree of purification was achieved in weightlessness, as compared to the experiments performed on earth. Another experiment performed was aimed at the isolation of hemagglutinin (one of the proteins constituting the viral membrane and used for the production of anti-viral, including anti-influenza, vaccines). A greater amount of pure hemagglutinin was obtained in space.

These are only the first experiments. A lot has to be done for the improvement of the equipment and methods used for the production of various compounds in space.

I have given only a few examples showing how wide and fruitful the international cooperation in the exploration of space today is. However, it could become still more intensive if all the states gave up the idea of the arms race in space and directed all their efforts and resources to peaceful purposes. This is the goal of the movement "International Physicians for the Prevention of Nuclear War". Nowadays, there is an imperative need for new forms of international relations, the states with different social systems should unite their efforts in the struggle to curb the arms race and radically improve the world political climate. The true peace programme put forward by the Soviet Union and aimed at the disarmament and prevention of space militarization is more urgent today than ever.

Dr. B. Lown, co-chairman of our movement said in his message to M. Gorbachev that our movement pledges to redouble the efforts to persuade the U.S. government to reciprocate and thus to create a mutual moratorium that would lead to an enduring and comprehensive test ban treaty.

The recent disaster at Chernobyl nuclear power plant has clearly shown the horrible consequences of nuclear power going out of control. It has once again elucidated the terrible dangers of nuclear war. Nuclear arsenals and tests harbour thousands of disasters much more appalling than the Chernobyl one.

Our nuclear epoch makes high demands on governments and peoples. Receiving a well known American public figure Dr. A. Hammer and Dr. Gale who have rendered concrete help in liquidating the consequences of the Chernobyl disaster, M. Gorbachev said that this was our idea of how the relations between our two great peoples should develop, provided the leaders of the two states had sufficient wisdom and good will.

We are now living in a difficult time. The prerequisites for the improvement of the international situation are far from being at the turning point: the arms race is going on, the threat of nuclear war remains.

However, we do believe in the triumph of reason. We believe that the people living on the Earth will do their best to hold back the attempts to involve the world into nuclear disaster and to turn space from the area of international cooperation into the area of military confrontation. The outer space should remain peaceful for the benefit and progress of mankind in space and on earth.

SCIENTIFIC PROGRAMME

Hiltrud Kier, Federal Republic of Germany

UNESCO Programme for the Protection of Culture in Wartime

T he Hague Convention on the protection of culture during armed conflicts was signed in 1954. This Convention includes provision for the identification of historical monuments with blue-and-white plaques to help soldiers recognise them as items of culture to be protected. The Federal Republic of Germany ratified this convention in 1967 and the Ministry of the Interior has been actively involved in fulfilling the plaque campaign since 1981. Around 8,000 monuments throughout the FRG are scheduled for this treatment, in order that they might be protected in time of war – but with the important reservation that they not be in the proximity of militarily important targets. As Cologne Cathedral is rather awkwardly positioned directly beside the strategically most important railway bridge of Central Europe, such a small blue and white plaque would serve solely as a decoration.

There are two comments to be made today on the Hague Convention, without casting any doubt on the good intentions of 1954:

1. Through the development of the categorisation of what is a monument to include objects form the more recent eras of the 19th and 20th century, the number of listed monuments in the FRG has increased to around 1 million, of which 8,000 would be an insignificantly small number. Cologne alone has around 9,000 listed buildings. The law on the protection of monuments in the Land of Northrhine-Westphalia does not differentiate between more or less important monuments, thus making a selection legally impossible. The relevant minister has therefore refrained from implementing the Hague Convention in Northrhine-Westphalia.
2. When the Hague Convention was signed in 1954, the threat of nuclear war to the world was unrecognised. Since that threat has been recognised, conventional war has been played down in an evil way as if it were a harmless stroll by a few soldiers, who would of course respectfully give each monument with a blue-and-white plaque a wide berth, so as not to damage it. What then wouldn't be more natural than for civilians to flee into such buildings, because there they would feel most safe? Around 10,000 people would find somewhat cramped space in Cologne Cathedral, people who, in time of danger, would have seen a sign of escape in the blue-and-white plaque, not knowing of the exception clause in the Hague Convention mentioned above. The nearby strategically important rail-

way bridge, the Hohenzollern Bridge, along with the nearby, also strategically important railway station, is also an important architectural monument!

In connection with this discussion about conventional war, during which the blue-and-white plaques are supposed to perform their functions, it seems important to portray how the protection of artistic treasures fared during the conventional Second World War, whose wounds of destroyed cities have still not yet been healed. But we should also realise, with an almost nostalgic melancholy, that we will never again see such a harmless conventional war, because conventional arms have also been further perfected. I should also mention that a Hague Convention from 1907 already existed, the consistent application of which should have provided for more than sufficient motivation for the protection of civilians and works of art. But how did it work out during the Second World War? Who gave any thought to the protection of the arts?

The Second World War saw the almost immediate use of air forces. At first they were used to destroy militarily or strategically important targets: e. g. the raids on Cologne in 1940 were concentrated on the bridges and factories in and around the city.

The military strategy of wearing down the enemy by consciously killing his civilians and of divesting him of his national identity by the destruction of his cultural heritage was initiated, above all, by the German military command in the second half of 1940. This was based on the assumed and available superiority of the German Luftwaffe and its strategic use in bringing about a quick end to the war with England. Joseph Goebbel's later comment on the use of the V-weapons against London betrays the disdain for humanity and art in a purely military mentality, "Boom! There it strikes into the sleeping, unsuspecting metropolis!"

By the end of 1940, London had been attacked on 57 nights by an average of 200 bombers, and the densely-occupied City of London had been subjected to area-bombardment. Like a miracle, the dome of St. Paul's Cathedral survived undamaged, just as the towers of Cologne Cathedral rose above the destroyed city. It wasn't however the intention of any of the bomber crews not to destroy these two unmistakable and universally known buildings. On the 12th of September 1940 a bomb, one of the heaviest available time-fused bombs, hit St. Paul's, penetrating 8 metres deep into the earth. It took specialists three days of feverish activity to remove that bomb and to defuse it outside the church. In the winter of 1940 the Luftwaffe transferred their attacks on to smaller towns of which the raid on Coventry during the night of 14th to 15th November 1940 proved to be the most fateful for the war history of Cologne.

Coventry, a city of about 250,000 inhabitants, was attacked by about 500 bombers during the night. The old city in particular was destroyed and 400 inhabitants lost their lives in this merciless raid. The artistically important 14th century cathedral was left a heap of rubble. On the following day, the German radio announced that other British cities would suffer the same fate as Coventry, and be "coventrisiert".

In the following weeks Glasgow, Bristol, Birmingham, Southampton and other cities were heavily attacked, and again and again the destruction of life and cultural identity stood in the foreground.

Whilst in 1940 it still seemed as if Britain would not launch any such similar raids against German cities, at the beginning of 1941 the Royal Air Force succeeded against all the objections of the other forces. This had much to do with raised prestige for the air force, which was at that time unrecognised by the other services. There had even been suggestions of disbanding the air force and deploying its forces as auxiliaries of the army and navy. Air

Marshall A. T. Harris was fighting not only for his idea of area bombardment, but also for the recognition of his "professional status".

On the 31ˢᵗ of May 1942 the first area bombardment of a German city took place. According to the Harris Plan, one of the most important German cities should be in one night obliterated from the map of Europe for ever, so as to demonstrate once and for all the strategic superiority of the Royal Air Force. The raid which had been planned for the night of 27ᵗʰ May 1942 in which for the first time in military history all available forces were assembled for "one go", had to be postponed because of bad weather until 31ˢᵗ May. The choice of targets lay between Hamburg and Cologne. The weather forecast decided in favour of (or rather against) Cologne. 1,046 bombers took off for a raid which lasted 90 minutes, in the course of which 1,500 tons of bombs were dropped. The German air defences were only able to bring down 50 British aircraft. The objective of the British attack had obviously been the historic centre of Cologne and its world-famous buildings, where the fire brigades tried quite unsuccessfully to extinguish the fires and nearly 500 people died. It was as Leonard Cheshire described it during the attack, "The first bomber battle is taking place here, and the bombers are the victors!" On the following night of 1ˢᵗ June the German Luftwaffe retaliated with a raid by 90 bombers on the mediaeval town of Canterbury, with the destruction of cultural heritage as a conscious strategic means once more to the fore.

The 1000 Bomber Raid on Cologne of 31ˢᵗ May 1942 was thought to have been so successful that the Allies, in their Casablanca Conference in January 1943, determined on the bomber offensive as the primary military strategy. Its aim should be "the destruction of the German military, industrial and economic structure, as well as the undermining of the morale of the German populace up to the point where the will to armed resistance will be decisively weakened".

The latter doubtlessly meant the deliberate destruction of all the cultural monuments of the enemy. The attack on 31ˢᵗMay 1942 had already resulted in heavy destruction of Cologne's old city, but this was further compounded by the raids of the following years, in particular those of 29ᵗʰ June 1943 and the numerous ones of October 1944. In more than 250 air raids, over 1.5 million bombs were dropped on the city. In the last air raid of 2ⁿᵈ March 1945 the ruins of Cologne's old city and its monuments were once more ploughed up. The strategically important Rhine bridges were only destroyed with German thoroughness by the German Wehrmacht on their retreat to the left Rhine bank on the 5ᵗʰ of March 1945.

Naturally, the proponents of labelling a few monuments with plaques in accordance with the Hague Convention are aware that these constructions can not be protected during a bombardment simply because the plaques cannot be seen from the air and bomb-sights are too inaccurate to be focussed plot by plot. And that is always assuming that the intention is not consciously to destroy the enemy in terms of his cultural identity, as was the case in the conventional Second World War.

But, in any case, the troops involved in ground combat should at least respect the plaques. But that is always assuming that the responsible bodies are able to keep up with the task of maintaining the plaques during a conventional bombardment. It seems unlikely, however, that during such ground combat, e. g. the taking of Cologne's old city by U.S. troops in early March 1945, that such a duty may be fulfilled, especially when factors directly threatening their lives preoccupy the thoughts of soldiers. Photographs of the taking of Cologne on 5ᵗʰ to 6ᵗʰ March 1945 say very clearly to us, "Who thinks at such a moment about cultural treasures? The defending or even the enemy troops?"

How was the protection of culture organised on the German side? What was done to limit war-damage? What excellent defence and rescue programmes had been filed away by those in power, especially as long before 1939 preparations for war had been set in motion, e. g. in the building of shelters? The answer is shamefully simple. There was no official protection of art or monuments during the Third Reich. Whatsoever was rescued was rescued on the initiative of individuals. In an internal memorandum of the President of the Rhine Province in June 1944 the situation was clearly set out, "In spite of the press accusing the enemy in floods of propaganda of intentionally destroying German cultural monuments, one can only see as weak in comparison our determination to rescue at any price the monuments of German history."

What were the grounds for this?

First of all, there was German arrogance, epitomised by Herman Göring's famous statement of "You may call me Meier if only one foreign aeroplane flies over Germany". This resulted in the firm faith that the air war would only affect foreign cities. Even after the 1000-Bomber-Raid on Cologne on 31st May 1942, which forced Hermann Göring, as chief of the German Luftwaffe, to recognise his opponent's superiority in aerial combat, the Minister for Construction, Albert Speer, was convinced that the enemy had exhausted himself with this one attack and wouldn't be able to organise such a raid again.

It was only on 31st October 1942 that Speer issued a general decree authorising immediate measures concerning monuments, which had to be approved by the local major and whose necessity had to be attested by the local conservationist. It was only after this decree that it was possible to install emergency roofs on important mediaeval churches before the winter of 1942/43. It was difficult, however, to obtain building materials and craftsmen. Most activity took place on the local initiative of the parochial councils and the relevant conservationist. There is little photographic documentation, as it was prohibited during that era to photograph any damage.

The valuable Renaissance houses, Heumarkt 77 and Alter Markt 20–22, received, after serious damage, a re-inforced concrete skeleton frame onto which were fixed the outer walls. For this reason, these two buildings are amongst the few that survived the total destruction of March 1945. Attempts were also made to rescue the gothic house Saaleck by means of props. A direct hit during the last days of the war rendered all efforts wasted. This was often the case with hasty measures, which were only really of use when a direct hit was not experienced, e. g. the bricked-up rood screen in St. Pantaleon or the measures taken at the Cathedral which was damaged but not destroyed. After heavy bomb damage on the night of 20th December 1943, which put the structural stability of the north tower in question, rapid repair work was necessary, but neither material nor craftsmen were officially available. A German pioneer captain set himself against this prohibition at risk to his own life and managed to obtain bricks and craftsmen – so the cathedral was saved. The brick plug is still in place today, regarded by Cologners as a memorial of the war. (And shall we really put a blue-and-white plaque in place on it in readiness for the next war?)

In many cases it only proved possible to save a few fragments of certain monuments, e. g. statues and architectural details, which are now in the conservationist's depot, where a bust of Hitler also managed to ingeniously land itself.

Particularly disastrous was the officially broadcast opinion that enemy bombers were not dropping incendiary bombs. After the first bomb-damage to St. Gereon's on 1st August 1941, a local construction engineer, Wilhelm Schorn, wanted to erect light steel protective scaffolding, but official permission was not forthcoming. Permission was granted for wooden scaffolding instead. When Schorn protested against this decision, saying that it would be set alight by incendiary bombs, he was told, "There won't be any incendiary bombs!". Of course, such bombs did fall, and the church was burnt along with its entire precious interior on 31st May 1942. The rood-screen of St. Maria im Kapitol was protected by wooden planking, lined with saw-dust, in order to protect the beautiful work from possible shrapnel splinters from high-explosive bombs. This was all set ablaze on 31st May 1942, the remnants of the rood-screen only afterwards being protected by brickwork and surviving only because it did not suffer a direct hit.

It seems likely that the damage to, above all, the churches, would have been much greater were it not for the efforts of primarily young people who stood fire-watch at the churches, again and again removing incendiary bombs from the buildings.

It was only the movable treasures of the Cathedral that were provided with relatively systematic protection. Two days after Hitler's troops effected the re-militarisation of the Rhineland on 7th March 1936, the cathedral authorities clandestinely commenced the construction of packing cases, etc. in order to safeguard its art treasures. A precise plan of evacuation was worked out so that within hours of the outbreak of war on 1st September 1939 it was possible to pack and secure the safety of everything. The cathedral curate, Loosen, who was in charge of these matters, has described in an essay in detail the numerous removals and storage points necessary to ensure the treasures' survival of the war.

At the close of the war, the threat to Stephan Lochner's altar-piece portraying the patrons of the city came under a German threat. The Nazis wanted to destroy the picture to prevent it from falling into enemy hands. So it had to be removed once more and hidden from the Germans. Movable art treasures were also saved, right up into the last days of the war, from other churches and secular buildings. But nearly all of this activity was left to individual initiatives and was carried out in the main against the wishes of the authorities.

Besides the above-mentioned certainty of victory, there was also a second motive for German officials not to think about the safeguarding of architectural monuments. As was the case in most German cities, new town plans had been drawn up for Cologne during the 1930s, plans which called for the demolition of most of the old city along with its historic buildings. Destruction by the enemy actually only fulfilled the plans which had already been drawn up. This can be seen in the promises of Hitler and Goebbels after air-raids to the effect that they would re-build the cities after the war, but more beautifully than they had been before.

At the end of the war, Cologne, which had had 768,000 citizens in 1939, had only 40,000 inhabitants, but there were 14 million cubic metres of rubble. The citizens of Cologne returned quickly to their city after the war's end, clearing rubble, commencing with the reconstruction and even started to celebrate traditional feasts amongst the ruins. The reconstruction of the city included endeavours to save historic buildings. Much was saved or rebuilt, but in the main the city consists of new buildings and many wonderful monuments and artistic treasures have been lost for ever.

Even the best urban conservation department equipped with the best documentation cannot heal the wounds of war, cannot rebuild historic buildings as originals, but only as reconstructions. And that is only after a war like the Second World War, a conventional one.

SCIENTIFIC PROGRAMME

William Gunn, Great Britain

Towards an International Disaster Relief Treaty

O ver the past decade large-scale emergencies and disasters have been increasing in frequency and magnitude, and international involvement has been growing in parallel. Fortunately for us and for civilization, despite the critical mass of the nuclear armamentarium, the disasters have not been of nuclear origin. Yet I believe that treaties concerning natural disasters would encourage and facilitate the introduction of conventions and accords against nuclear disasters. Having said that, I shall confine myself to international action against natural disasters, though, in the course of our discussion we may draw parallels between these and any action against man-made technological and nuclear disasters. Are there treaties regulating disaster relief? Before examining any existing instruments I should like to say a few words about natural disasters.

A disaster is primarily a socio-centric, anthropo-centric phenomenon. A volcanic eruption, if it does not hit man or society, remains a mere physical, geological phenomenon; it is only when such an event causes damage to man and his society or environment that it becomes a disaster. Unfortunately such catastrophes are becoming more deadly, not perhaps because they are occurring more often, but because they now involve greater numbers of people and human settlements – due, among other things, to the current population explosion, unorganized urbanization or inappropriate technological explosion. With the world's growing interest in disasters and with the increasing participation of innumerable agencies, governments and inter-governmental organizations, one would have expected that by now some kind of "International aid law" or "Disaster relief treaty" would exist. That, I am afraid, is not the case. However, one can extract from existing laws and international instruments certain elements of human rights or of international legislation that, I suggest, could serve as the basis for a more concrete Relief Treaty. The following are some of the existing agreements or conventions.

The Universal Declaration of Human Rights

Signed on 10 December, 1948, this Declaration has 30 Articles, of which Article 25 could respond to our concern. It states: "Everyone has the right to a standard of living adequate for the health and wellbeing of himself and of his family, including food, clothing, housing and medical care and necessary services, and the right to security in the event of unemployment, sickness, disability, widowhood, old age or other lack of livelihood in circumstances beyond his control." I submit that this could well apply to disaster situations.

Constitution of the World Health Organization

Signed eight months before the above-mentioned Declaration, the WHO Constitution added new dimensions to social thinking, let alone health. Its preamble states that the enjoyment of the highest attainable standard of health is a fundamental right for every being, and that governments are responsible for the welfare of their peoples, and can only fulfil that responsibility by taking appropriate health action and social measures – including assistance in disasters.

Health is further defined as "A state of complete physical, mental and social well-being and not merely the absence of disease or infirmity". The pertinence of such a statement to disaster situations can be easily grasped. Furthermore, the WHO Constitution makes it clear that health is a matter of international politics, since health is a prerequisite to the attainment of peace and security. Indeed it is on this basis and at the express wish of World Health Assembly Resolution WHA 34.38 that, in 1983, WHO established the Committee of Experts to study "The effects of nuclear war on health and health services", and whose famous Report of the same name is known to you all. If these remarks concern nuclear disaster – which I intended to keep out of this paper – natural disasters are equally clearly covered by WHO prerequisites for the primary health care strategy of "Health for All".

Two other elements of support come from the WHO Constitution: Article 2(d) stipulates that in case of emergency the Organization should provide the necessary assistance, while Article 28(i) authorizes the Executive Board to take the necessary measures in favour of victims of calamities.

The Universal Declaration on the Eradication of Hunger and Malnutrition

Adopted by the General Assembly of the United Nations in December, 1974, this Declaration proclaims that "every child has the inalienable right to be free from hunger and malnutrition". When we consider the slow or creeping disasters of drought and desertification, or the sudden destruction of crops due to hurricanes – calamities that have lacked no proof during the past 24 months – we can comprehend the importance of such a Declaration. But what is needed is to put teeth into it.

UNDRO

In 1975 the U.N. reinforced its capacity to deal with natural (and other) disasters by establishing a special Disaster Relief Coordinator's Office. As the name implies, UNDRO is a coordinating, not a legislative body. However, in 1982 it proceeded with a study on a "Proposed draft Convention on expediting the delivery of emergency relief". This has been adopted by the U.N. but still awaits ratification, which unfortunately may be a long time to come. Its implementation would greatly facilitate the thorny problems of sovereignty, cooperation, customs, transport, export, identification, security and assistance in disaster situations.

The United Nations Institute for Training and Research

UNITAR has formulated "Model rules for disaster relief operations" with the aim of filling the lacunae in international humanitarian law. Contrary to disasters arising from conflict or war, for which legislation exists in the form of International Humanitarian Law and the law of war, no guidelines or legislation exists concerning non-conflict, natural disasters! No law governs state responsibilities; there is no standard for assistance to victims; no instruments govern the rights and duties of the state in case of natural disaster. The model rules are attempts in the right direction at developing an international law of disasters, but here again their implementation is a distant wish.

Bilateral Agreements

Some bilateral arrangements between governments exist, such as the Cooperation Agreement between Sweden and Peru following the 1970 earthquake. There are also conventions between countries on downstream pollution risks. But we have seen how tenuous these can be when applied to the recent accident from a peaceful source of nuclear energy. In fact there is nothing to assist, let alone compensate, the injured parties, be they individuals or governments.

The International Red Cross

I referred earlier to International Humanitarian Law. Fortunately, according to the Geneva Conventions, such international laws exist for the conduct and regulation of wars. We are, however, not discussing military disasters or the role of the ICRC in conflicts. It is a sad reflexion on modern society that there is no equivalent International Law of Natural Disasters to regulate assistance, compensation and reconstruction. In the absence of such codes, the League of Red Cross and Red Crescent Societies plays a capital role in natural disaster. A well-functioning federation of many National Red Cross Societies, based on legal in-house resolutions and humanitarian ideals, renders most useful services in case of disaster. But these have no force of law.

Besides regulating its own activities, the Red Cross also calls upon other authorities to pull their weight in such emergencies. In 1969, the 21st International Red Cross Confernce, by Resolution XXV urged "all Governments which have not already done so to prepare and to pass necessary legislation enabling immediate and adequate action to be taken in conjunction with the Red Cross, along the lines of a pre-established plan based on disaster relief rules adopted by this Conference." In 1971, the 23rd Conference, regretting the lack of progress made, appealed again to Governments to facilitate relief.

* * *

This, I am afraid, is where the international community stands now. There are favourable instruments of law, and the atmosphere is conducive to the relief of victims of disasters, but, unfortunately, there exists no established or ratified International Law of Disasters or Relief Treaty.

SCIENTIFIC PROGRAMME

Albrecht von Müller, Federal Republic of Germany

Structural Stability at the Central Front

T hough the issue of stability plays an unprecedented role in official statements, the actual developments seem to head exactly for the opposite direction. This is true not only for the nuclear realm but also as far as conventional defense is concerned. The renewed cult of the offensive goes hand in hand with the desire to develop deep-interdiction capabilities, which the other side must perceive as means to cripple their own defense capabilities. The result is a dramatically increasing bonus for pre-emption that perverts the effects of our defense preparations completely: instead of providing incentives to de-escalate in a political crisis, those time-critical and, therefore, pre-emption prone force structures fuel an autocatalytic escalation process in crises.

These dangerous developments are probably not the result of malign intentions. Much more, I believe, they are the result of conceptual confusion for which at least four sources are to be found:

- the mixing up of "stability" and "symmetry",
- the lack of imaginative faculty for the non-linear processes of destabilization that occur in crises,
- the exclusive concern about higher weapons efficiency instead of an integrated approach which also comprises stability and arms control considerations,
- the "fallacy of the last step" that misses to analyse what happens if the other side reciprocates.

The task of this short paper is only to whet some interest for the issue of stability in the conventional realm and to offer a dialogue for all those military experts and politicians who are interested in developing comprehensive defense and security policies.

The phenomenon of stability

As this is not the place for a comprehensive discussion of stability we want to stress only four rather independent effects that might create some understanding for the phenomenon of stability.

It is "Net Deterrence" That Counts.   Deterrence works on the basis that the other side does not see a realistic chance to gain from a military exchange. Many people, therefore, believe that one must only increase the amount of prospective destruction in order to strengthen deterrence. But that is a dangerous over-simplification. Relative military advantages and especially bonuses for pre-emption play a crucial role and we will come back on that effect in the next argument. Also of major concern, but mostly neglected, is the factor of the political prospects in the deterrence equation. Why should somebody feel deterred from the use of military means if he will be manoeuvered to the "ash-heap of history" anyway, i. e. even if he does not recur to the use of military means? In this case it is much more rational to wage war against all odds than passively to wait for one's own extinction. From Sparta's desperate attack against the increasingly superior and, therefore, threatening Athens to the Japanese attack on Pearl Harbour a reasonable part of military conflicts started like that. Deterrence, therefore, equals not simply the amount of devastation in case of war, but correlates a sum of war and no-war prospects. If these no-war prospects are rather negative this inevitably diminishes deterrence.

Unfortunately, most right wing ideologists neglect this effect that it is "net deterrence" that counts. Or, in order to state it the other way round, a hard-headed detente policy (in the sense of Nixon and Kissinger) is not a deliberate addition but a logical prerequisite for successful containment and deterrence policies.

Symmetry Versus Stability   Symmetry is not at all a guarantee for stability, or, more technically speaking, stable and symmetrical relations are two different classes which may share some common elements but which are not at all identical.

One might hope that the MIRV-lesson, the prototype of technological destabilization, should not be forgotten. Even Henry Kissinger, once the most outspoken and influential proponent of MIRVs, acknowledges that his decision was wrong. But it seems the message never arrived at those who are responsible for conventional force planning in Europe.

Therefore, it may be useful to recall the effect of "destabilization despite symmetry" through a very simplified scenario: Imagine a situation in which side A and side B both have a hundred technically comparable ICBMs with single warheads. Given a kill-probability of fifty percent, a first strike by either side could only expect to destroy half of the enemy's silos. That in turn means that both sides possess a deterring second strike capability. Such a constellation can be regareded as relatively stable. The situation changes dramatically if we introduce MIRVs. Assume that each rocket now carries ten warheads. Under these conditions the side that strikes first has a thousand independently targetable warheads which have to destroy only a hundred silos. That is a comfortable edge and retaliation need not be considered a serious danger. Because of the fact that this situation is identical for both sides, we have a structural prescription for disaster. Even in a minor political crisis each side has to calculate the difference between the bonus in the case of pre-emption and the malus in case the other side decides to strike first. The result of that calculation must be the decision to strike as early as possible – if not even out of the blue before any crisis.

The crucial point is that while in both cases the criterion of symmetry is satisfied only the first relation is stable. Therefore, the essential question is not whether symmetry or asymmetry exists but whether or not there exists a built-in bonus for pre-emption.

While many other examples of symmetric but completely instable relations could be adduced, one from popular culture is perhaps as illustrative as any: A complete symmetry exists between the two cowboys who slowly approach each other on the dusty main street of Dodge City. They have the same Colts, the same amount of ammunition, comparable skills and so forth. Nevertheless, it is a deadly instable situation – due to the high bonus for pre-emption. Until this difference between stability and symmetry is really digested, especially in the political decision-making process, we will continue to "improve" our conventional defense capabilities by means that in the end create a less stable situation than we had before.

Stability and Structures   Now we want to go one step beyond this phenomenological analysis and ask somewhat more philosophically what stability is and how it works. Normally we mean by "stability" the capability of a certain object to resist distortive impacts. As soon as the object is not completely homogeneous we have a subset of somewhat more stiff or coherent components which we then tend to call "structures". So, in all more complex objects or systems the stability depends mainly on the robustness of these structures. But as structures are concerned we again have two rather different types. One is the so-called tectonic structure which we normally have in mind when speaking of structures. This is a structure which draws its resistance to distortive impacts from a specific stiffness or inflexibility. (Good examples are the rafters in the construction of a roof or the vertical frames in the hull of a ship).

But there exists a second type of structures. They also create a sort of stability, but not as a result of specific stiffness and coherence of their elements but as a result of their coordinated dynamic behaviour. If one turns on a water-tap, i. e., one often observes meander type structures along the stream. They seem to be static but we all know that this is only an optical impression and that the underlying phenomenon is a rapid but higly coordinated movement.

These structures, in which stability is created not through stiffness and coherence but through coordinated dynamic behaviour are called "dissipative structures", because they are maintained only through a flow of energy, i. e. their maintenance consumes and "dissipates" energy. The crucial phemonemon here is that principally we would have an enormous spectrum of divergent trends in those multi-component systems. But through a specific mechanism of auto-catalytic selfenforcement (or positive feed-back which is fuelled by the external flow of energy) – one of these trends becomes dominant and increasingly subjugates all others.

While the properties of static structures are rather simple to analyse, the assessment of those dissipative structures is very complicated because a bulk of non-linear relations is involved. Nevertheless, during the last twenty years great progress has been made in understanding these dissipative structures, especially in thermo-dynamics, chemistry and biophysics. Interesting for our context here is that this second type of structures is much more relevant for social systems and especially for our present concern, the phenomenon of military and crisis stability. The reason for that is the fact that the systemic organization of social systems depends mainly not on "tectonic structures" but on coordinated behaviour or, so to speak, autocatalytic "behavioural canalizations", i. e. on dissipative structures.

A crucial feature of those dissipative structures is the phenomenon of "bifurcation". Bifurcation is in a way comparable to a crossroad situation: the system's behaviour, respectively the present dissipative regime has been rather stable for quite a long while. Then, due to a rather small change in a critical parameter, the system comes to such a bifurcational crossroad situation in which for the future development several rather distinct pathes are possible. In this situation a very small impulse in one or another direction may have an enormous impact on the overall development of the whole system. In physical systems those bifurcations normally create a barrier for prognosis, beyond which the system's behaviour is impredictable. In social systems they have an somewhat different role, due to the fact that they are reflexively structured, i. e. that individual components can execute intentionally a steering impact.

Generally, one can describe history as a specific path through bifurcationary cascades along with rather stable phases (during which it is very hard to change the course of the future development) and bifurcationary phases (which are higly sensible to steering impulses) alternate. But looking at historical developments from this prospective, i.e. from the conceptual framework of bifurcation theory and dissipative structures, we can anticipate a new paradigm of policy-making: instead of the traditional, regulative approach which seems to bring with it an ever increasing degree of bureaucratic interference with private affairs, we could in the long run develop an approach which systematically focuses on those bifurcative phases, thus enabling us to shrink governmental interference, while at the same time maintaining and even increasing the steering competence, i.e. our ability to shape long-term developments intentionally. Personally, I am convinced that we will be able to cope with the challenges of our epoch only if we succeed in making such a dramatic progress as the craft of policy-making is concerned. Without those major improvements in the methodology of policymaking we will not be able to create a political environment in which the explosive instrumental capabilities of mankind won't backfire and exterminate our species from this planet. As far as international security is concerned, our long-term goal is the transition from the present paradigm (or dissipative regime) of confrontation-oriented power politics to a future-oriented global domestic policy.

All of the following argumentation that advocates establishing a defense-prone military regime at the central front can be seen also in the wider historical context as a trial to find an evolutionary path out of the vicious circles of the arms race and to create a nucleus for the establishment of a new regime in international relations.

Crisis Stability as a Regime of Dissipative Structures which Successfully Subjugate all Escalative Trends Having said all this, what does it mean now for the problem of a structural stability at the central front?

Also on the level below the long-term historical development we ought to describe military and crisis stability as a pattern of dissipative structures which are strong enough to subjugate all occurring irritations and escalative trends. This definition already implies one rather important conclusion: to avoid all irritations and causes of escalative trends is impossible. Political control can never be so strict that it would be absolutely impossible that a naval mishap in the Baltic or a super-power confrontation in the Gulf could not create major political strains. Those events are "fluctuations" in international relations and a policy that was based on avoiding them absolutely in order to maintain peace would be absolutely illconceived. The right strategy instead is to create a dissipative regime which is strong enough to subjugate all those disturbances and that means politically to guarantee continuous incentives that make it much more attractive to avoid the use of military means.

Regarding the situation in Europe, especially at the central front, such a stability-oriented, dynamic regime would comprise at least the following three components:

- An overall political situation which offers a "non-zero-sum game", i.e. positive returns for cooperative behaviour on either side. This does not mean that one should not have sanctions in case of severe violations of international law or human rights. It means only that there should always be the option for such a cooperation which does not require a political self-abandonment of the other side.
- A military situation in which either side is well aware of two facts: (a) that it does not have a chance to gain from a war and (b) that even if war should be unavoidable, it would not profit from gaining the role of the attacker, but would be better off as defender.

– Both sides must be convinced that the phase of cooperation does not serve as an umbrella for opposite efforts. This does not mean that the political competition between East and West should have an end. It means only that there could not be a long-term stability if both sides would try to misuse the phase of cooperation for building up a military superiority that would later on allow to crush the political system of the other side by means of violence.

These three components complement each other mutually and add up to an extremely stable pattern that makes the outbreak of war in Europe as unlikely as the flash-over of conflicts from other regions.

The field in which stability can be improved most during the next years is probably the second component. Until now, only (a) is realized and even that only through the recurrence to the threat of a nuclear escalation that becomes increasingly incredible. But this lack of deterrence credibility can be overcome by improved conventional defenses. The only problem for this goal is that most proposals forwarded up to now, especially the Airland Battle concept and Samuel Huntington's demand for conventional capabilities, but also the FOFA concept as developed by SHAPE, would result in a dramatic increase of the bonus for pre-emption, thus completely missing point (b).

The Status quo and the IFD proposal

Regarding the conventional stability the present situation is rather insecure and could become even much worse, were we really to embark for FOFA, Airland Battle or Samuel Huntington's proposal for conventional offense capabilities. But before analyzing and discussing the structural instability of the present situation I want to stress two political points. First of all and despite a shrinking credibility of nuclear escalation, there exists still a reasonable level of risk for the Soviet Union that a conventional war might get out of control and escalate. Secondly, the Soviet Union cannot possibly have an interest to conquer Western Germany or even Western Europe. Such an overexpansion would definitely destabilize the intrapact balance. A reunified communist Germany would probably be no less a threat for Moscow than a reunification under the auspices of NATO. Therefore, there is no need to be afraid of a deliberate attack. The only causes of war I consider realistic would be a horizontal escalation from a conflict in another region or an abrupt reaction of the Soviet Union in the context of a developing, SDI-based strategic superiority of the United States. For both scenarios it is crucial whether the military situation at the central front offers a high bonus for pre-emption and attack – thus attracting conflict like a magnet – or if it offers structural incentives to seek the defender's role – thus preventing both sides from attacking, even if a political will to do so should have developed.

Having said this, i.e. having stressed that there is no need for panic about deliberate attack, but much reason to seek a longterm structural stabilization of Europe, we can now start to analyse the bonuses for attack and pre-emption purely along the lines of conventional military capabilities.

Regarding military stability we clearly face an asymmetric situation. At present the Western Alliance has almost no chance for a successful conventional attack against the Soviet Union. All the second, third, fourth echelon forces, all the dated tanks (which do no longer fulfil the requirements for a rapid attack), all this equipment and the enormous personal reserves would come into play in case of a protracted WTO-defense. And a Guderian type of success (i.e. winning due to initiative and velocity, despite extensive numerical inferiority) is no longer possible due to the lacking logistical infrastructures on the Western side and due to improved Eastern anti-tank and anti-aircraft capabilities. So, summing up, the only scenario the Kremlin has to be afraid of would be a synchronized revolt in more than two East European countries with NATO providing (limited) military support or trying to exploit it militarily. But the best remedy against this is to concede some more room for socio-economic experiments – a strategy that would fit even the economic interests of Moscow in providing a buffered and controllable (i. e. "placenta-type") coupling to the Western economies.

The Soviet Union instead would have a good chance to win a surprise attack against NATO – if it consequently exploits the momentum of surprise and pre-emption. Had I to plan such an attack, I would first of all throw out the nuclear war heads of ninety percent of the SS 20 force. Equipping them with state-of-the-art conventional war heads provides the option to take out or at least seriously damage on German soil

- all air bases
- all major command, control and communication centers
- all barracks
- and all the infrastructures relevant for mobilization.

Executing such a preventive strike even on Christmas Eve, the Bundeswehr being reduced to roughly 50,000 men, would cripple the Western defense irrecuperably. Only after that strike, which has to come perfectly out of the blue, I would alert my own forces – and it would be completely sufficient, if the first tank columns cross the inner German border 12–24 hours after the initial strike.

Having said this, I already hear our Western mainstream strategists cry: "We need roughly the same options in order to maintain the military balance." That would be as clever as fighting a leak in the hull of a ship with a second one. Only one thing is more instable than a situation in which one side enjoys an extensive bonus for pre-emption: if both sides could enjoy it. While in the first situation all depends still on the political will to exploit it (which due to the nuclear threat and for political reasons does not exist in Europe at that time), the second situation is a prescription for disaster in any minor political crisis. Therefore, we should think twice before adopting one of these deep interdictions or offense-oriented proposals to modernize NATO's conventional forces, even if the problems regarding cost efficiency and technical feasibility should be overcome: Looking at the military capabilities, we would gain certain options, but a symmetry of pre-emptive bonuses would be even worse than the present, asymmetric situation.

But this means not at all that we should not improve our conventional defense capabilities. We only should do it not by creating a second bonus for pre-emption but by eliminating the first one and creating a structural advantage for the defender. The most important steps toward this goal would be

- to reduce the possible targets for any pre-emptive strike
- to increase our anti-tank and our anti-air capabilities, thus denying any options for a rapid break-through and exploiting it by OMG's
- to complement our forces with "close interdiction" (40–60 km) capabilities, which also prevent second and third echelon forces from arriving at the battle-field
- to create additional light infantery components which systematically exploit the specific advantages of the defender, like fighting from prepared territory and protected positions, etc.

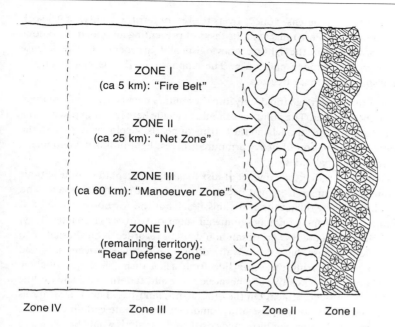

ZONE I
(ca 5 km): "Fire Belt"

ZONE II
(ca 25 km): "Net Zone"

ZONE III
(ca 60 km): "Manoeuver Zone"

ZONE IV
(remaining territory):
"Rear Defense Zone"

Zone IV   Zone III   Zone II   Zone I   Figure 1

In this way we would create the capabilities for an "Integrated Forward Defense". After a period of incremental changes we should then arrive at the following force structures (see also Fig. 1).

– Directly at the border is the first zone, the so-called "fire belt". It is characterized by an enormous concentration of fire power and the almost complete absence of our own troops. The fire power comes from artillery rockets (MLRS), mortars, attack drones and a wide variety of intelligent passive ammunition (sensor mines, communicating mine fields, autonomous manoeuvred mines, helicopter mines, etc.) The fire belt should have a depth of only some five kilometers on our side, but it could be extended some forty to sixty kilometers into the enemy's territory should war break out.

– Directly behind the fire belt is the second or so-called "net zone". It has a depth of between twenty-five and fifty kilometers and is covered with light infantry components that confront the intruder with a wide variety of precise fire power from indetectable opponents. This zone, like the fire belt, presents no military targets for the opponent's artillery. There is no traditional battlefield, but rather a dense field of well-directed fire power that fully exploits the advantages of guerilla warfare and of third generation PGMs. Scenario analyses in battlefield simulations indicate that even a very concentrated attack by heavy armoured forces should break down in the first two zones of IFD.

– But in case some formations of the intruder should break through the second zone, they have gained nothing but entry into the third zone, the so-called "manoeuver zone". Here the traditional heavy armoured units are deployed. Their task is to block and destroy any residual intruders. They function as sort of an "internal rapid deployment force;" their tactics resemble somewhat those of the traditional cavalry and they are dispersed so that they do not offer targets to the enemy's artillery or air force.

– The fourth or so-called "rear defense zone" covers the rest of territory. This is a network of local, partially mobile, defense units with the tasks of preventing airlanded operations and sabotage, and of supporting the fighting zones logistically. In general, the rear defense zone is, as today, not of major importance. The emphasis in IFD is placed on the functional synergisms of the first three zones.

It is not the purpose of this paper to go too deeply into the military details, and many of them still have to be researched further. The point that should be made here is that in place of the current "all armour / all purpose" model and the "string of pearls" deployment pattern the IFD model proposes a combination of heavy armoured forces, light infantry components and new close interdiction capabilities.

The Air Force would have rather the same set of tasks as today, except that some anti-air and choke-point interdiction missions would become too risky for manned airplanes and would have to be taken over by rockets or cruise missiles. Thus the Air Force would be at liberty to concentrate more strongly on maintaining air superiority over our own territory.

It has to be stated clearly that the IFD proposal should not be regarded as an alternative to the doctrine of Flexible Response, but as an advanced form of it. Nuclear weapons would have the main purpose of deterring the other side from using theirs. It is questionable whether a "first use" policy has a positive or a negative net result. It definitely increases the risks for somebody who considers attack. On the other hand, land-based nuclear weapons are attractive targets, especially for surprise attack and they also create certain escalative dynamics in case of conflict. A rather sophisticated cost-benefit analysis would be needed to decide whether the risk of a "First Use" or a "No First Use" policy is smaller. I would assume that one could stick to a "first use" policy, if (a) the opponent has not to fear pre-emption and attack due to a generally defense-prone military context, and if (b) all nuclear systems with European missions are sea-based.

So, summing up, the IFD proposal is not an alternative to Flexible Response, but a modernized version of it and in how far it is the hardware component for an integrated security on defense policy we shall see now in the final section.

Outlines of an integrated security and defense policy

In order to explain from which considerations the IFD model has been derived and which purposes it should serve, the following arguments focus on three topics, (a) stability, (b) military efficiency and (c) last not least arms control prospects.

Structural Stability or Only Who Attacks Faces Defeat   As we saw in the first section a quantitative assessment of military and crisis stability would normally require a mathematically rather complicated analysis of non-linear relations. But for the point I want to make here this is not required. We do not want to analyse the system's behaviour in those critical regions where rapid changes, so to say "phase transitions", occur, we only want to know roughly where these critical regions are and where, instead, we are in less troubled waters. In order to make such a very provisional assessment we just use a two-dimensional graph in which along the x-axis we have the conventional strength of one side (for example, in division equivalents) and the y-axis stands for the strength of the opponent. If we had now force structures and exchange ratios on the battle field which provide same chances for the attacker and for the defender, the "region of stability" would be nothing else but the diagonal (see Fig. 2).

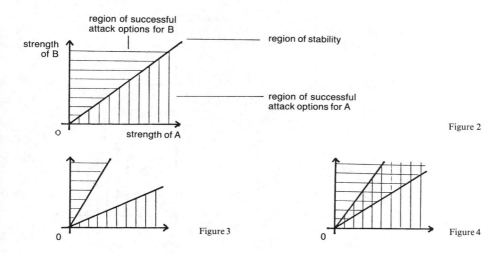

Figure 2

Figure 3

Figure 4

Would we instead have a structural advantage for the defender, let us say of 2:1, a "corridor of stability" would open up and all the force ratios that are in that region could be considered as stable because neither side could win. (See Fig. 3).

If we instead have a relevant bonus for pre-emption, this can be translated into our model as an advantage for the attacker. Assuming such an advantage of 1.5:1 (see Fig. 4), we get a certain "corridor of absolute instability". It is characterized by the fact that all force ratios in this region imply a situation in which either side can win, if it only gains the role of the attacker and the advantages of pre-emption.

Obviously, in the real world we never know precisely what our actual force ratios are because motivation, training and many other factors for which a quantitative assessment is very difficult, play a crucial role. Translated in our model this means, we do not really have clear lines but more or less foggy zones at the borders between different regions. But we should keep away from these borders anyway, and, therefore, it does not matter too much.

Turning now to our present situation, I would say that today's force structures provide only a rather small corridor of stability. It is true that the attacker has certain disadvantages in the exchange ratios on the battle-field and, therefore, has to have a certain quantitative and/or qualitative superiority. On the other hand, we do have a not too small bonus for pre-emption, especially as the air-force is concerned, even if we still let aside the conventional SS 20 attack I referred to above.

As these contradictory factors mutually compensate, I would say that we have a rather small corridor of stability at present. But that in turn means that our present force ratio, with its clear numerical advantage for the WTO, lies outside the corridor of stability and in the region of a Soviet victory (see Figure 5). But this only relates to the conventional stability and it is most likely that the nuclear risk, together with the fear of over-expansion, cause the Soviets not to exploit their conventional superiority.

In this situation it is highly legitimate for NATO to try to improve the conventional balance, especially because the nuclear guarantees seem to lose their credibility. The problem is only that we would not gain anything if we would reinforce our conventional forces mainly by time-critical weapon systems, which are efficient only in attack, but which are vulnerable and thus could be taken out by a pre-emptive strike.

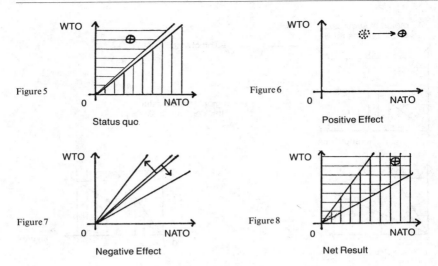

Though creating more of a symmetric conventional situation, it would not at all improve the stability in Europe. It would bring the force ratio more towards the diagonal but this would not mean stability because at the same time and due to the same improvements, the regions of stability would be changed in a way that a disastrous overlapping of the regions of possible victory is created (see Figures 6-8).

Based on the analysis of this trap, the IFD proposal tries to improve our defense capabilities *and* to widen the corridor of stability at the same time. This effect is reached through the synergism of close interdiction, light infantry components and the traditional heavy armoured mobile components. Zone I and Zone II being more or less static, i.e. not being easily carried into foreign territory, only the Zone III is useful for attack. In this way a clear advantage for the defender is created that becomes transparent if we imagine the decision-making process in an acute political crisis:

- It is very clear that NATO is unable to attack, having only today's mobile components and having interdiction capabilities which do not allow for extensive disarming and crippling strikes.
- Much more interesting are the alternative options for the Soviet decision-makers. If the WTO forces do not attack there is no danger that they could lose a war, firstly because NATO will not attack and secondly, even if she should, the Western Alliance would not have the slightest chance, its mobile components being dramatically outnumbered.
- If instead the Kremlin decided to attack, obviously Zone I and Zone II would come into the play and the WTO would have to calculate the loss of forty to seventy per cent of its forces already in these first two zones of the Western defenses. But if that happens, then – and only then – the conventional balance is shifted in favour of NATO. Now the NATO forces would have the opportunity of far-reaching counter-attacks, maybe even of conquering Eastern European territory.
- This effect can be called a "Conditional Conventional Retaliation Capability (CCRC). It strengthens deterrence, it makes NATO less dependent of nuclear weapons (thus fulfilling even Samuel Huntington's demand for a conventional retaliation capability), but at the same time avoids the destabilizing side-effects of FOFA, AirLand Battle and Huntington's proposal.

Exactly such a situation, in which either side knows that it cannot win as attacker, but is clearly able to defend itself against any attack, can be called "structural stability". Fortunately, the creation of such a structural stability does not even require arms control agreements or reciprocity – it just takes a somewhat more sophisticated force planning and procurement.

The Pareto Optimum of Military Efficiency   The above argumentation, hopefully being rather cogent, raises the question why we don't have such force structures already. The answer is twofold: one factor is that only recent progress in micro-electronics and data-processing provided the necessary target acquisition capabilities for the systems of Zone I. The other factor is bureaucratic inertia and the inclination of the services to opt for representative weapon systems like huge tanks, airplanes etc. – even if the same military functions could be realized through much cheaper but less spectacular weapon systems. Nevertheless, I am rather optimistic that the necessary course corrections will occur and that the obstacles in the service will be overcome. The reasons for that optimism are the shortages in funding which we face in the coming years and which will force us to use our resources more thoughtfully, if we want to maintain a credible conventional deterrence.

Unfortunately, also the scientific debate about these issues was rather confused. Proposing IFD has very little in common with proposing to defend NATO with a bunch of PGM equipped moresque dancers. Nevertheless, those who want to block any serious debate, continue to argue exclusively about their private caricatures of modified force structures – and this makes it extremely hard to overcome their fixation on thinking in terms of evermore expensive successor generations.

But maybe the following arguments help a little. In military action we have basically four components, namely fire-power, mobility, protection and reconnaissance. And there are opportunity costs for each of these factors which imply a certain integrated optimum for the combination. If then a major technological break-through occurs in one of these fields, this translates into a change in the optimum mix. But this in turn means that it is simply impossible that force structures which provided the optimum at the technological level of World War II continue to provide the optimum today. So, we have to ask how the dramatic progress that has been made in micro-electronics and data-processing, which especially affects reconnaissance and the allocation of fire-power, translate into modernized force structures. Obviously, some additional considerations have to be taken into account, too. One is for example that we do not want to have a technological monoculture which invites for counter-optimization on the side of the opponent. We, therefore, have to maintain a certain mix of technologies, like HE-warheads and kinetic energy, like mines which threaten the bottom-side of tanks and submunitions which threaten the top-side etc.. In this way one creates a complexity of the threat which is hard to evade by counteroptimization.

The same is valid for different operational procedures and tactics. For example Zone I, Zone II and Zone III are completely different environments for the intruder, thus creating a real synergism in the various defense efforts.

So, summing up, one can state that the IFD proposal does not only provide a high degree of structural stability, but also dramatic increases in the military efficiency of our conventional defense capabilities.

Structural Stability as a Means to Curb the Arms Race   As finally arms control is concerned, the IFD proposal provides two major advantages. The first is that the number's game is rendered obsolete, the second is that one side can start to transarm autonomously and it then lies increasingly in the interest of the other side to reciprocate. Were we, for example, to invest seriously into FOFA capabilities, this would result in a strong incentive for the other side to beef up its first echelon forces, thus rendering obsolete most of our deep interdiction capabilities. Are we instead focusing on close interdiction, the opposite incentive is created, namely to withdraw expensive heavy armoured components beyond the reach of these systems. But also for the negotiating tables new options are created – if there should be a serious interest in reaching arms control agreements and stabilizing the situation in Europe. The leitmotiv of the negotiations should be no longer purely quantitative force reductions (which in many cases would not even increase stability) but the state of "structural defensivity" on either side. I personally believe that under these auspices far-reaching arms control agreements could be found. But even in case this should not happen, we are no longer locked into a stalemate situation. We, the free Nations of the West, can act and can seriously improve the situation in Europe, no matter if the other side reciprocates or not.

So, having gone through the topics of stability, military efficiency and arms control we see that the IFD proposal is in fact the military component of an integrated approach to European security policy – or in other words, it is the state-of-the-art hardware for the political goals of NATO, as outlined in the Harmel report.

Annex: SDI stability revised

One cannot speak of stability today, without referring to the SDI program, too. But as I already mentioned, there is much talk about SDI stability but very little substantial research. The following arguments, therefore, have to be regarded as very provisional problems and dangers that are inherent to any conceivable transition from the present Mutual Assured Destruction regime to the desired Mutual Assured Survival regime.

In our model the x-axis defines the interception capability of the United States (IC-us) and the y-axis stands for the interception capability of the Soviet Union (IC-su). In a first step we now can identify three different regions of stability. The first one, the MAS-region, is the one where either side can intercept all attacking war-heads, no matter who is striking first. Then we have two regions of full superiority (FS-us and FS-su). They are characterized by the fact that only one side is able to intercept all attacking war-heads (Total Number of Warheads = TNW) while the other side is not. (See fig. 9).

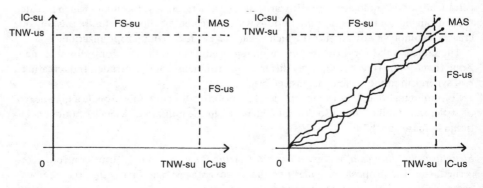

Figure 9   Figure 10

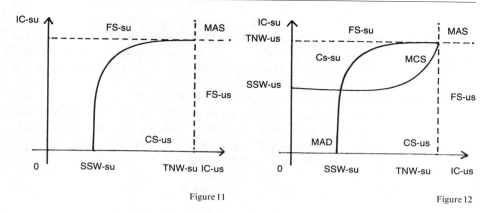

Figure 11   Figure 12

Any transition from the present situation to the MAS-regime can now be described as a path from 0/0 (it is probably no irresponsibility to neglect the Galosh system) into the MAS-region. (See fig. 10). But here we already observe a first dramatic obstacle: most of these pathes cross an FS-region – and that means full superiority for one side. And it is very doubtful that the side that once gained full superiority will not try to keep it, but will allow for a renewed deterioration of its world hegemony. The superior side must not even start a war in order to utilize its superiority, it simply can tell the other side: either you stop any further development of your interception capabilities, and we will start our on-site inspections tomorrow, or we will blow you up. Therefore it seems at least likely, if we look at history, that there will be no transition to the MAS-regime at all, but that the development will come to end in unilateral superiority for one or the other side.

The only way to circumvent this problem is to have a transition path that crosses exactly the intersection point. But in the real world that is most unlikely and it would require the most precise arms control agreements one could imagine. If one side cheats only with ten penetrating war-heads it can gain full superiority. Therefore, we have maximum premia for minimum cheatings – not exactly the environment in which arms control agreements are likely to be reached and kept. But the question how to enter the MAS-regime without crossing a FS region is only one problem. Our prospects deteriorate even more as soon as we start asking what happens during the transition process itself.

Here we face the phenomenon of "conditional superiority" (CS), i. e. a situation in which one is not yet able to handle all the enemy's war-heads but could successfully defend against the enemy's ragged retaliation in case oneself executes a disarming first strike. This region starts at the point where one is able to intercept all those war-heads which one cannot destroy by pre-emption (Second Strike Warheads = SSW). The shape of this region then depends on the interception capability of the other side, too, because the more the other side can intercept of one's pre-emtive strike, the bigger is its retaliatory capability, and therefore one's own required intercept capability. (See fig. 11).

But that is true for both sides, so we get two regions of conditional superiority which are even overlapping. (The reason why the CS-region for the Soviet Union is smaller, is that the United States have a much bigger fraction of sea-based and, therefore, rather survivable systems). (See fig. 12)

These CS-regions are already highly instable because the side which enjoys superiority knows that it can gain a clear victory by starting a war or that it faces annihilation together with the other side if they start the war. So, the superior side must fulfil high ethical standards not to opt for its own security by crushing the other side. Again history gives no reason for optimism. It is hard to imagine, but the MCS-region offers even worse prospects. Here both sides know that victory is possible – but only if they gain the role of the attacker. If instead the opponent attacks first, oneself is annihilated. Such a situation can also be defined as a structural prescription for disaster. It is the paramount of instability.

Now we see rather clear, what is the real problem with SDI. It is not only the technical feasibility, but the fact, that there seems to be no path from the MAD-regime to the MAS-regime which would not cross one or more regions that are characterized by superiority. According to my assessment such a stable transition path simply does not exist. Maybe I am wrong, I do hope so. But we really should press every advocate of SDI to come up with plausible arguments how he could avoid these instabilities.

Final remarks

But let me end our excursion to the SDI problematic with some more optimistic remarks. All what we said until now was immanent SDI-argumentation – and I am sure the proposal can be beaten on its own ground. But as soon as we make some additional considerations we see much better prospects.

(a)   It is simply wrong to believe that a modern industrialized society like the United States could be crushed only by ballistic or cruise missiles. What about small biological and chemical weapons which both superpowers could smuggle in many of the most important urban areas of the other side? The point I want to make is: a modern industrialized society is by far too fragile to be comprehensively protected. Even if we forget about all nuclear weapons, there will remain capabilities for mutual assured destruction for all the foreseeable future. The only way really to protect us would be a totalitarian police state of historically unprecedented dimensions. But in this case it would not even take a totalitarian attacker any longer, we would lose our freedom already by our own preparations to protect it. So, I definitely hope that at least the U.S. House of Representatives and the Senate will understand during the next three to five years that there is no chance for a comprehensive protection whatsoever. The net-result of going ahead with SDI would be only to push the arms race into the even more devastating and uncontrollable direction of hidden B and C weapons. (We would look back to the nuclear age with nostalgia because the weapons of mass destruction were so large and complex that they could be easily controlled.)

(b)   The second intellectual progress I am waiting for in the years to come is the desillusion about the long-term goal. Let's assume that we had the technical capability to create a perfect astrodome. And let's even imagine that the Russians would never have the idea of circumventing it by smuggling alternative means of mass destruction into our countries – even under these completely unrealistic assumptions we would not at all live in the paradise of stability which the SDI-advocates are promising. To the contrary. Today we have a multi-stable situation, meaning that even if there were a break-through in anti-submarine warfare, for example, there would be the other two legs of the triade which guarantee stability. But, if both sides have a perfect astrodome and one side makes a marginal technological progress which allows for the penetration of only ten war-heads – that would immediately create a situation of full superiority. So, instead of being the paradise of stability and the end of the arms race, the MAS-regime would offer maximum incentives for the most marginal technological improvements. Instead of having a multistable equilibrium as today, you would have unprecedented instability and an all-out arms race. Again, I do hope that the House of Representatives and the Senate will understand that even the long-term goal of the SDI-program is not at all attractive but would, compared with the present situation, mean a dramatic deterioration of U.S. security.

(c)   My third reason for hope is a rather practical one. The technological spill-over of the SDI-program is much overestimated today. What can be done with a giga-watt laser in brain surgery? There is no doubt that spending a fraction of the funds directly for civil technology would create much more of a technology push for the United States' economy than the detour of SDI. So, even the technological and economical impact of the SDI-program is negative and thus only strengthens the other competitors, especially Japan and the European Community.

* * *

Each of these three arguments I consider strong enough to stop the SDI-program, not to speak of them together. Therefore, what I expect, is a post SDI hang-over to come during the next three to five years. And that is, paradoxically, the great chance for world peace that is created by the SDI-program: everybody will understand that the preservation of peace is not mainly a technical problem but needs political solutions. I do hope that this hang-over will make us ripe for the necessary paradigm-shift in international politics that leads us from the paradigm of confrontation-oriented power politics to the paradigm of a future-oriented world domestic policy. What Europe should do during the next years is to develop a sound conceptual framework for a second detente. When the post SDI hang-over has come there will be a demand for a new orientation. And I do even believe that the crucial elements of such a new grand strategy for the Western Alliance can be identified already today:

– we should stabilize the military situation in Europe and elsewhere by utilizing modern technology for creating defense-prone environments;

– that makes it no longer necessary to compensate for conventional insufficiencies with nuclear weapons;

– this in turn paves the way for adopting, even unilaterally, a minimum deterrence posture (and 1000 SLBM plus 300 Midgetman plus 300 ALCM would be more than enough);

– and all these military changes should function as a catalyst for the paradigm shift in international relations towards a world domestic policy.

SCIENTIFIC PROGRAMME

Carl Johnson, U.S.A.

Short and Long Term Effects from Nuclear Bomb Detonations

The United States Nuclear Regulatory Commission estimates that long term effects of worldwide fallout from nuclear weapons testing will include 29,000 to 72,000 deaths from cancer (whole body exposure) and 168,000 birth defects, all generations[1]. However, about one-half of the fallout induced by a nuclear bomb will fall back to earth in the first 24 hours as "local fallout". While short-term and more serious long-term effects on local populations downwind from nuclear bomb test sites could be expected, there have been few investigations. The Hiroshima and Nagasaki survivors received direct radiation from a nuclear bomb and little radioactive fallout[2]. The acute effects on these populations were well-documented and late effects are still being recorded[2-4]. There was a peak in leukemia deaths among the survivors in the first five years, followed by a persistent increase in other cancer deaths. The excess cancer death rate increased by 2,4 times in the last study period, 27 to 32 years after, caused by cancer of the esophagus, stomach, colon, lung, breast and urinary tract, lymphoma and multiple myeloma[2]. The number of cases of cancer of thyroid and benign tumors was also larger than expected.

A fifteen megaton hydrogen bomb was detonated at the Bikini Atoll (March 1, 1954) and radioactive fallout arrived at Rongelap 180 kilometers distant in 4–6 hours and at Utirik, 440 kilometers distant, in about 22 hours[5]. The islanders were evacuated within 72 hours[5]. About 90% of those exposed on Rongelap had skin burns and hair loss (175 rads); 78% had

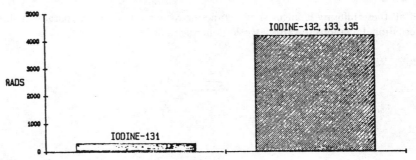

Figure 1:
Radiation Doses to the thyroid of Rongelap islanders from fallout from a thermonuclear bomb test at Bikini Atoll on March 1, 1954

TEST	DATE	HEIGHT (m)	EXPLOSIVE kt	RADIO-ACTIVITY (kg)	FALLOUT (t)
Hiroshima	August 5, 1945	560	12	0.6*	4
Nagasaki	August 9, 1945	560	20	0.9*	4
Grable	May 25, 1953	160	15	0.7	301
Apple II	May 5, 1955	150	29	1.4	972
Boltzman	May 28, 1957	150	12	0.6	225
Met	April 15, 1955	120	22	1.1	936
Nancy	March 24, 1953	90	24	1.3	1277
Harry	May 19, 1953	90	32	1.6	1734
Simon**	April 25, 1953	90	43	2.1	2330
Trinity	July 16, 1945	30	19	0.9*	1500*
Bravo	Feb. 28, 1954	2	15,000		

Table 1

Selected nuclear bomb explosions with yields in kilotons of high explosive; kilograms of radioactivity and tons of fallout, in order of decreasing height above ground at time of detonation. – Source: Hearings before the Subcommittee on Oversight and Investigations, of the Committee on Interstate and Foreign Commerce, U.S. House of Representatives , 96th Congress, First Session (96–129), Washington, D.C. (April 23, May 29 and August 1, 1979).

* Estimated
** Simon contaminated the Troy-Albany, N.Y. area on the following day, resulting in a dose commitment from the ground of gamma radiation alone of 110 mrads (17.2 million nuclear disintegrations per minute per square meter).

superficial skin lesions and 18 % had hair loss at Ailinginae Atoll (75 rads); and no one had skin lesions or hair loss on Utirik (14 rads)[5]. The Rongelap Islanders received a thyroid dose of 300 rads from iodine-131 "but about 4,200 additional rads in iodine-131 equivalents" from the short-lived iodine isotopes (iodine-132, -133 and -135) (Figure 1)[5]. Children received a larger dose, to 2,000 or more rads for a one year old child. Estimated thyroid doses at Utirik ranged from 30 to 90 rads[5]. Primary hypothyroidism and thyroid nodules were first recognized in 1964, about ten years after exposure, and were earlier and more severe in children. About 77 % of Rongelap children younger than ten years at the time required surgery later for benign and malignant thyroid nodules[5].

A 19 kiloton nuclear bomb "Trinity" was detonated on a 30 meter tower at Alamogordo, New Mexico (July 15, 1945), entraining an estimated 1500 tons of radioactive earth in its fallout plume, which travelled principally to the east, exiting the U.S. over the Carolinas (Table 1)[6]. The first population exposed to nuclear fallout was American. Construction of the Nevada Test Site (NTS) began in January, 1951 and nuclear bomb detonations began at that time (Figure 2)[7]. Of 691 detonations there to date, 183 were above ground ("atmospheric") (1951–1962). Nuclear bombs were usually detonated when winds were not blowing toward Las Vegas and Los Angeles. Las Vegas is 140 kilometers from ground zero (GZ) and Los Angeles is 420 kilometers from GZ. At least 87 of the nuclear bombs caused offsite contamination between 1951 and 1958 and 28 laid down a swathe of radioactive fallout over Utah[6]. These 28 bombs had a total force greater than 620 kilotons.

Exact patterns of fallout deposition were unpredictable and could be determined only where there were functioning monitoring devices in local areas. An unpublished University of California/Atomic Energy Commission document reported "a low (fallout) cloud will most likely follow the valleys. In that case, the cloud will probably not disperse the one mile in six assumed" and "with higher winds the greater local turbulence would likely increase local deposition, particularly on reverse slopes". The nuclear bomb "Small Boy" of less than one kiloton was detonated on a tower three meters high (July 14, 1962) and produced a "hot spot" of 100 rads/hr 540 kilometers downwind (48.5 degrees) from GZ in the Orem, Utah

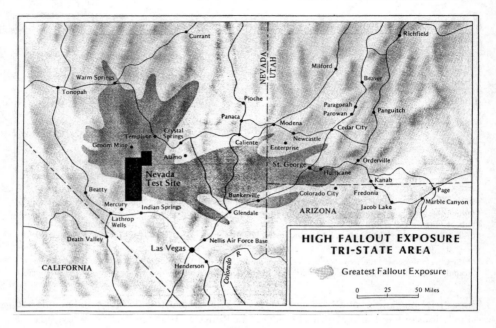

Figure 2
Location of Nevada Test Site and area of high fallout exposure

area, according to a federal report[8]. Within a radius of 8–16 kilometers around this spot the radiation dosage increased by 25 times. Because of the sparse number of monitors, few such areas are detected.

An infinite dose of 100 rads was calculated for an area in Utah on the highway between St. George and Cedar City (228 and 276 kilometers from GZ, respectively), after the detonation of "Harry", and offsite doses of similar magnitude were reported for detonations of "Nancy", "Simon", "Badger", and "Boltzman"[9].

High explosive tests were later made to study the dispersion of plutonium and uranium, measurably contaminating over 250,000 square kilometers, with most contamination occurring in northern Nevada and Utah. The highest offsite plutonium concentration reported was 9.6 picocuries per square centimeter (pCi/cm^2), two orders of magnitude greater than that produced by weapons fallout in nearby states downwind from NTS, and three orders greater for states more distant from NTS[10–12].

After the atmospheric nuclear bomb tests ceased in 1962, radioactive plumes and clouds from at least forty sub-surface nuclear bombs escaped into the atmosphere and traveled beyond site boundaries. Eleven of these further contaminated Utah (1962–1979), including the 100 kt "Sedan" in 1962 and "Coulomniers" in 1977. Official monitoring of fallout was compromised by failure to activate radiation monitoring apparatus during nuclear tests[13].

After a test on May 19, 1953, radiation greater than 300 millirads per hour (mR/hr) was observed "in and out of cars" in St. George. Former Atomic Energy Commission Chairman, Lewis Strauss, noted that "East they got over Pioche and over St. George, which they apparently always plaster"[14]. "Estimates of dosage delivered by radioactive iodine to the thyroid of children in St. George, Utah who were less than 5 years old in 1953 vary between

500 and 2500 rads"[15]. These doses are of the same order of magnitude as those sustained by the Rongelap children who also received 175 rads of whole body radiation[5].

Testimony by officials in a recent federal court trial in Salt Lake City, Utah supported this information[16]. As the pink dust fell, radiation instruments went off scale in city streets and records were later falsified. U.S. Public Health Service agents burned their clothes and showered to decontaminate themselves, but under AEC orders reassured local people that no precautions were needed. Children played outside during periods of peak fallout, pregnant women worked in the gardens and families ate their locally-grown produce, milk and meat contaminated with fallout radionuclides. Public notices were released to convince local residents that there was no hazard, no need for even the simple measures to protect themselves against nuclear fallout.

Farm animals received much higher doses of radiation, and deaths of more than 4,000 sheep in 1953 were associated with the passage of radioactive plumes and clouds. Sheep are more radiosensitive than man, dying after whole-body exposure to 240–300 rads, compared to a lethal dose range of 300–600 rads for man[17]. Foraging animals like sheep "are virtually vacuum cleaners for fallout" deposited on foliage. Dr. Harold Knapp reported fetal lambs had received doses of 20,000–40,000 rads to the thyroid, and sheep had received 1500–6,000 rads to the gastrointestinal tract where external doses were estimated to be only 4 rads[9]. Beta radiation in nuclear fallout may be several orders of magnitude greater than the gamma radiation. Sheep near Cedar City received 38–269 rads of external gamma radiation alone[18].

People living in the high fallout communities complained of a sudden change in health consistent with large and prolonged radiation exposures. Those who were outside as the fallout plumes came through complained of burning of the eyes and skin, of hair loss and changes in hair color, of nausea and diarrhea. A housewife told of the 50 families she knew in her small community[19]. Only four families were free of cancer. One family had 12 miscarriages and seven cancers. She herself developed four types of cancer, dying finally at age 42 of leukemia after surviving 13 surgical operations[20]. A man who grew up in another downwind town in the 1950's was shocked at a high school reunion to learn that none of his nine boyhood friends had survived beyond the age of 28, all dying of cancer or leukemia[20]. Another family reported nine cases of cancer in the family since the testing began[21]. Again, in another small community with a population of 450 people, there were six cases of leukemia after the testing began[20]. In Parowan, a town of 2,000 in Utah, it was reported that 30–40% of the livestockmen and outdoor people had contracted some form of cancer after the testing began. Eighteen people on one street were reported to have contracted cancer, including four teenagers with leukemia who died in 1960[21].

Despite reports of high levels of radiation in Utah and Nevada, in Salt Lake City, Denver and points more distant, there have been few investigations. Important exposures of the Los Angeles population went virtually unnoticed[22]. An increase in leukemia deaths in an area-based study of southwestern Utah (1950–1964) was reported in 1965[23] and corroborated in a follow-up area-based study of leukemia deaths in children 14 years later[24].

About 30 years had passed since the first exposure of people in southwestern Utah to radioactive fallout. There had been external exposures to radioactive gases and particulates in the air, and from contaminated soil, and internal exposures to alpha, beta and gamma radiation emitted by isotopes inhaled or ingested in food and water, and stored in body organs. In this area of Utah many persons milk cows and grow their own produce and meat, and are exposed to resuspended contaminated dust from agricultural activities, in addition to the fallout plumes. Personal air monitors may indicate radionuclide concentrations several orders of magnitude greater than indicated by area monitors, according to the International Commission on Radiological Protection, Publication Nr. 12. However, no such observations were made for the residents of the high fallout area.

Of some 240 longer-lived radionuclides released by the fissioning of uranium and plutonium, there are radioactive isotopes of every trace element and other elements important in human nutrition[12, 25]. Most are cumulative and become concentrated in the food chain[26]. The molecular, cellular and developmental effects of these radionuclides have been poorly studied. This is especially true of long-term effects on human reproduction. Because of the possibility of long-term effects on the residents of the high fallout areas in the United States, an empirical investigation of the incidence of all cancer in Mormons was conducted in communities in southwestern Utah and adjacent parts of Nevada and Arizona.

Methods

Selection of the study group required that religion be considered as a confounding factor. Utah has the lowest cancer incidence of any state, attributed to the lifestyle of members of the Church of Jesus Christ of Latter Day Saints, or Mormons[27]. Utah Mormons (72 % of the population) have a cancer incidence 23 % less than the national average. Utah non-Mormons have a cancer incidence 16 % greater than that of Mormons. Church members are urged to abstain from tobacco, alcohol, coffee, and tea, avoid extra-marital sexual activity, conform to certain family customs and pursue higher education. Furthermore, the Mormon population in Utah seems to have greater stability. The beneficial effects of the Mormon lifestyle were also reported in California. Because of these considerations, the cancer incidence in Mormons in the high fallout area in southwestern Utah[4, 125] was compared with the cancer incidence in all Utah Mormons (population 781,735 in July 1971). This comparison is conservative, since "all Utah Mormons" include the more highly exposed Mormons in southwestern Utah, and all Mormons in Utah received exposure to fallout, though less than the study population.

The incidence of cancer (that is, the recording of cases of cancer as they occur by date of onset) was studied rather than cancer deaths because of serious problems in the use of death data. Death certificates are known to have recording errors. Further, about one-half of all cancer cases do not die of cancer but of some other cause and so are not counted in studies based on death certificates or "mortality data". Persons with cancer may survive for years or decades, and the wide variability of survival periods can further confound death certificate data. A study of long duration will also be affected by the trend toward longer survival periods of persons contracting cancer since cancer therapy has improved greatly over the years. Further, information from mortality studies is delayed for many years because of the survival period. There is insufficient information on death certificates to permit correction for such factors as religion, smoking and occupation. Persons contracting cancer are known to move from rural areas to reside near regional medical centers for care of their disease, and so they are lost to a study of cancer deaths.

In the earlier area-based studies of leukemia deaths in Utah, thousands of persons exposed to fallout left the area to have their cancer elsewhere, but their loss is unrecorded in an area-based study. Many tens of thousands entered the area who had not been exposed to fallout, but who became part of the study population of such area-based studies. This type of confounding is a more serious problem with study periods of long duration. For this reason a specific cohort of Mormons was chosen to be followed forward in time in this investigation of the incidence of all cancer.

Towns with heavy fallout exposure included the St. George area, Parowan, Paragonah and Kanab, Utah; Fredonia, Arizona; and Bunkerville, Nevada. A high risk population was defined as those Mormon families or persons listed in 1951 telephone directories in these towns who were still listed in the 1962 directories and who could be located in 1981. This roster was checked against church records. "Family" included all persons related by blood or marriage in each household including children born to these families during the period 1951–1962 and those who died in 1962 or after. The period 1951–1962 was chosen to define the study population because they received their major exposures to fallout in this time. However, the choice of 1962 as the end of this period is not intended to imply that fallout-induced neoplastic diseases of short latency such as leukemia could not have appeared before 1962.

Volunteers were trained in the smaller towns to carry out a survey of this population between April and December 1981. In St. George, the larger population there required that trained volunteers be augmented with persons hired for this purpose. The survey form was completed by the surveyor and the head of the family and included an inquiry about church membership. Other questions concerned effects felt immediately after fallout (skin burns, eye burns, hair loss, change in hair coloration, nausea and diarrhea), smoking experience, employment and diagnosis of cancer. Those who had a medical diagnosis of cancer were asked to supply information for a supplementary form: diagnosis, date of diagnosis, date of death if deceased, hospital where last treated, name of physician, and current address of the cancer patient or surviving relative. Cancer is a major life-threatening event that will be remembered by a person and by members of the family. The treating physician will inform the patient and/or the family of the diagnosis of the disease. A recent study reports that diagnosis in life correlated with death certificate cause and with unpublished data from the Utah Cancer Registry more than 90% of the time[24].

Information was also requested about spontaneous abortions, stillbirths and malformations, to be included in later reports. When necessary, telephone interviews were conducted. Telephone companies reported that about 2.5% of residents in this area did not have telephones. About 40% of the defined population could not be located in 1981. Loss of this portion of the population was thought to have a conservative effect on the data, i.e. to be more likely to understate any association present. Mormons who leave the church have been found to have higher cancer incidence rates. Less than 1% refused to cooperate. The year of diagnosis of cancer could not be recalled with certainty in about 18% of cases occurring between 1958 and 1980. These were assigned at random to periods 1958–1966, 1967 through 1971, or 1972–1980. Skin cancers not melanoma and benign tumors were not considered, although a high rate of the former was reported and an increase of benign tumors could be expected in a population with radiation effects[3].

The 1951 cohort at high risk was identified by 1962 telephone directories and availability for this study in 1981. The population was too small to follow annual cancer incidence rates. Cancer incidence data for all Utah Mormons were available for a nine year period (1967 through 1975) and two nine-year periods were selected for study of the cohort. Assuming that substantial radiation doses from fallout might have been sustained by the major part of the study population by 1953, an increase in leukemia incidence could be evident by 1958, and so an early period (1958–1966) was selected. Other cancers of more radiosensitive organs have longer latency periods, and the latest nine-year period available for study was selected (1972–1980). This design provided internal as well as external controls. Cancer incidence in the early period may be compared with cancer incidence in the later period, as well as with the control population (all Utah Mormons). Cancer incidence in the early period for the subgroup complaining of fallout effects may be compared with that of the subgroup in the later period, with the study population as a whole, and with all Utah Mormons. Further - more, the ratios of cancer of more radiosensitive organs to all other cancer may be compared between the study and control populations.

Cancer incidence in the study population, the fallout effects group and the comparison group (all Utah Mormons) were each adjusted by the direct method, with the 1970 U.S. white population as a standard. Expected case numbers were calculated in each category by the average annual age-adjusted cancer incidence rate for Utah Mormons divided by the average annual age-adjusted cancer incidence rate for the study population, times the number of cases of cancer in the study population. Although the hypothesis to be evaluated is that there may be an excess of cancer of the more radiosensitive organs in a population exposed to radioactive fallout, a more conservative two-tailed test of significance was selected[28].

Cancer registry data could not be used in this cohort study (1951–1980) because the registry was not established until 1966, fifteen years after the testing of nuclear weapons began. The registry could not be used to establish a specific high-risk cohort in 1951 and follow it through time. Registry data include large populations that have immigrated into the area in recent years with smaller, more recent exposures of fallout and insufficient time to permit any latent cancers to appear. Many early residents would have left the area and had cancer develop elsewhere.

MALE (× 1,000)	AGE						
	0–14	15–44	45–54	55–64	65–74	75 +	Total
Utah Mormons 1971	122.1	175.6	32.2	26.2	14.5	10.0	380.6
Southwestern Utah, 1962	593	955	250	167	110	56	2,131
Fallout-effects group, 1962	15	47	35	20	14	3	134

FEMALE (× 1,000)	AGE						
	0–14	15–44	45–54	55–64	65–74	75 +	Total
Utah Mormons 1971	123.4	181.0	35.1	28.5	19.6	13.3	400.9
Southwestern Utah, 1962	541	937	246	145	87	38	1,994
Fallout-effects group, 1962	18	43	25	13	6	0	105

Table 2

Age distribution by sex in 1962 of members of Latter Day Saints families compared with the age distribution of Utah Mormons in 1971. – Latter Day Saints families consisting of those listed in both 1951 and 1962 directories of communities in south-western Utah. Some of the families could not be located in this 1981 survey and are not included in this table or in the survey of cancer incidence. The study area includes St. George, Kanab, Parowan, Paragonah, Gunlock, Hurricane, Ivins, Leeds, Santa Clara, Washington, and Veyo, Utah; Fredonia, AZ; and Bunkerville NV. In some cases, respondents were uncertain of exact age of some family members, and these were placed in the broad age categories above by position in the familiy. Age distribution of Utah Mormons from Lyon J. L., Gardner J. M., West D. W.: Cancer Incidence in Mormons and non-Mormons in Utah during 1967–1975 (JNCI 1980; 65: 1055).

TYPE (b)	CLASS (International Classification of Diseases No., Rev. 8)	RATE Utah Mormons 1967–75 (c)	HIGH-FALLOUT AREA (e) 1958–1966			HIGH-FALLOUT AREA (e) 1972–1980			FALLOUT-EFFECTS GROUP 1958–1966			FALLOUT-EFFECTS GROUP 1972–1980		
			Rate	Observed (d)	Expected (d)	Rate	Observed	Expected	Rate	Observed	Expected	Rate	Observed	Expected
A + B	All sites (140–207)	228	354	118**	76.0	377	170**	102.8	1,322	31**	5.3	1,064	33**	7.1
A	Lung, respiratory (162, 160, 163)	16.5	20.0	7	5.8	12.8	6	7.7	21	1	0.8	22	1	0.8
	Upper GI tract (141–150)	4.4	11.4	4	1.5	8.9	4**	2.0	...	0**	...	26	1**	0.2
	Stomach (151)	7.0	34.5	9**	1.8	12.5	5**	2.8	138	3**	0.2	36	2**	0.4
	Colon (153)	19.7	14.0	5**	7.0	34.1	14**	8.1	66	2**	0.6	87	3**	0.7
	Breast (174)	31.9	29.1	8**	8.8	60.7	27**	14.2	96	2**	0.7	347	8**	0.7
	Thyroid (193)	3.7	16.3	6**	1.4	30.8	14**	1.7	...	0**	...	26	1**	0.1
	Leukemia	7.9	41.7	19**	3.6	28.1	12**	3.4	307	9**	0.2	70	1	0.1
	Lymphoma	10.7	10.1	4	4.2	20.7	10	5.2	48	1		199	5**	0.3
	TOTAL	101.8	177.1	62**	34.1	208.6	92**	45.1	676	18**	2.7	813	22**	3.3
B	Melanoma (172)	5.7	9.0	3	1.9	19.5	9**	2.6	85	2**	0.1	13	1	0.4
	Brain, CNS (191, 192)	4.7	15.0	5*	1.6	8.2	4	2.3	131	2**	0.1	70	1	0.1
	Bone, joint (170)	0.8	8.3	3**	0.3	10?1	5**	0.4	...	0	...	...	0	0.1
	Other	115.0	144.6	45	35.8	130.6	60	52.8	430	9**	2.4	168	9	6.2
	TOTAL	126.2	176.9	56*	39.6	168.4	78	58.1	646	13**	2.6	251	11	6.9
A/B		0.807	1.001	...	...	1.239	...	...	1.046	...	...	3.239	...	...
$\left(\dfrac{A/B (subpopul.)}{A/B (Utah) -1}\right) \times 100$ ...			+ 24 %	...	...	+ 53.5 %	...	...	+ 29.6 %	...	...	+ 301.4 %	...	...

Table 3
Cancer incidence in a mormon population residing in Southwestern Utah exposed to radioactive fallout compared with cancer incidence for all Utah Mormons (a). – For explanation, see legend Table 4.

Results

The age and sex distribution of the study population in 1962 is compared with that for all Utah Mormons in 1971 (Table 2). Although 59.3 % of women in the study group were of childbearing age in 1962 or the decade before (1,183/1,994) compared with 53.8 % for all Mormon women in Utah, only 27.5 % of the study population are children, compared with 31 % for the state, an apparent deficit in the fallout area for 1948–1962 of about 20 %.

Average annual age-adjusted cancer incidence rates in Mormons in southwestern Utah in 1958–1966 and in 1972–1980 are compared with all Utah Mormons in 1967–1975 (Table 3).

The ratio of cancers of the more radiosensitive organs (identified in studies of Japanese survivors exposed to whole body radiation) to other cancer in the study population in 1958–1966 is compared with that ratio in the same population in 1972–1980 and to that for all Utah Mormons in 1967–1975. In addition, cancer of certain other organs thought to be sensitive to radiation are considered separately. These are cancer of bone, brain and malignant melanoma.

There was an excess of 42 cases (p = .01)* of all cancer in the early period (1958–1966) and an excess of 67 cases (p = .01)* in the later period (1972–1980) (Figure 3). The excess cases reflected principally an increase in the incidence of cancer of more radiosensitive organs.

Most notably, there were 19 cases of leukemia (p = .01)* (3.6 expected) in the early period, and this persisted into the later period, with 12 cases observed (p = .01)* (3.4 expected) (Figure 4). There was a borderline increase in lymphoma in 1972–1980 (10/5.2, p = .04). An early excess of cancer of thyroid (6/1.4, p = .01)* was followed by a sharp increase later (14/1.7, p = .01)* (Figure 5). The incidence of cancer of the breast was unremarkable in 1958–1966 (8/8.8) but a sharp increase was noted in 1972–1980 (27/14.2, p = .01)*.

There was a persistent excess of cancer of the upper gastrointestinal tract (4/1.5 and 4/2.0) that was not significant (Figure 6). The incidence of cancer of the stomach showed an early increase (9/1.8, p = .01)* that persisted later (5/2.8). An excess number of cases of cancer of colon occured later (14/8.1, p = .037). No increase in incidence of cancer of the lung was observed (Figure 7). There were more brain tumors, cancer of bone and melanoma than was expected in the early period (5/1.6, p = .05; 3/0.3, p = .01*; and 3/1.9, respectively) and this persisted (4/2.3; 5/0.4, p = .01*; and 9/2.6, p = .01*, respectively).

Differences in the incidence of cancer by sex are given in Table 4. Although both sexes had an excess of leukemia, males had more cases. Males did not have an excess of lymphoma, as females did later (6/1.9, p = .05). Females had a larger excess of cancer of the thyroid (6/1.0, [p = .01]* early, and 9/1.3, [p = .01]* later) than males, who had no cases in the early study period but had an excess (5/0.4, p = .01)* later. Females had a greater excess of stomach cancer early (6/0.6, p = .01)* that did not persist later (2/.09). There were an excess number of cases of cancer of the colon later among the females (11/3.7, p = .01)* but not among males. Both males and females had an excess of melanoma later (4/1.2, p = .34; and 5/1.4, p = .05, respectively). Females had more brain tumors (3/0.7, p = .34 early; and 3/1.1, later) and males had more bone cancer (2/0.2 [p = .05] early and 4/0.3 [p = .05] later). Females had two more cases of bone cancer than expected throughout the study periods.

Comment

There was an excess of 109 cases of cancer (288 cases observed [p = .01]*, 179 expected) in this southwestern Utah population of 4,125 during the period of study in this report (1958 through 1966 and 1972–1980), a total of about 72,000 person-years. Leukemia was preponderant early and persisted later, compatible with a prolonged period of exposure to radioactive fallout during 1951–1962 and afterward from 11 of the 40 underground nuclear bomb tests that escaped into the atmosphere (1962–1979). This contrasts with the peak of leukemia deaths at about five years among the Hiroshima-Nagasaki survivors after their one exposure to direct radiation in 1945. There was an increase of lymphoma in females of marginal significance (p = .05) in 1972–1980. There was only one case identified as multiple

---

* significant (28)

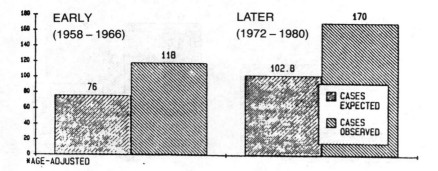

Figure 3
Incidence of all cancer in a Mormon population residing in Southwestern Utah exposed to radioactive fallout compared
to all Utah Mormons: comparison of an early period (1958–1966) to a later period (1972–1980)

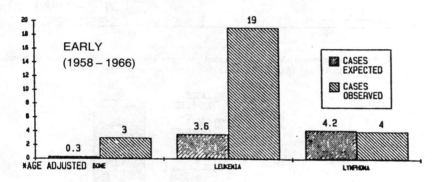

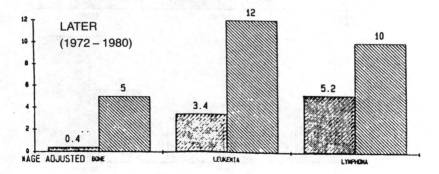

Figure 4
Incidence of leukemia, lymphoma and cancer of bone in a Mormon population residing in Southwestern Utah exposed
to radioactive fallout compared to all Utah Mormons: early (1958–1966) / later (1972–1980)

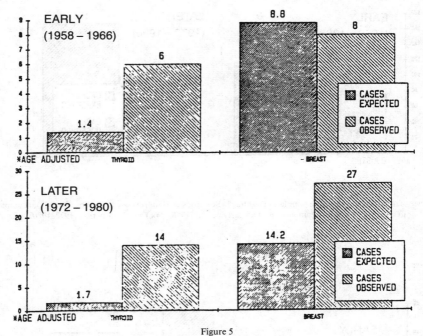

Figure 5
Incidence of thyroid and breast cancer in a Mormon population residing in Southwestern Utah exposed to radioactive
fallout compared to all Utah Mormons: early (1958–1966) / later (1972–1980)

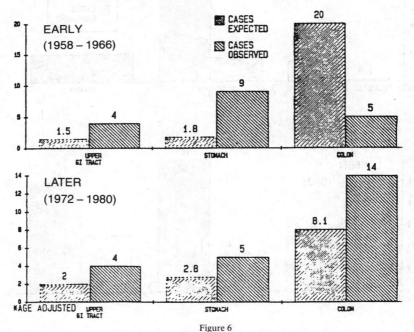

Figure 6
Incidence of cancer of the gastrointestinal tract in Mormon population residing in Southwestern Utah exposed to radioactive fallout compared to all Utah Mormons: early (1958–1966) / later (1972–1980)

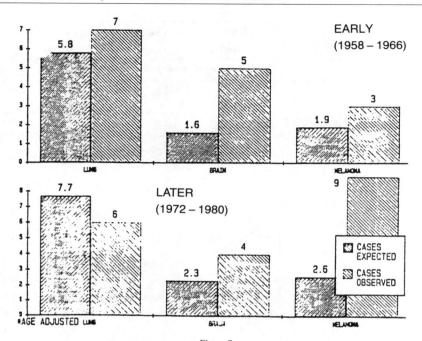

Figure 7
Incidence of melanoma and cancer of lung and brain in a Mormon population residing in Southwestern Utah exposed to radioactive fallout compared to all Utah Mormons: early (1958–1966) / later (1972–1980)

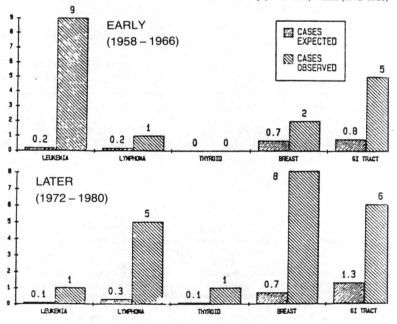

Figure 8
Incidence of leukemia, lymphoma, cancer of thyroid, breast and gastrointestinal tract in a cohort of Mormons with history of acute fallout effects in SW. Utah compared with all Utah Mormons: early (1958–1966) / later (1972–1980)

TYPE (b)	CLASS (International Classification of Diseases No., Rev. 8)	RATE Male Utah Mormons 1967–75 (c)	MALE MORMONS IN THE HIGH-FALLOUT AREA (e)					
			1958–1966			1972–1980		
			Rate	Observed (d)	Expected (d)	Rate	Observed	Expected
A + B	All sites (140–207)	253	294	18	45.6	318	73	58.1
A	Lung, respiratory (162, 160, 163)	28.3	27.4	5	5.2	20.3	6	7.0
	Upper GI tract (141–150)	6.9	23.4	4	1.2	13.9	3	1.5
	Stomach (151)	9.4	16.7	3	1.7	14.0	3	2.0
	Colon (153)	21.0	10.1	2	4.2	13.2	3	4.8
	Breast (174)	0.7	0	0	. . .	0	. . .	. .
	Thyroid (193)	1.9	0	0	. . .	22.6	4	0.4
	Leukemia	9.4	43.1	12**	2.6	37.0	8**	2.0
	Lymphoma	13.8	15.6	3	2.6	16.2	4	3.4
	TOTAL	91.4	136.3	29	17.5	137.2	31	21.1
B	Melanoma (172)	5.6	12.8	2	0.9	18.9	4	1.2
	Brain, CNS (191, 192)	4.9	11.7	5	0.8	3.7	1	1.3
	Bone, joint (170)	1.1	11.3	2*	0.2	16.6	4**	0.3
	Other	150.0	121.9	18	22.1	141.6	33	35.0
	TOTAL	161.6	157.7	24*	24	180.8	42	37.8
A/B		0.566	0.864	. . .	. . .	0.759	. . .	. . .
$\left(\dfrac{A/B\,(\text{subpopul.})}{A/B\,(\text{Utah})\,-1}\right) \times 100$		. . .	+ 52.6 %	. . .	. . .	+ 34.1 %	. . .	. . .

Table 4

Age-adjusted cancer incidence by sex in a Mormon population residing in southwestern Utah exposed to radioactive fallout compared with cancer incidence for all Utah Mormons (a)

(a) Radioactive fallout occuring from atmospheric detonations of nuclear weapons at the Nevada Test Site between 1951 and 1962. Data have been adjusted for age and sex; age adjustment for the three populations by the direct method with the 1970 U.S. white population as the standard (JNCI 1980; 65: 1169).

(b) A = cancer of more radiosensitive organs   B = other cancer

"A" classes of cancer (of the more radiosensitive organs) are those fouund in excess among the survivors of the nuclear bomb detonations at Hiroshima and Nagasaki; leukemia, lymphoma, cancer of thyroid, lung, esophagus (included here are other cancers of the upper gastrointestinal [GI] tract 141–150), stomach, colon, and breast.

(c) All rates are average annual age-adjusted incidence of cancer per 100,000.

TYPE (b)	CLASS (International Classification of Diseases No., Rev. 8)	RATE Female Utah Mormons 1967–75 (c)	FEMALE MORMONS IN THE HIGH-FALLOUT AREA (e)					
			1958–1966			1972–1980		
			Rate	Observed (d)	Expected (d)	Rate	Observed	Expected
A + B	All sites (140–207)	205	410	65**	32.5	432	97**	46.0
A	Lung, respiratory (162, 160, 163)	5.3	2.8	2	0.6	5.6	1	0.9
	Upper GI tract (141–150)	2.1	. . .	0	. . .	4.1	1	0.5
	Stomach (151)	4.8	51.5	6**	0.6	11.0	2	0.9
	Colon (153)	18.4	17.7	3	3.1	54.0	11**	3.7
	Breast (174)	61.6	56.9	8	8.6	118.5	27**	14.0
	Thyroid (193)	5.5	31.9	6**	1.0	38.5	9**	1.3
	Leukemia	6.4	40.4	7**	1.1	19.6	4	1.3
	Lymphoma	7.8	4.9	1	1.6	25.0	6**	1.9
	TOTAL	111.9	216.1	33**	16.6	276.3	61**	24.5
B	Melanoma (172)	5.8	5.3	1	1.1	20.1	5*	1.4
	Brain, CNS (191, 192)	4.5	18.2	3	0.7	12.4	3	1.1
	Bone, joint (170)	0.5	5.5	1*	0.1	4.0	1	0.1
	Other	82.3	164.9	27**	13.5	119.2	27	18.6
	TOTAL	93.1	193.9	32**	15.4	155.7	36**	21.2
A/B		1.202	1.114	. . .	. . .	1.775	. . .	. . .
$\left(\dfrac{\text{A/B (subpopul.)}}{\text{A/B (Utah)}} -1\right) \times 100$		. . .	× 7.3 %	. . .	. . .	+ 47.7 %	. . .	. . .

(d) The number of cases observed is compared with the number expected. Expected case numbers were calculated by the following approach: the number of cases in each class times the average annual age-adjusted cancer incidence rate for Utah Mormons divided by the average age-adjusted cancer incidence rate for the study population (Environ Res 1981; 25: 86).

(e) High-fallout areas consist of the St. George area, Parowan, Paragonah, and Kanab, Utah; Fredonia, AZ; and Bunkerville, NV. For some cases dates of diagnosis of cancer were not recalled with certainty. These were allocated to the broad time periods indicated in the table above. Those not clearly falling in a time period were assigned to a time period in the sequence in which they appeared, with conservative effect, i.e. assigned equally to the early (1958 through 1966), interim (1967 through 1971), and intermediate (1972 through 1980) time periods. The interim period was not studied because the design is to compare an early period with a later period.

 * Indicates significant at p = .05 (Two-tailed test)
** Indicates significant at p = .01

myeloma, in a fifteen-year-old boy. One person was reported to have had aplastic anemia (woman aged 23 years). Another was reported to have polycythemia (man, aged 73 years) and one death was attributed to radiation sickness. Major classes of cancer (chiefly breast, colon and lung) in the early period (1958–1966) had virtually the same incidence as that for all Utah Mormons, consistent with the longer latency period for these cancers.

Cancer of the thyroid was prominent in the exposed group. A significant ($p = .01$) excess was noted early in females and a notable excess was found in both sexes in 1972–1980. Many others in the study group complained of thyroid problems.

There was not an excess of cancer of the breast until the later period (1972–1980). There was a slight excess of cancer of the upper gastrointestinal tract, stomach, and colon occurring later in females. The incidence of lung cancer was not higher in the study population than for all Utah Mormons. The low prevalence of smoking in this group would decrease retention of inhaled radioactive particulates of respiratory size. Moreover, most Utah Mormons live in urban areas with greater air pollution than in southwestern Utah, and so lung cancer rates here similar to those for all Utah Mormons may actually represent a local increase. Considering the excess incidence of other classes of cancer associated with radiation in this area, a larger study population may demonstrate an excess incidence of lung cancer.

A significant ($p = .01$) excess of melanoma was found in the later period (1972–1980) about equally in both males and females. An excess incidence of melanoma has been reported in plutonium workers, and a possible mechanism for induction of melanoma by actinides has been described[29, 30]. Tests of plutonium dispersion devices at the NTS, as well as the detonation of weapons with plutonium components, have scattered plutonium over a wide area and this may be related to the excess cases of melanoma found here. Isotopes of plutonium, uranium and other transuranics can contribute as much as 40% of the total radioactivity of the nuclear bomb debris in a period from 20 hours to two weeks after detonation[31]. Plutonium workers have been reported to have a proportional morbidity ratio of brain tumors (gliomas) eight times greater than expected[29] and a significant ($p = .05$) excess of brain tumors were found in the early period of this investigation, slightly more in males than females. Females had a slight excess of brain tumors in the later period. Throughout both periods there were five more brain tumors than expected. Plutonium and other actinides are known to be able to induce bone cancer, and a significant ($p = .01$) excess of this cancer was found both in early and later periods. Although females had a slight excess of bone cancer, males had the most cases, and a larger number of cases in the later period than earlier. In total, there were eight cases of bone cancer, and 0.7 cases were expected.

Plutonium is a potent carcinogen, and produced a cancer incidence rate of 114.5% in one animal study, with a mean latency period of about one year (many animals had two different types of cancer)[32]. Plutonium is known to induce leukemia and cancer of bone, lung, soft tissue, mammary gland and kidney, and must be considered as an important component of the fallout radionuclides deposited in the body[32, 33]. The radiotoxicity of plutonium in man is indicated by a study of plutonium workers, which found that plutonium body burdens of 400 to 4,000 picocuries were associated with an average increase in the rate of chromosomal aberrations of 33%, compared to other workers with less than 400 picocuries[34]. Plutonium is found in all organs of plutonium workers[29].

The lower range of whole body radiation associated with fallout signs and symptoms is about 50 rads, and the subgroup of 134 men and 105 women with a history of fallout effects probably had much larger doses of radiation than did the rest. That this is true is supported by the high age-adjusted incidence of cancer found for this group. In general, this group had excess numbers of cancer in the classes found to be in excess for the group as a whole, but proportionately greater. Persons exposed to large doses of carcinogens have a large cancer risk[35].

Comparison of the ratio of cases of cancer known to be in excess for the survivors of Hiroshima and Nagasaki with all other classes of cancer can help to confirm that the excess incidence of cancer in a population exposed to radiation is actually related to this exposure[30]. In this investigation this comparison provides assurance that the excess incidence of cancer is actually caused by exposures to radioactive fallout. No other explanations of these effects were discovered in the investigation, i.e., smoking, occupational history, or industrial point sources of carcinogens.

The temporal trend of excess incidence of cancer seems to be consistent with the experience of the Japanese survivors, considering that the exposures to the southwestern Utah group began six years later and were sustained during a twelve year period and, to a lesser extent, during a subsequent eighteen year period. The Japanese survivors have had a sudden acceleration of the increase in the cancer death rate by about 2.4 times in the period 1972–1976, that could have been anticipated by an estimate cited in a National Research Council report of seven radiation-induced cancer deaths in an exposed population for each radiation-induced leukemia death (relative risk model)[3, 36]. It seems probable that the largest increment of cancer in Utah is yet to come. Additional study periods (1981–1990, 1991–2000, 2001–2010) are necessary to evaluate this later phase of cancer induction. Further, there is a need for more basic scientific research into the molecular, cellular and developmental effects of the multitude of radioisotopes to which people have been exposed. These include the radioactive isotopes of all trace elements and other elements important in nutrition. Many of these are concentrated in the food chain and retained in body organs for long periods of time.

The Nuclear Regulatory Commission's memorandum on casualties expected from worldwide fallout should lead us to anticipate greater effects in local populations exposed to much higher concentrations of radionuclides from fallout in the environment. The exposed cohort of Mormon populations in southwestern Utah and adjacent parts of Arizona and Nevada have certain statistical advantages for such investigations, because the cancer incidence data there may be compared with that for all Mormons in Utah, permitting comparisons of cancer incidence free from some of the variables that must be dealt with elsewhere. Allowance should be made for cancer induced by fallout for all Utah Mormons (although less than in southwestern Utah). A burden of radiation-induced cancer throughout the state can be expected, because an excess of childhood leukemia has been reported for the entire state, and this observation is an early warning of other classes of radiation-induced cancer to appear later.

The basic design of this investigation is strong, providing for internal and external controls, selection of a specific cohort of exposed individuals, and use of cancer incidence data rather than death certificates. The household survey of communities known to be exposed allows consideration of religion, occupation and use of tobacco, alcohol, caffeine and other factors, in addition to age, sex and race. This design should be most useful in assessing population effects downwind of other nuclear bomb detonation sites and nuclear facilities such as those at Hanford, Savannah River, Three Mile Island, Windscale and Chernobyl.

BIBLIOGRAPHY

1. Alexander R. E.: Written communication, U.S. Nuclear Regulatory Commission, Office of Standards Development; Washington, D.C., (Feb. 26, 1979).
2. Beebe G. W.: The atomic bomb survivors and the problem of low-dose radiation effects. American Journal of Epidemiology 1981; 114: 761–783.
3. Kato H., Schull W. J.: Life span Study Report 9: I. Cancer Mortality Among A-Bomb Survivors, 1950–1978. Hiroshima, Radiation Effects Research Foundation, 1980, pp. 12–80.
4. Ishikawa E., Swain D. L.: Hiroshima and Nagasaki: The Physical, Medical, and Social Effects of the Atomic Bombings. Basic Books New York, 1979.
5. Larsen F. R., Conard R. A., Knudsen K. D., et al: Thyroid hypofunction after exposure to fallout from a hydrogen bomb explosion. JAMA 1982; 247: 1571–1575.
6. Colter M. W., Moghissi A.A.: Three decades of nuclear testing. Health Phys 1977; 33: 55–71.
7. Final Environmental Impact Statement, Nevada Test Site, Nye County, Nevada, ERDA–1551. Government Printing Office, 1977.
8. Compilation of Local Fallout From Test Detonations, 1945–1962, extracted from Dasa 1251, vol 1, in Continental U.S. Tests, report 1251-1 Ex. US Defense Nuclear Agency, 1979.
9. Knapp H. A.: Oral Communication, U.S. Defense Communication Agency, Washington, D.C. (Nov. 5, 1982).
10. A picocurie of a radioactive Isotope of an element is a quantity sufficient to produce 2.2 nuclear disintegrations per minute. Each disintegration releases ionizing radiation. There are eight important isotopes of plutonium, but plutonium-239 is the predominant isotope and has a half-life of 24,390 years.
11. Johnson C. J., Tidball R. R., Severson R. C.: Plutonium hazard in respirable dust on the surface of soil. Science 1976; 193: 488.
12. Kocher, D.C.: Dose rate conversion factors on calculations for 240 radionuclides of potential importance in routine releases from nuclear fuel cycle facilities. Health Phys 1980; 38: 543–621.
13. Anon: Deseret News, Salt Lake City, Utah, P. 8–B (Dec. 4, 1979).
14. Health Effects of Low Level Radiation, official minutes of the Atomic Energy Commission meeting No. 1062, Feb. 25, 1955. Government Printing Office, vol 1, 1979, serial 96–41.
15. May M. E.: Written Communication, Lawrence Radiation Laboratory, Berkeley, California (Nov. 29, 1965).
16. Jenkins B.: Memorandum Opinion, Irene Allen et al, Plaintiffs vs. (Department of Energy) U.S.A., Defendant. C79-0515-J, U.S. District Court, District of Utah, Salt Lake City, Utah (May 10, 1984).
17. Anon.: Hearings before the Subcommittee on Oversight and Investigations of the Committee on Interstate and Foreign Commerce, U.S. House of Representatives, 96th Congress, First Session (96-029), Washington, D.C. (April 23, May 24, August 1, 1979).
18. Smith R. J.: Atom bomb tests leave infamous legacy. Science 1981; 218: 266–269.
19. Gregerson G.: The National Catholic Reporter (April 23, 1982).
20. Ball H.: Justice Downwind: America's Atomic Testing Program in the 1950's Oxford University Press; New York, Oxford (1986).
21. Anon.: Transcript of the Special Town Meeting conducted by U.S. Senator Orrin Hatch in St. George, Utah (April 17, 1979).
22. Public Health Service Transcription of the Nov. 10, 1958, Meeting of the National Advisory Committee on Radiation. Public Health Service, 1958.
23. Weiss E. S.: Unpublished manuscript on leukemia mortality in Utah, U.S. Public Health Service, Atlanta, Georgia (1965).
24. Lyon J. L., Klauber M. R., Gardner J. W., et al: Childhood leukemias associated with fallout from nuclear testing. New England Journal of Medicine 1979; 300: 394–402.
25. Radiological Surveillance Studies at the Oyster Creek BWR Nuclear Generating Station. Cincinnati, US Environmental Protection Agency, Office of Radiation Programs, Eastern Environmental Facility, Radiochemistry and Nuclear Engineering Branch, 1976.
26. Franke B.M., Kruger E., Steinhilber-Schwab B., et al: Radiation Exposure to the Public From Radioactive Emissions of Nuclear Power Stations: Critical Analysis of the Official Regulatory Guides. Heidelberg, West Germany, Institut für Energie und Umweltforschung, translated into English by the US Nuclear Regulatory Commission, 1980.
27. Lyon J. L., Gardner J. W., West D. D.: Cancer incidence in Mormons and non-Mormons in Utah during 1967–1975. JNCI 1980; 65: 1055–1061.
28. Bailar J. C., Ederer F.: Significance factors for the ratio of a Poisson variable to its expectation. Biometrics 1964; 20: 639–643.
29. Johnson C. J.: An Investigation of brain cancer, melanoma, and other neoplasms in employees of the Rocky Flats Nuclear Weapons Plant in Jefferson County, Colorado. Read before the annual meeting of the American Public Health Association, Los Angeles, Nov. 3, 1981.
30. Johnson C. J.: Cancer incidence in an area contaminated with radionuclides near a nuclear installation. Ambio 1981; 10: 176–182, 1982; 11: 377–378, 1983; 12: 280–281.

31. Feld B. T.: Mechanics of fallout. In The Final Epidemic by Adams R. and Cullen S., Eds.; Educ. Foundation for Nuclear Science, Chicago, IL 60637 (1981).

32. Sanders C.L., Jackson T. A.: Induction of mesothelioma and sarcoma from "hot spots" of plutonium-239 dioxide activity. Health Physics 22: 755–759 (1972).

33. Svovoda V., Sedlak A., Bubenikov A. D., Klener V.: Biological effects of bone-seeking alpha emitters with respect to the risk of internal contamination in man. Czech Med. 5: 80–89 (1982).

34. Brandom W., Bloom A., Saccomanno G., Archer P., Archer V., Bistline R., Lilienfeld A.: Somatic Cell Chromosome and Sputum Cell Cytology Changes in Humans Exposed to 222 radon and 239 plutonium (Progress Report, Department of Energy Contract Nr. E (2902)–3639. Rocky Flats Plant, Golden, CO (1976).

35. Hogstedt C., Aringer L., Gustavsson A.: Epidemiologic support for ethylene oxide as a cancer-causing agent. JAMA 255: 1575–1578 (1986).

36. U.S. National Research Council: The Effects on Populations of Exposure to Low Levels of Ionizing Radiation. Committee on the Biological Effects of Ionizing Radiation, National Academy of Science, Washington, D.C. (1980).

This study was supported by a grant from the Nuclear Radiation Research Foundation. The survey received valuable support from many citizens in the high fallout area; Philip H. Williams, M. S., trained and coordinated the persons carrying out the survey; Bruce Ellis, M. S., assisted with the statistical tests; Frederick A. Johnson assisted with the data; Kathryn Van Deusen, M. A., Mina F. Coffey and Colleen Kozel helped prepare the manuscript.

SCIENTIFIC PROGRAMME

Gordon Thompson, Australia

Nuclear Power and the Threat of Nuclear War

Present and Anticipated Future Use of Nuclear Power

Table 1 shows the status of nuclear power plants, both in operation and under construction, for all countries, as of the end of 1984. It is difficult to accurately project the use of nuclear power in the future. Indeed, the nuclear industry has consistently over-estimated future use. Table 2 shows a medium-term estimate (up to the year 2000) made by the International Atomic Energy Agency (IAEA).

Connexions between Nuclear Power and Nuclear War

There are two distinct types of connexion between nuclear power plants and the threat of nuclear war. First, nuclear power plants and other nuclear fuel cycle facilities (such as re-processing) plants could release radioactivity into the environment as a result of the direct or indirect effects of nuclear detonations. Such releases might or might not be intended by the attacking country. Second, nuclear power programmes could, either inadvertently or deliberately, lead to the growth of nuclear arsenals. This could be true for existing nuclear-weapon powers and for countries not currently in possession of nuclear arsenals.

Vulnerability of Nuclear Power Facilities in Wartime

Nuclear power plants can release radioactivity to the environment through:

- Detonation of a nuclear weapon at close range, causing evaporation or pulverisation of the reactor core, with entrainment of radioactivity into the weapon cloud.
- Longer-range nuclear weapon detonation (or attack by conventional weapons), leading to damage to reactor coolant and containment systems, with the release of radioactivity following core melting.
- Damage to electrical power and control systems from nuclear-weapon-induced electro-magnetic pulse, leading to a core melt accident.
- Loss of external electricity supply following damage to the electrical grid, potentially leading to a core melt accident.

	In operation		Under construction		Total operating experience (to end 1984)
	No. of units	Total MWe	No. of units	Total MWe	Years – Months
Argentina	2	935	1	692	12 – 7
Belgium	6	3 473	2	2 012	56 – 9
Brazil	1	1 632	2	1 245	2 – 9
Bulgaria	4	1 632	2	1 906	26 – 6
Canada	16	9 521	7	5 630	135 – 7
China			1	300	
Cuba			1	4 408	
Czechoslovakia	3	1 194	10	4 394	18 – 0
Finland	4	2 310			23 – 4
France	41	32 993	23	28 255	297 – 0
German Dem. Rep.	5	1 694	6	3 432	52 – 5
Germany, Fed. Rep.	19	16 133	7	6 881	196 – 3
Hungary	2	805	2	820	2 – 4
India	5	1 020	5	1 100	49 – 3
Italy	3	1 286	3	1 999	66 – 10
Japan	31	21 751	10	9 186	254 – 2
Korea, Republic of	3	1 790	6	5 622	11 – 5
Mexico			2	1 308	
Netherlands	2	508			27 – 9
Pakistan	1	125			13 – 3
Philippines			1	620	
Poland			2	880	
Romania			3	1 980	
South Africa	1	921	1	921	0 – 9
Spain	7	4 690	3	2 807	49 – 5
Sweden	10	7 535	2	2 100	87 – 7
Switzerland	5	2 882			48 – 10
United Kingdom	37	9 564	5	3 130	657 – 1
U.S.A.	85	68 867	33	37 093	870 – 9
U.S.S.R.	46	22 997	39	36 575	483 – 8
Yugoslavia	1	632			3 – 3
World total*	345	219 715	179	162 303	3 467 – 10

Table 1

Status of nuclear power plants worldwide, at the end of 1984.

Table based on data available to IAEA as of 11 March 1985. During 1984, construction was cancelled for 10 reactors and suspended for another 10. – Source: International Atomic Energy Agency Bulletin, Spring 1985

* In Taiwan, China, there were five units with a total capacity of 4,011 MWe in operation and one unit with a total capacity of 907 MWe under construction. Total operating experience was 20 years and 2 months at the end of 1984.

Other nuclear fuel cycle facilities, especially reprocessing plants, can release radioactivity in similar ways. Figure 1 shows that a nuclear power plant contains more long-lived radioactivity than is produced by detonation of a large nuclear weapon. Thus releases from a nuclear power facility can lead to long-term land contamination much more severe than that from a nuclear weapon detonation, as shown by Figure 2.

Potential Contribution of Nuclear Power to Growth of Nuclear Arsenals

Historically, nuclear power programs have been closely related to nuclear-weapon programs. Present trends in the application of nuclear power will make it easier for additional countries to acquire nuclear arsenals, and for present nuclear-weapon states to expand their arsenals, should they choose to do so. Notably, current plans call for the commercial separ-

REGION	1985		1990		2000	
	GWe	% of elec.	GWe	% of elec.	GWe	% of elec.
North America	93 – 101	17	124 – 126	20	130 – 160	20
Western Europe	89 – 94	28	121 – 125	35	130 – 190	40
Eastern Europe*	34 – 38	11	72 – 89	16	140 – 240	28
Industrialized Pacific	23 – 25	17	28 – 32	17	40 – 60	25
Asia	10 – 12	5	14 – 17	6	30 – 45	8
Latin America	1.5	2	6 – 7	6	30 – 45	8
Africa and Middle East	1.8	3	1.8 – 2.7	2	5 – 15	6
World total	252 – 273	15	366 – 398	18	485 – 725	20
Industrialized countries	236 – 253	18	335 – 361	23	420 – 620	25
Developing countries**						
in CPE Europe	4 – 6	9	10 – 12	15	25 – 35	18
Others	12 – 14	3	21 – 25	4	40 – 70	6
Total	16 – 20	4	31 – 37	6	65 – 105	8

Table 2

IAEA forecast of nuclear power capacity worldwide, and of nuclear share of total electricity

The lower values for operating capacities are estimated by assuming that no planned reactors not yet under construction will achieve grid connection during this period and that half of the capacity scheduled to achieve grid connection in a given year will slip to the next year. The high case values are estimated by assuming that all reactors under construction and all planned reactors will achieve grid connection exactly as currently scheduled. Capacity figures for Eastern European countries in 1990 are IAEA estimates based on project information, which is, however, not complete. The official target for Eastern Europe is about 100 GWe in 1990. – Source: International Atomic Energy Bulletin, December 1984.

 * Including Asian part of U.S.S.R.
** Developing countries in the Centrally Planned Economies (CPE) in Europe: Bulgaria, Czechoslovakia, Hungary, Poland and Romania. – Other developing countries: Argentina, Brazil, People's Republic of China, Cuba, India, Republic of Korea, Mexico, Pakistan, Philippines and Yugoslavia. This entry also includes figures for nuclear power in Taiwan, China.

ation of plutonium in quantities greater than in present nuclear weapon inventories, as shown by Figure 3. Yet, commercial separation of plutonium is occuring in advance of an economically demonstrable need. Figure 4 shows that uranium reserves are ample to meet the needs of the nuclear industry until well into the next century.

What Can Be Done?

The risk of wartime releases from nuclear power facilities can be reduced by:

– Limiting the size of nuclear power programs.
– Limiting the amount of radioactive material which can be released by any one accident (e. g., by not allowing storange of spent fuel adjacent to reactors.
– Adopting safer designs for all future construction, and improving present facilities where possible.
– Pursuing international agreements not to attack nuclear power facilities.

The potential contribution of nuclear energy to nuclear arms production can be reduced by:

– Deferring commercial separation of plutonium, at least until it is economically favourable.

- Strengthening international agreements and institutions which promote separation of nuclear power and nuclear weapon programs.
- Limiting the size of nuclear power programs.

This discussion cannot take place without consideration of world energy needs. However, it should be noted that these needs can be met through a combination of:

- More efficient use of all energy forms.
- Increased use of solar-derived energy.
- Nuclear power on a limited scale.

Figure 5 provides an illustrative scenario showing the respective contributions of these elements. It will be noted that the use of energy in the industrialised countries declines, without any loss in standards of living. Less developed countries enjoy substantial increases in their standard of living.

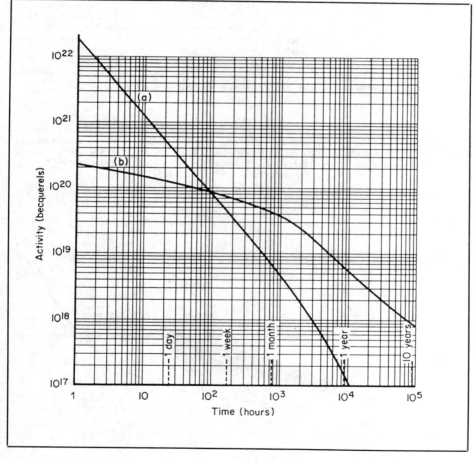

Figure 1

Decay of radioactivity from: (a) A 1 Mt bomb, (b) A 1 GWe reactor. – Source: Nuclear Radiation in Warfare, SIPRI, 1981

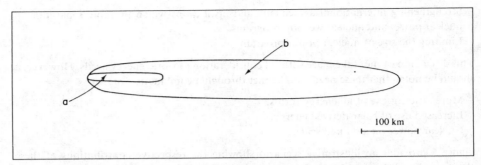

Countours of 1 Gy fall-out dose in one year, starting one month after the detonation of
(a) a 1 Mt bomb, (b) a 1 Mt on a 1 GWe nuclear reactor. (1 Gy = 100 rad)

DOSE* (Gy)	AREA (km²)		
	1 Mt bomb	1 Mt bomb on 1 GWe reactor	1 Mt bomb on a storage tank
1	2 000	34 000	61 000
0.5	4 000	46 000	87 000
0.1	25 000	122 000	164 000

Areas affected by detonation of nuclear weapons alone and on nuclear power facilities

Figure 2

Areas incurring given radiation dose after detonation of a nuclear weapon, alone or on nuclear power facilities.
Doses from inhalation or ingestion of radioactivity are not considered here. It is assumed that about one-fifth of the
reactor's radioactive inventory is released. A surface detonation of the bomb is assumed. The radioactive waste storage
tank mentioned in the table is similar to one at the former West Valley reprocessing plant in the U.S.
Source: Nuclear Radiation in Warfare, SIPRI, 1981

* Dose accumulated in one year starting one month after detonation

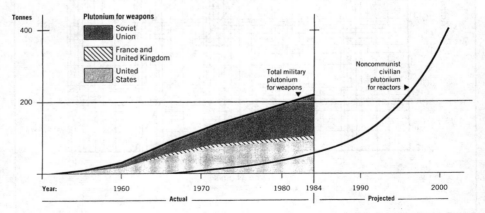

Figure 3
Supplies of separated plutonium worldwide, actual and projected.
Source: Bulletin of the Atomic Scientists, March 1986

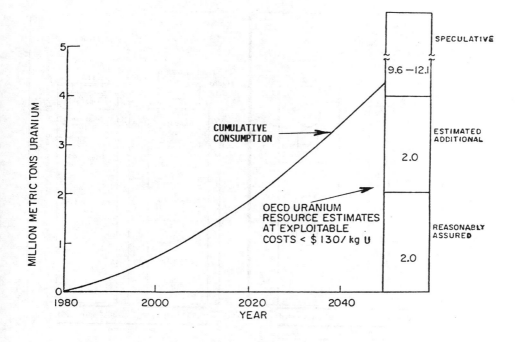

Figure 4
Estimated cumulative worldwide uranium consumption, and uranium resource estimates, excluding CPE countries.
Up to 2000, nuclear power capacity projections by the U.S. Department of Energy are used; after that it is assumed that
nuclear capacity will continue to grow at the projected 1995–2000 rate of 8 GWe/year. Total nuclear capacity under this
scenario is 364 GWe in 2000 and 764 GWe in 2050.
Source: D. Albright and H. Feiveson, Plutonium Recycle and the Problem of Nuclear Proliferation, Center for Energy
and Environmental Studies, Princeton University, Princeton, NJ (forthcoming)

Figure 3, note:
The amount of plutonium in the nuclear weapons stockpiles of the United States, the Soviet Union, France, and the
United Kingdom at the beginning of 1984, compared with the growing stockpile of separated civilian plutonium in noncommunist countries intended as fuel in civilian power reactors. Most, but not all, of the weapons plutonium is actually
in weapons. Estimates of the inventories are based primarily on the following data:
    United States: historical data on the heat output of Department of Energy plutonium-production reactors; *Soviet-
Union:* estimate of the releases of krypton-85 to the atmosphere from Soviet reprocessing, assuming the same proportionality between this krypton-85 release and plutonium production as in the United States; *France and th e United
Kingdom:* the capacity of their production reactors. The historical estimates of the civilian inventories of plutonium are
based on public information; the projections are based on the capacities of the major commercial reprocessing facilities
operating, under construction, and planned, in noncommunist countries. The uncertainties in the estimates of the 1984
stockpiles are all on the order of 15 percent.
    Source: Frank von Hippel, David H. Albright, and Barbara G. Levi, Quantities of Fissile Materials in the U.S. and
Soviet Nuclear Weapons Stockpiles; David H. Albright, World Inventories of Plutonium (Princeton, NJ: Princeton
University, Center for Energy and Environmental Studies, forthcoming).

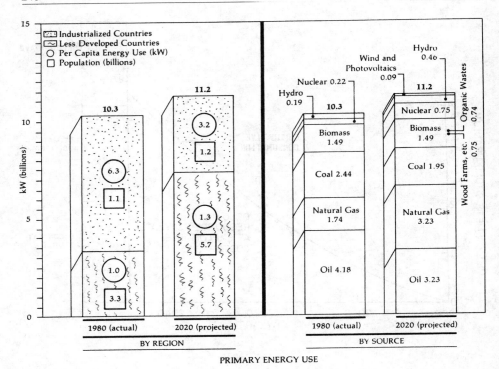

PRIMARY ENERGY USE

Figure 5
A potential world energy future based on efficient energy use.
Source: Goldemberg, Johansson, Reddy and Williams, "An End-Use Oriented Global Energy Strategy", Annual
Review of Energy, 1985

SCIENTIFIC PROGRAMME

John Andrews, Australia

Nuclear Testing in the Pacific: The Biological Consequences

An Introduction to Nuclear Testing in the Pacific

Pacific peoples have more reason than most to fear the consequences of nuclear war: they have been treated as the guinea-pigs in weapons testing from the very start of the nuclear age. The main radiation dose from short lived radionuclides come from the Pacific nuclear tests of the United States, Britain and France, and from long-lived radionuclides mainly from Northern hemispheric nuclear testing, which accounts for up to eighty per cent of long-lived fission products. These sources of fallout lead to a total effective dose commitment given as 3.1m Sv. Specific fallout products will be given for each radionuclide described, the most important being Carbon 14[1]. The main shortcomings in dose estimation are, that most information is for countries in the temperate zone with few data from tropical and subtropical regions, few data on trophospheric fallout, and none at all for iodine 131 in milk supplies up to 1958.

The American Pacific Nuclear Tests

The Marshall Islands are part of the United Nations Trust Territory of the Pacific, administered by the United States since 1945, and including the Marshall, Mariana and Caroline (which includes Palau) Island group. Despite the 30,000 inhabitants, the U.S. chose the Marshall Islands for atmospheric nuclear testing. Between 1946 and 1958, sixty-six thermonuclear bombs were exploded on Bikini and Enewetak Atolls, the inhabitants having been resettled beforehand on Kwajalein[5].

Discussion is confined to the 1954 "Bravo", 15 megaton nuclear test at Bikini Atoll which produced the heaviest radioactive fallout ever recorded. This involved 238 local inhabitants on three atolls, 28 American servicemen and 23 Japanese fishermen. The highest estimated dose to 64 people and 3 in utero was on Rongelap Atoll at 1.9 Gy over a two day period prior to evacuation.[2] Nausea occured in 66 per cent and vomiting and diarrhoea in 10 per cent in this group on Rongelap, many of whom developed epilation, "beta burns", and depression of peripheral blood elements to about half normal values.[3] The most widespread late effects

Atoll	Number	Nodules	Percent	Carcinoma	Percent	Hypo function	Percent	Total Lesions
Rongelap	67	23	34.3	4	5.4	7	10.4	50.1 %*
Ailignae	19	6	31.8	0		1	5.3	36.8 %
Utirik	164	17	10.4	3	1.8	0		12.2 %
Matcheo								
Controls	600	35	5.1	5	0.8	2	0.3	7.0 %

* 88 % in those < 10 years when irradiated

Estimated Maximum Whole Body and Thyroid Dose in Gy**

Atoll	Total Number	in utero	Whole Body Dose	Thyroid Dose*
Rongelap	67	3	$\cong 1.9$	$\cong 18$
Ailignae	19	1	$\cong 1.1$	$\cong 4.5$
Utirik	164	8	$\cong 0.11$	$\cong 0.95$

* Highest in those < 10 years when irradiated.   ** 1 C.Gy = 1 RAD, 1 GY = 100 RAD

Thyroid abnormalities in Marshall Islanders to 1981

of fallout exposure to the Marshallese population have been related to radiation injury of the thyroid gland[4]. Risk of developing thyroid cancer in children is 2.5 cases per million persons per C.Gy, per year. The number of cases of hypothyroidism (TSH $\geq 6 \mu$U/ml.) was greater than would be expected on the basis of ^{131}I therapy for thyrotoxicosis and is probably due to the more energetic short-lived radionuclides of iodine e.g. ^{132}I, ^{133}I, ^{134}I etc.. No thyroid lesions attributed to fallout appeared before 1963[6], and before 1953 the importance of radioiodine in fallout was not fully appreciated.

Recommendations   The continual close monitoring of the exposed population is essential, and adequate medical and social care should be given to the victims of these tests and to those people displaced from their homes and Islands.

The British Nuclear Tests in Australia

By mid 1950 the British Government realized its atomic bomb program was sufficiently advanced that a device would be ready for testing in mid 1952. The U.S. McMahon act meant that the U.S. testing sites would not be available to the U.K. Government, so British eyes turned to Australia. Thus on October 3rd 1952 a third nation entered the nuclear club, the first nuclear breakout from the superpowers. The main testing ground was in Central Australia at Maralinga, an Aboriginal word that means "field of thunder". In the second test in 1956 fallout covered most of Northern Australia and the fallout from the third 1956 test was complicated by a secondary wind shear which resulted in a very wide fallout pattern. The peoples at risk were those at the test sites, the general population and the Aboriginals who were still largely nomadic, despite the assurance of the Prime Minister of the time who said that there would be "No danger from radioactivity whatever, to the health of the people or animals in the Commonwealth". However, people who had worked at the sites subsequently became concerned at the apparently large numbers of their colleagues dying from various cancers and there were increasingly persistent stories of Aborigines who had been killed or contaminated. More and more veterans came forward to tell their stories and in 1984 the Federal Labour Government, then in power, established a Royal Commission on the subject of the tests. It concluded that although it was unable to quantify increased cancer risks, it was probable that cancers which otherwise would not have occurred have been caused in the Australian population and that exposure to radiation increased the risk of cancer amongst "nuclear veterans".

The Commission reviewed a South Australian Government survey of Aborigines which recorded 30 cancers including 2 of the thyroid and 2 leukaemias, higher than would be expected statistically, and also noted the distress and deaths amongst Aboriginals related to their removal from traditional lands and resettlement at Yalata Mission amongst other places. During the commission another serious problem emerged concerning the more than 600 "minor trials" which involved nearly 25 kg of plutonium as well as uranium and beryllium. Plutonium now represents the major residual problem, with a half-life of 24,400 years and a maximum body burden of less than 0.1 g, with over 25,000 fragments widely scattered in the area and plutonium contaminated material buried in a number of waste pits. The commission recommended clean up of the major contaminated areas.

Recommendation   This forum strongly endorses the recommendations of the Australian Royal Commission into British nuclear weapons tests, that the test sites be decontaminated to enable the area to be returned to the traditional Aboriginal owners.

The French Pacific Nuclear Tests

Since initiating the French Pacific test program in 1963, successive French Governments have reassured Pacific peoples and the International community that there would be absolutely no harmful effects. Between 1966 and 1974, 41 atmospheric tests took place with 39 of these on Moruroa Atoll, and from 1975 underground testing began and has continued ever since. It is from 1966 that the official publication of health statistics ceased, although in 1983 the French embassy in Canberra issued a statement accompanied by some statistical information in response to a protest from the Australian Government. The statement claimed low levels of radioactivity on Moruroa and in the waters of French Polynesia, and that the incidence of cancer is lower than in some countries, such as Australia and New Zealand, with no increase in tumours of radiosensitive organs. These statements have been seriously questioned. It is claimed that there has been gross radiological pollution on the Atoll including plutonium and that the number of cancer cases is incomplete because they show only the numbers from the Government Hospital and one Private hospital in Papeete. Beta activity in air sampling in 1974 is given as 1460 mBq/m^3 in Papeete compared to 3 mBq/m^3 in Auckland[7] (37 mBq = 1mCi) at the time of the last atmospheric tests.

Over 75 underground tests have taken place, all but the first two on Moruroa, a low narrow reef around a 30 × 10 km lagoon, easily washed over by sea in the event of a cyclone, of which there have been several. During one of these it has been admitted that plutonium and other radioactive waste has washed into the lagoon.

Finally after many requests the French Government invited a small group of scientists from New Zealand, Australia and Papua New Guinea to visit Moruroa and Tahiti for twelve days. No physician was included in the party. The objectives were to investigate, and report on, possible radioactive contamination on Moruroa, effects on the structural integrity and hydrology of the Atoll, and health statistics assessment of French Polynesia. This took place in October/November 1983 and the report was published in 1984[8]. The mission tended to support the French claims that the tests have presented no hazards thus far, but pointed out that some desirable objectives could not be met due to constraints imposed upon the mission. The report fails to provide estimates for likely risks and consequences if testing continues[9] and has left many questions unanswered[10].

Recommendations This forum supports the resolution tabled by Mrs. Piermont et al. in the European Parliament in March 1986[11] on the sending of an independent International Commission of experts, including relevant medical specialists, to French Polynesia. However, the most important public health measure is to stop nuclear testing in the Pacific.

Ciguatera in the Pacific

Ciguatera, the commonest type of ichthyosarcotoxism, or marine food fish poisoning, is a major public health problem for Pacific peoples. The clearly demonstrable links between this important non-ionizing radiation related disease and nuclear explosions have previously received only scanty attention. The importance of ciguatera derives from three factors:

- the high level of morbidity and occasional mortality it causes;
- its impact on the life and nutrition of traditional peoples for whom fishing is way of life and fish the major source of protein;
- its effect on the development of local fishing industries – virtually prohibiting commercial fishing in affected areas (WHO, 1981).

Ciguatera is caused by toxins produced by a unicellular plankton (Gambierdiscus toxicus) which is ingested by coral reef fish, the toxins thereby being concentrated up the trophic levels of the marine food chain (Gillespie, 1986). The disease is polymorphous, being characterized by variable combinations of constitutional, gastrointestinal, neurological and cardiovascular manifestations. The typical pattern is of an acute syndrome of vomiting, abdominal pain and diarrhoea, accompanied by neuromuscular, particularly sensory, disturbances. Muscular weakness sometimes necessitating assisted ventilation, along with bradydysrhythmias, hypotension and myocardial depression may also occur. The diagnosis is a clinical one and therapy entirely symptomatic and supportive (Sutherland, 1983).

The most striking etiological factor in outbreaks of Ciguatera is disturbance of coral ecology, which may be natural or human in origin (WHO 1981, SPC 1981). Specific ciguatera outbreaks were described, e. g. in Hao Atoll in French Polynesia, where a massive outbreak followed the construction of a staging base for the French nuclear explosion programme (Bagnis 1969, Banner 1974, Danielsson and Danielsson 1986); in the Gambier Islands near Moruroa Atoll (SPC 1981); and in the Marshall Islands following the U.S. test explosion programme there (Banner 1974, Randall 1980).

Official incidence statistics were presented (WHO 1981, SPC 1981 and 1985, Bagnis 1985), but these reflect only a small fraction of the affected population. In some outbreaks half the local population has been affected in one year, and it is estimated that 5–20 per cent of South Pacific populations may be affected by the chronic sensitivity to any fish which may follow an attack of ciguatera (WHO 1981).

The low mortality of the disease is in contrast to the morbidity it causes, which may be severe and produce long-term disability (Bagnis 1982).

The link between ciguatera and nuclear test explosions in the Pacific is both direct e. g. via physical disruption to atolls; and indirect, related to the ecologically damaging effects of extensive and technologically sophisticated military infra-structures. These effects impinge both on fragile island and coral reef ecosystems, and on the human populations they support. It was noted that these military activities have been and still are carried out in the name of natives far removed from the affected regions.

Nuclear colonialism is but the latest in a long series of ravages that Pacific peoples have suffered at the hands of "metropolitan" powers. In the Pacific basin, as in the case of British nuclear tests in Australia, nuclear test explosions exact a very real cost in lives and health even if a nuclear conflagration never occurs.

Recommendations

(1) On medical criteria alone the cessation of nuclear test explosions is clearly indicated and long overdue.

(2) This forum supports the sending of an independent, international commission of experts, including relevant medical specialists, to French Polynesia to evaluate the risks to health posed by the continued French nuclear explosion program; as proposed in the European Parliament and as repeatedly requested by the French Polynesian Territorial Assembly since 1981.

BIBLIOGRAPHY

1. Unslear. United Nations. 1982.
2. Brookhaven National Laboratory. 1982. BNL 51761.
3. Brookhaven National Laboratory. 1980. BNL 51261.
4. Late Radiation effects in Marshall Islanders exposed to fallout 28 years ago. R. A. Conard in Radiation Carcinogenesis. Epidemiology and Biological Significance. Ed. J. D. Boice & J. R. Fraumeni. Raven press N.Y. 1984 pp 57–81.
5. A test of the model based on experience in Marshall Islanders exposed to mixed types of irradiation. From NCRA report No. 80. 1985.
6. The effects of early fallout. S. Glasstone & P. J. Dolan in The effects of nuclear weapons. 3rd ED 1977. U.S. Depts. of Defense & Energy. pp 594–603.
7. AMBIO. B. Danielsson. 1984. Vol. 13. No. 5–6 pp 336–341.
8. Report of a New Zealand, Australian and Papua New Guinea Scientific Mission to Moruroa Atoll. 1984. Ministry of Foreign Affairs. Wellington.
9. M. Tomezak. Marine Studies Centre. Un. of Sydney. 1984.
10. J. Jasperse. SANA/Greenpeace. Auckland. 1984.
11. European Parliament. Doc. B 2-1657/85/rev. 1986. Piermont et al.

Ciguatera.

Bagnis R. (1969) Naissance et développement d'une flambée de ciguatera dans un atoll des Tuamotu. Revue des corps de Santé 10 (6): 783–795.
Bagnis R. (1982) Poisoning from Eating Fish. Medicine International 420–423.
Bagnis R. (1985) Epidemiology of ciguatera in French Polynesia from 1960 to 1984 in Gabrie C. and Salval B. eds. Proceedings of the Fifth International Coral Reef Congress, Tahiti 27 May to 1 June 1985, Vol. 4 Antenne Museum-Ephe: Moorea, 583 pp.

Banner A. H. (1974) The Biological origin and Transmission of ciguatera, in Humm H. J. and Lane C. E., eds.,
    Bioactive Compounds from the Sea, pp. 150–36, Marcel Dekker Inc. New York.
Danielsson B. and Danielsson M.-T. (1986) Poisoned Reign: French nuclear colonialism in the Pacific. Penguin Books,
    Ringwood, Hammondsworth, New York, Auckland 323 pp.
Gillespie N. C. (1986) Ciguatera Fish poisoning in Australia in poisonous animals and plants of Australia, Queensland
    Museum, in press.
Randall J. E. (1980) A survey of ciguatera at Enewetak and Bikini, Marshall Islands, with notes on the systematics and
    food habits of ciguatoxic fishes. Fish. Bull. 78 (2): 201–49.
South Pacific Commission (1981) Expert Committee on Ciguatera Suva, Fiji, 26 Feb. 1981 report South Pacific
    Commission, Noumea, New Caledonia, 26 pp.
South Pacific Commission (1985) File data.
Sutherland S. K. (1983) Fish Poisonous to Eat, in Sutherland. S. K. Australian Animal Toxins. The creatures, their
    toxins and care of the poisoned patient. p 453–468 Oxford University Press, Melbourne, 504 pp.
World Health Organization Regional Office for the Western Pacific (1981). Final Report: Working Group on Public
    Health Aspects of Marine Food Fish Poisoning, Suva, Fiji, 23–25 Feb. 1981
Regional Office for the Western Pacific of the World Health Organization, Manila, Philippines 69 pp.

* * *

This lecture resulted from a discussion held between J. T. Andrews (An Introduction to Nuclear Testing in the Pacific; The American Pacific Nuclear Tests; The French Pacific Nuclear Tests), F. P. J. Robotham (The British Nuclear Tests in Australia), and T. A. Ruff (Ciguatera in the Pacific).

SCIENTIFIC PROGRAMME

Peter Starlinger, Federal Republic of Germany

Biological weapons

T he regrettable trend to use every aspect of scientific knowledge for the development of weapons systems has not stopped short of biological research. Too well is it known that many living organisms can cause harmful diseases of man or of animals and plants. Scientists and the military have not refrained from an investigation, how these pathogens could be converted into weapons. They plan to use their knowledge in order to inflict disease rather than to prevent or to cure it.

On the other hand, there are scientists who have actively participated and played a leading role in the attempt to prevent and stop these disastrous developments. Particularly the well-known U.S. molecular biologist Matthew Meselson has played a leading role in this endeavour that led to one of the first international arms control treaties which not only limit the use of biological weapons, but rather forbid their development. This is the Biological Weapons Convention of 1972.

In the following, I shall try to give a brief overview of this dark field of biological research. I shall also address new developments in biological knowledge that may lead to a circumvention of existing treaties and must be stopped right at the beginning.

What are biological weapons?

For the biologist or for the practicing physician, this question is easily answered. Any living creature capable of and destined to harm man or its living environment is a biological weapon, if used for this sinister purpose. The question of definitions may be slightly harder to answer for the lawyer or for the philosopher and some of these questions have a real bearing on arms control.

It is obvious that bacteria, the causative agents of many infectious diseases, can be used for biological weapons. Any textbook contains a more or less comprehensive list of them, that need not be repeated here. Are all bacteria equally well suited to be used as weapons? The answer is no. Several requirements have to be fulfilled, before a bacterium can play this role. The bacteria must not be too sensitive to the environment, to extreme temperatures or to drying, if they are too reach their target, an adversary population. The agents causing venereal disease are typically not suited for weapons, because they are so sensitive that they do not live very long and are transmitted only by intimate body contact. On the other hand, spore-forming bacteria might well be suited. Among them, Bacillus anthracis may serve as an example. It causes severe, very often lethal disease and its spores are very persistent. During World War II, the British army prepared for bacteriological warfare, in order to be capable to retaliate, should the German army use such weapons. The British carried out limited experiments on the small island Gruinard off the Scottish coast and were so successful that the island is still off-limits to civilians, because the remaining anthrax spores cannot be neglected. Only recently has it been discussed to clear this up in a final operation and to return the island to civilian uses. The persistence of the causative agent has several aspects. The bacteria or their spores must be capable of storage for extended periods of time. If their biological activities are changing from month to month, the effects of the weapons will not be exactly predictable. If the spores had to be replaced at frequent intervals, the operation will become expensive and potentially unsafe.

Once used, the bacteria must be distributed over a wide range. It may not be necessary to discuss details here, but it is fairly obvious that a dissemination of these bacteria by aerosol or similar means puts a severe stress on them.

Once applied, these bacteria will be quite persistent, as exemplified by the experiment on Gruinard island. Now, however, the persistence can become a problem. If a war is over and enemy territory occupied, no endless epidemic is desired. Even if one's own troops are pro-tected by vaccination, an epidemic among the population of the occupied territory may not be desirable. And can it be assured that the vaccinated soldiers do not carry bacteria or their spores into their home territories? Will this necessitate the vaccination of whole popula-tions? All these questions have to be addressed and show that the use of a biological weapon is more complicated than just the finding of a dangerous infectious disease in a textbook.

Every physician knows that many bacterial diseases are mediated by a toxin that is either secreted into the environment or liberated upon lysis of the bacteria. Severe disease symptoms can be caused by the isolated toxin. It has been a matter of concern whether toxins should be incorporated among biological weapons, or whether they should be classified as chemical weapons. From a humanitarian point, this distinction is meaningless. Both biological and chemical weapons should be banned and the incorporation into either chapter should be a matter of convenience. In the present situation, however, the distinction does have a meaning. Biological weapons are regulated by a convention that forbids not only their use but even their deployment and their development, as will be discussed below. Chemical weapons are also banned, but to a much lesser degree. Under these circumstances, the incorporation of bacterial toxin among biological weapons ensures a greater degree of protection from their weapons use and is therefore preferable. At present, the toxins are indeed subsumed under biological weapons.

Next to bacteria, viruses rank highly among the military research establishment. The fatal disease of yellow fever, the eradication of which has become one of the triumphs of modern preventive medicine could be quoted as an example that shows how criminal it would be to reintroduce such a disease again. Many other viruses could be quoted, but this can presently be left to a specialist.

Likewise a matter of the specialist is it that not only bacteria and viruses, but other living organisms including protozoa and fungi have been considered as potential weapons.

It is important to note that biological weapons have been developed not only against man. Research has been applied to develop plant or animal pathogens to inflict damage to an adversary's agriculture.

Potential Uses of Biological Weapons

If one can believe the open literature in the field, biological weapons are not seriously considered for the battlefield. Their effects are too slow and too unpredictable and there are too many other very effective weapons. Therefore the military has not been particularly attracted to this use.

It is a different matter, whether such weapons should be used deep in the enemy's territory, in order to cause epidemics and by this to weaken the ability to resist war actions brought about by other weapons. We should not take this possibility too lightly. If we think of major war between the great powers, we cannot avoid thinking about nuclear weapons. Many of us are convinced that their use would lead to immediate disaster. We should not forget, however, that more recently, the discussion of protracted war, even with the use of nuclear weapons, has begun to play a role in the strategic debate, at least in the West. In such a war, biological weapons could be used.

We should also not forget that wars are possible and are being fought between non-nuclear states, some of which do not have the enormous financial resources for their military that are presently spent by the great powers. For them, biological weapons might become attractive, as they are relatively cheap and need relatively less sophisticated facilities for their production.

Weapons can be used in a war. This is not their only use, however. It is conceivable that such weapons could be used by covert action against a hostile population or its government short of real war. Allegations of this type have several times been made, though they never have been proven.

This brings to mind the possibility that covert action cannot only be taken by governments, though the latter have the best capabilities for it. Biological weapons might also be used by terrorists, either in the desperate wish to inflict damage, or at least in blackmailing attempts.

All of these considerations should show that biological weapons, though probably not of the global danger brought by nuclear bombs, should not be taken lightly and should be prevented to every degree possible.

Have Biological Weapons Been Used in History?

There are anecdotal reports dating back long time. It is told that the plague epidemics raging through Europe in the 14th century was started during the siege of a Tartar city on the Crimea by the Genoese, who were purposely infected by the Tartars who threw the corpses of the victims of a plague epidemic within the city into the enemies quarters. It is also told that smallpox was deliberately spread among American Indians during their wars with their British occupiers. The truth of these reports is hard to verify.

Much better known are events during World War II. The experiment by the British army on Gruinard island that fortunately did not lead to any practical application has been reported above. More sinister were the experiments carried out by the Japanese army during the Chinese-Japanese war. The Japanese have experimented on prisoners of war who were infected with various agents and were eventually killed. Several thousand soldiers, most of them Chinese, have been murdered that way. Most of the scientists and physicians involved in these experiments have never been punished, because they became exempt of persecution when they were employed by the U.S. army for the development of the biological warfare capabilities of the latter.

It is known that the U.S. army after World War II had an active biological weapons project going on. This research was done in Ford Detrick in Maryland. It was reported that six antipersonal weapons were developed as well as two weapons consisting of fungi directed against major crop plants. The British also have continued their weapons development. It is not known whether the Soviet Union has engaged in similar activities. Allegations of this kind have always been denied by this state, but it has been more difficult to assess the validity of this statement due to the less open society and press system in this country.

Legal Constraints on B-weapons

As early as 1925, biological weapons were banned along with chemical weapons by the so-called Geneva protocol. This protocol forbids use, but not development and deployment. Many states became part of this protocol, with one notable exception: the United States. Due to legal complications not pertaining to biological weapons but other parts of the protocol, the U.S. Senate never ratified it.

It was as late as 1969 that President Nixon was convinced by his then Secretary of State Henry Kissinger to renounce the use of B-weapons by the United States unilaterally and to declare that stockpiles of such weapons could be destroyed. This development was partly helped by the lucky coincidence that Professor Meselson, a well-known molecular biologist of Harvard University and a foremost fighter against biological weapons happened to know Henry Kissinger from the time when the latter was still a Harvard Professor. The declaration by President Nixon, soon followed by its likewise unilateral inclusion of bacterial toxin into the bacterial weapons paved the way that led to the signing of the Biological Weapons Convention of 1972, in which the parties undertake to "never ... develop, produce or stockpile ..." these weapons.

There is, however, a qualifying statement which says that the above constraint applied only to actions "that have no justification for prophylactic, protective or other peaceful purposes". This latter clause has been and still is a cause of debate. It is often interpreted as allowing research into defensive measures, including the development of effective vaccinces against potential B-weapons. Secretary of State Kissinger went so far as to say that a certain amount of research into potential offensive uses of biological agents must be allowed if it is necessary to carry out the appropriate defensive research. It is obvious that in this field, as in many others, defense and offense cannot be cleanly separated and that particularly developments potentially leading to mass vaccinations of a certain army might be perceived by a potential adversary as a preparation for biological war. It will therefore be desirable to carry such measures not too far and, if still being done, to do it to the greatest possible degree in a cooperative manner with potential adversaries.

It may even be a legal consideration whether the phrase "... other peaceful purposes" might not actually forbid defensive research and might be meant only to allow medical research proper in a non-military sense. As often, law experts do not completely agree on the correct interpretation. From the point of view of the biologists, the real world facts of the uses of such agents should have precedence and the legal instruments should be adapted accordingly, if possible.

What Is New About B-weapons Since the Biological Weapons Convention?

Several allegations of the use of B-weapons have been made both by Western and by Eastern states. The U.S.A has alleged that the Soviet Union has used toxin weapons in Afghanistan, and by proxy in Cambodia and Laos. Particularly, it was said that a phenomenon called "Yellow rain" was man-made and served the spread of mycotoxins. None of these allegations have ever been proven. In the case of yellow rain, very thorough research was directed towards the solution of these allegations. Professor Meselson from Harvard University again played a leading role. He was eventually able to show that yellow rain is a natural phenomenon caused by swarms of beas defecating collectively. The British and Canadian government have been unable to confirm the use of mycotoxins as means of warfare. The position of the United States has been eroded strongly by these recent reports.

It might be noted in this connection that one of the weaknesses of the Biological Weapons Convention is the lack of a verification procedure (which would indeed be very hard to draft). There is, however, a provision in Articles V and VI by which the Security Council of the United Nations might be addressed, if one party to the treaty wants a particular allegation to be confirmed. It is notable that neither side has ever felt itself sure enough of its allegation to invoke these provisions.

What else Has Happended in the Field of B-weapons?

It has not gone unnoticed that the U.S.A has increased its budget in this field. From 15 million US-dollars in 1981, this budget has risen to over 50 million US-dollars now. This is a sharp increase, though the subtotal is still small when compared to the defense budget of 300 billion US-dollars.

A point of controversy is the intended construction of a new test facility for infectious aerosols in Dugway, Utah. Initially, it was tried to sneak the necessary sums into a budget amendment that is usually less thoroughly scrutinized than the normal budget. Due to the attention of a U.S. senator, the question came to the public and then suddenly found powerful supporters, including Secretary of Defense, Casper Weinberger. Eventually the sum was alloted, though well-known scientists, including Nobel Prize winner David Baltimore pointed out that a purely defense-oriented establishment need not be classified and might be open if not to the public in general, then at least to investigation committees not related to the defense establishment. For reasons unknown, this has been denied by the army.

The question is still pending, since environment activists have reached a court injunction postponing the construction work until the army can produce an official environmental impact statement. This takes some time, though nobody doubts that it eventually will be issued. The discussion will then be taken up again.

B-weapons and Gene Technology

Particular attention has been drawn from several quarters to the fact that biology in general and bacteriology in particular are in a stage of rapid change due to the development of modern methods of gene technology. Will these be able to create weapons unheard of, and will these be built either by circumvention of the Biological Weapons Convention or by outright breach of the treaty? I am not sure, how revolutionary the impact of genetic engineering will be on biological weapons. Obviously, bacteria can be made resistant to anti-biotics, thus making therapeutic measures more difficult. Troops or populations can be protected by newly engineered vaccines. More than one gene for a toxin can be combined in a single bacterium. Whether this means a new quality as compared to quite lethal agents like Bacillus anthracis, is not clear at the moment.

Not in the year, but maybe in the midterm future, the construction of new toxins designed to particular biological targets still to be revealed by biological research, may become a reality. We have seen so many astonishing developments in biological sciences in the last decades, that it would be surprising if this trend would not continue for a while and might also open up possibilities for biological warfare. Attention is therefore asked for. At the moment, however, the new toxins do not seem to be around the corner.

What Should We Do?

If my description of biological warfare capabilities is correct (which I hope it is), a few conclusions come to mind:

1. Biological weapons do not seem to be too well-suited for battlefield use. They lend themselves more to covert action, including terrorism. That raises suspicion with the military, and may turn some military people into our allies if we try to ban these weapons altogether.
2. As compared to chemical weapons, biological ones seem less useful. We therefore should not only concentrate on the strengthening of the Biological Weapons Convention, but at least to the same extent we should try to get a chemical weapons convention as powerful as the BWC already is. This means, not only the use, but also the deployment and development of chemical weapons must be forbidden.
3. Both of these weapons are dangerous and inhumane and deserve our efforts to prohibit them. We never should forget, however, that nuclear war is still the biggest danger. This is reflected not only in general considerations, but also in the fraction of budget alloted to the different kinds of weapons. Our work against biological weapons should therefore not distract us from rather incite us to a simultaneous effort to eliminate nuclear weapons.

BIBLIOGRAPHY

M. Meselson (1970) Chemical and Biological Weapons. Scientific American 222 (5): 15–24.
S. Murphy, A. Hay, S. Rose (1984) No fire, no thunder. Pluto Press, London.
J. B. Tucker (1984) Gene Wars. Foreign Policy 57: 58–79.
E. Geißler (1984) Implications of genetic engineering and biological warfare. In: SIPRI-Yearbook 1984, pp. 421–455.
T. D. Seeley, J. W. Nowicke, M. Meselson, J. Guillemin, P. Akratanakul (1985) Der gelbe Regen. Spektrum der Wissenschaft, Nov. 1985, 126–139
J. P. P. Robinson (1985) Chemical and biological warfare: developments in 1984. in: SIPRI-Yearbook, pp. 159–219.
J. Palca (1986) Yellow Rain – another treaty threatened. Nature 321: 554.
J. Palca (1986) Biological Weapons. Nature 321: 805.

Friedrich Jung, German Democratic Republic

Chemical Weapons

T his theme reminds me of the Spring of 1945. There had been a number of poisonings by chemical weapons at a Wehrmacht munition dump and I had been called in as a physician and a specialist. A few days later, as leader of a truce party, I surrendered the dump to the allies. It contained several tons of a new, to me as yet unknown, chemical and posed a deadly danger to the immediate surrounding of the towns of Isny and Leutkirch. This threat was eliminated with the unconditional surrender, at least as far as there and then was concerned.

This danger is at present once more of immediate concern. In this lecture I would like to first examine part of the history of this type of weapon and then go into detail about the most important types, continuing with their methods of effectiveness as well as possibilities of protection and assistance. I will then come to the attempts to ban this particular weapon technology from the military arsenals.

* * *

The earliest evidence for the military use of poisons are to be found in the two Indian epics of Ramayana and Mahabharata. It is also to be found in such classical writers as Thucydides and Plutarch and then further in Leonardo da Vinci and up to the present. Something like burning sulphur or an arsenic bearing vapour was deployed. It is interesting to note that in the very earliest Indian texts mention is made of a highly toxic agent, Abrin, which also appears today in the inventories of the U.S. Army. Lewin made mention of several of these occurrences in his book on the role of poison in world history. He did not, however, document the observations of a certain Austrian, not called Hitler, rather Senfftenberg, who commented around 400 years ago on the use of arsenic vapour by the Hunyadi in the siege of Belgrade, "It is a terrible thing. Christians should never use such murderous weapons against other Christians. It is, however, highly appropriate against Turks and similar monsters." Fanatical crusaders – against dissidents (communists, for instance) or those of another colour – are still with us despite our so-called civilising progress and they are as brutish as in those days.

The development of modern technical sciences, including chemistry, made accessible new murderous weapons (e. g., the use of chlorine in the American Civil War, of prussic acid by Napoleon III, of organic arsine compounds in the Crimean War) and shortly before the outbreak of the First World War ethylbromacetate, a so-called tear gas, made its appearance with the French police. In October 1914, a few weeks after the beginning of the First World War, the German army, on the proposal of Professor Nernst deployed "a nose- and lung-irritating agent" on the Western Front. It then remained to a research group under Professor Fritz Haber to push ahead the systematic development with German thoroughness. They embraced new toxic agents as well as various delivery techniques. At the end of March 1915, around 200,000 kilograms of chlorine in gas bottles were waiting, ready for use, near Ypres. With the arrival of a favourable wind they were released on April 22nd. There are no reliable casualty figures, but they are estimated at 5,000 dead and 15,000 injured. This success convinced the military on both sides and so set in action a rapid further development, which led to phosgene, mustard gas and a whole group of highly toxic arsine compounds. A million gas grenades were used at Ypres in the Summer of 1917, and gas was thereafter a fact of every large-scale offensive action. Gas claimed around 1.3 million victims in the First World War. That war started from German soil, and the same may also be said for the development of this new and cruel weapon, in fact the first real weapon of mass destruction.

The Hague Conventions forbade the use of poisonous gases. It is interesting to note that immediately after their first use German propaganda claimed that German troops had not used grenades with a poisonous or suffocating gas. The credibility of certain militaries already existed at that time. There was, however, also the conscience of certain scientists who were aware of their responsibilities. I understand from the correspondence of the novelist Romain Rolland that a German chemistry professor had made an anonymous appeal to the Red Cross in Geneva to intervene, even before the use of the new weapon. It was the later Nobel laureate, who then perceived that mankind can be blind to the danger that threatens it. Now, was Staudinger a traitor or was he a German patriot, was the moral integrity of his homeland closer to his heart than the power of its rulers?

It is difficult for us to learn from history, as we can see from the period between the wars. It was also during that period that a scientist, Dr. Schrader, who was employed by Bayer, took out a secret patent on 23rd December 1936 for a highly toxic agent and delivered a sample to the fascist Wehrmacht in the following year. Pilot production commenced in Munsterlager in 1939 with field trials in Raubkammer. Large-scale production followed and more than 12,000 tons were ready by 1945. There is one French estimate of the discovery of 13,500 tons in the western occupation zones. I assume that a great part of this was stored in the ammunition depot of Urlau near Leutkirch which I mentioned in the introduction. The chemical was called Tabun and was not the end-point of the development. Schrader delivered a still more deadly product to the Wehrmacht in 1939, Sarin. Yet more deadly still was the derivative developed by the Nobel Prize winner Richard Kuhn, Soman. None of these chemicals were put into military action in the Second World War. I do not know to what degree they were tested and used for crimes in the extermination camps of the SS. Experiments with the older chemicals were carried out on humans by SS doctors and were condemned at the Nuremberg Trials. The Second World War also started from German soil and in the form of these new weapons sprang up once more a new and terrible means of mass destruction.

New super-poisons were also the subject of further intensive research after 1945. In 1957 Schrader received a new patent in this group of substances and ICI in England as well as Swedish research teams marked new achievements. It was from these super-poisons, known in the U.S.A as V-agents, that the Pentagon selected a derivative designated as VX, beginning its production in 1961, already possessing around 10,000 in 1971 and far more today. Some of it may be stored in the Palatinate or elsewhere in the Federal Republic of Germany.

The manufacture and handling of these super-poisons is complicated. During storage the canister (grenade or bomb) may leak. With the so-called binary weapons the canister contains two primary substances which on use can be brought into reaction with each other in order to produce the super-poison. This is a technological innovation easing the deployment of such weapons and is the cause of our current concern since Reagan's instruction to produce this variant.

Although these new post-war developments function quickly and with certain lethality, there are also two other important trends:

- The development of psycho-poisons which disrupt or even destroy the coordination of humans. In this respect highly effective derivatives have been developed which can be used in sabotage or militarily to induce disorientation. I would not categorise these as methods of mass destruction.
- An accidental discovery was that of the high toxicity of the dioxins (used as admixtures in certain herbicides), the use of one of which in Agent Orange-G had grave consequences. It is also the poison of Seveso and it is also feared as a by-product in refuse-burning installations. Its effects are not acute and a military-tactical significance cannot be attributed to it. The examples of Vietnam and Seveso nevertheless show its suitability for sabotage uses as a long-term and difficult to counter poison.)

✳ ✳ ✳

The most important current chemical weapons today are:
- Poisons specially produced for this purpose: the so-called nerve-gases, all organic phosphoric acid compounds, the V-agents, Sarin and possibly Soman; mustard gas, also known as schwefellost or sulphur-yperite and its derivative nitrogen-yperite; Adamsite (diphenylaminechlorarsine), an arsenical compound, an intensive irritant, especially in the respiratory tract; CN (2-Chloracetophenone) and CS (2-chlorobenzylidine malononitrile) gas, mucous membrane irritants, tear-gas; and finally the BZ (benzilate) weapon, a psycho-toxic compound and also the well know hallucinogen LSD.
- Some highly toxic chemicals which are also important in the chemical industry: Phosgene and hydrocyanic (or prussic) acid

One may also here include several older weapons whose production has been halted, but which are nevertheless still stored in quantity in combat readiness. They are in part the remnants of the First and Second World Wars. I would mention here Tabun and a few arsenic-potassium compounds such as Lewisite, Clark and arsine.

Many of these remnants of earlier wars come into the possession of illegal international arms dealers and can lead to unforseen events in smaller wars.

General physical and chemical properties determine usefulness as chemical weapons. Above all, none of the substances, with the exception of phosgene and hydrocyanic acid is as gas. Most of them are fluids, some of which easily evaporate, whilst others, such as Adamsite or BZ, solidify. They have to be deployed as either a cloud of vapour or as finely sprayed dust, these requirements being obtained on the detonation of a grenade or rocket. There are, however, also specially developed aerosol generators available to spray in the field. We know this principle from asthma sprays. Critical factors are their persistency and durability in the field, stability in storage and also on detonation of the carrier round. A gas such as phosgene is spread by the wind, and on a change in wind direction it can affect its own side. On the other hand, it enters protected areas much more easily than an aerosol. Aerosols are much

	L mg × l × min	I	Factor L/I	Effect on entry Inhaled	Effect on entry Skin
V Agents	.01	.005	2	immediate	30–60 min
Sarin	.1	.03	3	immediate	protracted
Mustard Gas	1	.2	5	1–2 hours	6–24 hours
Phosgene	3	1.5	2	1–6 hours	—
Prussic Acid	5	—	—	immediate	—
CN	8	.01	800		immediate/eyes
Adamsite	30	.005	6 000		minutes/ respiratory tract
CS	60	.005	12 000		immediate/eyes & respiratory tract
BZ	200	.1	2 000	30–60 min	Psycho-toxic

Alle values are approximations. L refers to the respective air concentration × period of inhalation that leads to death in 50 % of exposed cases. I is the dose that leads to incapacity. — means no information available. (N.B. exact information on the lethal dosage for humans is impossible, all figures are approximations based on animal experiments.)

more persistent. Higher persistency can be attained by, amongst other means, the addition of adhesive substances.

We can therefore see that special substances on the list were chosen from a multitude of possible poisons on the criterion of stability: Sarin will keep for up to four days in the field in summer, whereas in winter for only a day. The V-agents, in contrast, are active in summer for up to ten days, in winter for several weeks. Mustard gas is very resilient and can remain active for several decades. The sabotage poison dioxin is extremely resilient and the same is true for the arsenic compounds, after whose destruction the inherent poison arsenic remains in every case. Sarin, V-agents, mustard gas and Adamsite survive the heat of the detonation of the carrier round without any problem. Hydrocyanic acid would burn and a drug such as BZ would be extensively destroyed.

Chemical stability naturally also plays a role in the desired poisoning (or decontamination), beginning with the skin of the afflicted person and on to objects or open spaces: Low chlorine acids and their derivatives such as chloride of lime, sodium hypochloride and also chloramine can destroy mustard gas and the weaker V-agents. Whilst Sarin and its group break down under treatment with lixivium the V-agents do not.

In assessing the toxicity, it is necessary to determine the amounts or concentrations which cause death and which lead only to incapacitation. There are great differences to be observed in this area depending on whether the chemical reaches the lungs, or whether it comes into contact with external mucous membranes, such as the eye, or whether it is taken in through the mouth. The most-commonly used measure from the standpoint of science is the dose which leads to the respective effect (death or incapacitation) in fifty per cent of those effected. In absorption via the lung it is customary to measure the dose, not in mg, but rather in terms of the so-called CT-product, i. e. the product of air-concentration and time of inhalation.

We can further ascertain that

– In respect to fatal effects Mustard gas is 5 times more toxic when inhaled than the well-known to lay persons prussic acid; Sarin is approximately 10 times more toxic than mustard gas; the V-agents yet another factor of 10. This victory of a sickening development is easy to determine.

- In respect to ability to incapacitate: CN and CS gas as well as Adamsite have effective doses similar to the V-agents or mustard gas. But whereas with the latter substances, as well as with hydrocyanic acid or phosgene, a slight raising of the dose leads to death, the lethal threshold is only reached with the former with a 1–10,000 increase of the amount. This means a clear division into two groupings.
- And further, that there is an enormous difference with respect to the onset of the effects. The V-agents and sarin work rapidly as does hydrocyanic acid. The irritants also work quickly. Humans perish slowly after several hours with phosgene and mustard gas. Slower still are the effects of the pseudo-toxic chemicals. This is important with regard to the deployment tactics.
- It is important to note finally that a number of the chemicals enter the body via the skin or the membrane of the eye. This is the case with the V-agents, Sarin, mustard gas and also hydrocyanic acid. Larger amounts are required for this and the poisoning is slowed down. This is also important for protective measures, particularly in the case of the V-agents leaving time for attempts at treatment.

$$* * *$$

I would now like to turn to the method of working, the physiological effects and therapeutic possibilities. I will look in each case at a representative type.

Organic Phosphorus Compounds

As is known, the stimulation of one nerve cell by another, or of a muscle or gland cell by a nerve cell is carried by a chemical carrier or transmitter. This is secreted at the synapse, stimulating the receiver cell and must then be disposed of when its task is completed. One of the most important of the transmitters is acetyl choline, its removal being effected by the splitting enzyme cholinesterase. The V-agents, e. g. Sarin are very similar in their chemical configuration to the acetyl choline, are seized by the enzyme, during that time the splitting reaction proceeds incompletely and the enzyme is thus blocked. An analogy would be a key which at first fits in a lock but then breaks apart, thus blocking the lock. All synapses in the nervous system which rely on acetyl choline are then disrupted and cease to function. The symptoms are typical for every mild poisoning. The iris muscles of our eyes have a very fine nervous control – if the required enzyme is missing the acetyl choline builds up and you suffer a lasting excitation: the pupil contracts and becomes very small. You become night-blind and suffer from other sight problems. Recovery begins a few days later as the body builds new enzymes. From this example we can also demonstrate the two therapeutic principles possible:

- Atropin limits the effects of acetyl choline. It can neutralise the over-excitation but cannot re-institute the normal functions. The pupil becomes broader but remains immobile.
- Certain oximes can reactivate the blocked enzyme. In this way the normal functions of the pupil can be restored. But the poisoning does not stop with the narrowing of the pupil. Nasal, salival and bronchial secretions begin to flow. Asthmatic conditions follow. Vomiting, diarrhoea and cramps set in with severe poisoning. Muscular spasms and discharges of urine and faeces occur. Death through severe poisoning is caused by respiratory paralysis. First aid can only be effective for a very short period after a case of severe poisoning. The intra-muscular administration of the antidote – e. g. atropine +

obidoxime – has to be performed within minutes. Repetition is necessary after an hour. It is, of course, necessary at the same time to prevent further effects of the poison. The decontamination of the skin through washing with a sodium bi-carbonate solution or diluted liquid ammonia or even with soap is recommended. Artificial respiration may be necessary. After effects, particularly in the nervous system are to be expected on recovery. The urgency of a very rapid and differentiated treatment of the poisoning should particularly teach us that in the event of mass poisonings we physicians are relatively helpless. Added to this is the fact that the effects of the antidotes are in no way certain.

Mustard Gas

The way of working of mustard gas was unclear for a long time. It seems that the poison or a by-product transposes itself with the genetic material, nucleic acid, leading to a disruption of DNS reproduction and other processes responsible for the re-synthesis of cellular protein. A decisive signpost for this was that mustard gas itself, and then its useful further development, cytostatica, are cancer chemotherapy agents. A poisoned cell at first continues to function until the restricted regeneration of its protein leads to its demise. It is also no longer able to separate. Mustard gas goes in the first instance very easily through the skin, without any initial signs of irritation. The germinal epithelium of the skin and its underlying tissue then slowly dies. This leads to boils and ulcers that are extremely slow in healing. If the gas should be inhaled, the lung tissues then meet the same fate. The picture is very similar to that of phosgene poisoning to which we shall later turn. The eyes and the gastro-intestinal tract are highly sensitive.

Possible consequences are general physical debility and lingering and often fatal sickness. There is no specific antidote. First aid is limited to the decontamination of the skin and the eyes. Salves containing chloramine can destroy remnants of the poison, but the treatment of the eyes is limited to rinsing with a sodium bicarbonate solution. On surviving the poisoning a higher cancer expectancy is to be awaited.

Phosgene

Phosgene is a true gas, the closely related diphosgene an easily vapourising fluid which is also a little more persistent. Both are only effective on inhalation. The bio-chemical action is unclear. They have no direct irritating effect. The walls of the lung vesicles, the alveolar endothelia, are destroyed. Blood plasma then enters the alveoli and the gaseous interchange is disrupted. This results in deficient oxygen supply, breathing difficulties and, finally, suffocation. The poisoning is complicated by the thickening of the blood, a consequence of the entry of the blood plasma into the lungs. The process generally develops quite slowly, and it can take for up to six hours before the first symptoms emerge.

Poisoning is not inevitable. A short examination of the victim during the symptomless phase is critical. It is important that patient be given complete rest and be kept warm in order reduce the oxygen requirement. After the onset of breathing difficulties, oxygen may be administered with caution as some mechanical breathing assistance may nevertheless be dangerous. Hexamethylentetramin may be administered as a specific antidote during the latency period. Glucocortocoids may also be of use. On surviving acute poisoning there are high risks of infection.

Irritants

CN functions primarily on the membrane of the eye, Adamsite particularly in the respiratory tract and CS at first on the eye, but later in the respiratory tract. Lethal quantities are not in general deployed, although they were occasionally used by the US Army in Vietnam. The causes of death in those cases were lung oedema and suffocation. Longer lasting damage to the eyes may be expected after careless use. Assistance can be rendered by the rinsing of the conjunctival sacs with a bicarbonate solution or camomile tea. In the case of inflamed respiratory tracts the inhalation of certain vapours, similar to those used against severe coughing, may be of help. It may thus sound all relatively harmless, but death and severe injury can be caused by this agent. There is a problem of dosage, and the dosing of this chemical cudgel in field deployment is difficult to master. It is therefore incorrect to try to exclude these compounds from the category of chemical weaponry. Even when there is only an inflammation resulting from their use by the police, this remains in fact a physical injury.

Any form of assistance is made yet more difficult by always having to reckon with having to face these compounds in combination with various other weapons.

General Prophylactic Measures

The experiences of the First World War showed that a well-prepared military unit could be well protected against the chemical weapons of the time – a least by the end of the war. Protection against a surprise attack with the rapidly working V-agents is altogether more problematic.

Modern gas-mask technology provides extensive protection against inhalation, even against certain aerosols, such as Adamsite, which were developed to penetrate masks. There is also protective clothing which can reliably hinder a poisoning of the skin. I know of expensive technology which was used by the fascist Wehrmacht for the protection and decontamination of men and machines. It wasn't entirely useless, because it could also be used against lice. This is all better understood today and still more is known about the neutralising of the important properties of certain chemicals.

But, what is the situation for the civil population? I do not doubt that thorough analyses, such as those which the IPPNW has carried out with regard to nuclear war, would show anything but similar results for a comprehensive chemical attack. Comprehensive help would be impossible, we would lack the means to render effective help to the injured and, moreover, what do we have for effective therapy? Practically nothing.

So, you can prophylactically drive the millions of a great city underground into shelters and attempt at the end to crawl out once more to decontaminate with strong chemicals homes, workplaces and the entire surrounds. Or, you can do nothing and then experience what the inhabitants of the Indian city of Bhopal lived trough. The gas in Bhopal was nevertheless relatively harmless compared to the V-agents. However, we are not in the situation of the people of Bhopal before the catastrophe – there the gas was in a container and a safety-valve blew. What would happen if some sort of an accident occurred in a V-agent depot and the explosive in the grenades that are stored there blew the rest into our countryside? We have heard of Harrisburg in the U.S.A., of Windscale in England; Chernobyl touches us in a wide vicinity just as the Pershing accident did the citizens of Heilbronn.

* * *

I will now turn to the real protection which sensible people have striven for for a hundred years. That is the banning of such weapons!

For over a hundred years there have been attempts to introduce humanistic principles into international laws for military conflicts. The St. Petersburg Declaration of 1868, the Hague Declaration of 1900 and the Hague Land Warfare Convention of the same year committed the treaty partners to renounce weapons which inflicted unnecessary suffering or death, as well as to abstain from military measures which would fail to respect civilian populations. Article 23 of the Land Warfare Convention specifically forbade the use of poisons or poisoned weapons. These agreements in international law are still in effect and have been ratified by nearly all nations of the earth. There is an important provision whereby, in the case of one warring party violating the treaty, the other party is released from its commitments. It is therefore clear that the way leading to preparation for a chemical war is not blocked by these regulations. The Geneva Convention of 1925 strengthened the agreements of 1900 and is in accord with the regulations of the 1932 World Disarmament Conference (never ratified). The latter made provisions for control measures, but at the same time stood by the right of retaliatory attack. There are thorough analyses of why we were spared the catastrophe of chemical warfare during the Second World War despite massive chemical weapon reserves and the already mentioned new developments. Military-strategic considerations certainly played a role as did the world-wide proscription of chemical weapons. There were naturally accusations, as for instance in the case of the British attack on Kassel in October 1943. There I experienced myself how people suffocated in the smoke of an area-fire and not from a chemical weapon. In April 1942, Churchill offered Stalin the delivery of 1,000 tons or more of mustard gas, an offer which Stalin refused in his answer of 22. 4. 1942. At the end of the First World War the Soviet Union had already called for a full and effective ban of chemical weapons. Such a ban is in accord with today's world opinion. There are resolutions of the United Nations to that effect which are regrettably only recommendations and not binding in international law. The Geneva disarmament commission has been discussing the implementation in international law for decades. There are some very good proposals, but also lot of propaganda tactics. So, a proposal from Reagan called for a total ban which would be confirmed by a comprehensive control of all state controlled production possibilities. In the socialist Soviet Union, that is naturally everything. But where is state sector in the mighty chemical industry of the USA? The latter would remain fully uncontrolled. It is understandable that the principles of equality and equal security are infringed by such proposals, thus making them unacceptable. What is the reasoning behind the required proscription?

- Chemical weapons are cruel in their immediate and their after effects.
- A differentiation between armed forces and the civil population is impossible. The latter would suffer the most.
- They are weapons of mass destruction, not only bringing a harrowing death but also rendering the environment uninhabitable.
- In densely-populated Europe alone there are thousands of tons of these weapons. A technical failure could also lead to a terrible disaster even in peacetime.

What should a general and internationally legally binding agreement contain?

- The confirming of the already existing regulations in regard to the ban on their use, moreover without the reservation of the right to a retaliatory attack in the case of the treaty being violated.

– New developments, production and storage would be forbidden, adherance to the treaty to be secured through an effective control system.
– Existing stores to be destroyed.

And further: A critical current question is that of the new developments related to the production of binary weapons by the USA. With the realising of the production and storage of these weapons the danger multiplied many-fold and, in addition, can lead to a new round in the arms race. Control would be made generally more difficult. Transport, storage and preparations for deployment would be simplified. New and more dangerous chemicals can be utilised in these systems. It is therefore also as important to have controls over the preparatory chemical stages related to production and storage as to have them over the development and production of the respective technical delivery systems.

The required treaty system is realisable, as a glimpse at the relative convention on biological weapons shows. The latter also teaches us that a proscription on the development of weapons in no way serves to limit research which is useful to mankind. We carry a heavy historical burden – two world wars were launched from German territory as was the development of the cruel weapons of mass destruction which we have here examined. The FRG and the GDR are situated on the dividing line between two differing systems. They, like their neighbouring countries, are densely populated and their citizens are consequently more threatened than anyone else on the planet. A heavy responsibility rests therefore not only on their politicians, but also on each of us.

Good, I know that the government of the GDR is in favour of a global proscription, and I have heard that the government of the FRG has also expressed itself to be of this opinion. But, doesn't the current situation call on us to do more than make such verbal confessions? The proposal from the SPD and the SED for the creation of a chemical weapon-free zone in central Europe lies on the table. In contrast to the global proscription this does not require global consent but its realisation comes into the sphere of responsibility of the affected states, insofar as these are sovereign. It would remove the permanent danger of the storage of thousands of tons of chemical weapons and decisively reduce the risk of a chemical war in Europe. It would also be a decisive step on the way to the global proscription and curtail the escalation of the chemical armaments, especially with regard to binary weapons. The government of Czechoslovakia supports this proposal and the Soviet Union is ready to provide the necessary guaranteeing statement. It is perhaps unnecessary to state that we in the GDR, that is to say, every citizen up to the state leaders, stand fully behind this. I feel from the news of the last few weeks that recent statements give rise to the hope that the current depots may be removed from there before the end of the decade. Who can guarantee this, however? Security comes from an international legally binding treaty, and the proposal for this is on the table.

The treaty proposal that accompanies the proposal is carefully designed to guarantee equality and equal security but also takes care of sensitive problems of control such as verification. It explicitly contains provision for extension to neighbouring countries such as Poland, Belgium and the Netherlands. I can provide you with detailed information of its contents.

* * *

I take it for granted that we are united in believing that these weapons should disappear. Their repercussions are almost as terrible as those of nuclear weapons, which are in the foreground of the concerns of those of us in the IPPNW. To be committed to democratic ideals means that we cannot pass the responsibility for these things upwards, but rather that we ourselves must feel responsible for whether we live or whether we ourselves, our children and friends perish in an inferno. It is not my task to advise how to set about achieving that in the bounds of your constitutions, but it challenges you, just as much as us.

SCIENTIFIC PROGRAMME

Peter Safar & Martin Silverstein, U.S.A.

Questions Concerning Military Medicine

W hen I was asked by the IPPNW leadership to organize a discussion session on military medicine, I did so with the intent of inviting as Chairman someone who is more knowledgeable than I about military medicine. I would merely ask questions. When I searched for a leading, active medical officer in the U.S. Armed Forces, I found volunteers, but they were not permitted by their superiors to participate in the IPPNW congress. What they had to say would have to be approved in advance. This is not possible for open panel discussions. I then explored the composition of this discussion session with young physician friends who experienced recent wars personally, as past medical officers and who would not be censored. They suggested that I invite a retired medical officer who also has a scholarly background in military medicine. I invited Dr. Martin Silverstein to introduce and chair this discussion session and he graciously accepted. He and I have both served as consultants for NDMS planning in the U.S.A. He is Professor at the Center for Strategic and International Studies of Georgetown University in Washington, D.C.

Peter Safar

* * *

I am grateful to Drs. Safar, Chazov, Lown and other leaders of IPPNW for the invitation to attend this meeting and the opportunity to discuss some very pertinent aspects of warfare which I feel have been neglected by single-minded concentration of peace groups on massive nuclear weapons sitting atop enormous missiles. Indeed, I present you with the thesis that this tunnel vision performs a disservice to the peace process by ignoring other weaponry which has progressed technologically in recent years. It is the presence of these weapons which stimulate the development and deployment of nuclear weaponry. It is these weapons which unlike nuclear weaponry have killed and maimed people in the period which has followed World War II and at this very time are killing and crippling in many parts of this globe. When I last counted wars, based on information supplied by the Defense Information Center, there were between forty and forty-five undeclared wars in progress.

I would present you with the further thesis that the killing power and mobility of non-nuclear weapons has progressed relatively unobserved by the general public. These weapons in the hands of violent men and women are the vectors of an epidemic spreading over the globe, while maximum political attention is being paid to the potential of nuclear warheads and bombs which have not killed anyone since 1946. The concentrated attention on nuclear weapons has, in fact, diverted the eyes of well meaning people from the actuality of the appalling violence which has occurred by the use of nonnuclear weapons. Indeed, the single minded clarion call for nuclear disarmament, with which no one can disagree, has given a de facto acceptance to other forms of warfare which are equally destructive to human life and society. The politics of nuclear disarmament can be compared to the stage magician's obvious right hand which diverts our eyes from the left hand which is actually doing the trick. We as physicians are familiar with the wounds of violence and recognize the horror of all man's inhumanity to man. We least of all should be diverted to a single issue which then becomes politicized.

I have spent some thirty-seven years repairing the wounds and attempting to salvage the lives of civilians as well as military and I am familiar with the devastation to a family that is caused by a single violent death and with the horror of mass death which is presently caused by terrorists and other misguided people who would seek power and redress by the killing of innocents.

To my mind, the stability of the world and the safety of civilians are principally threatened by the development of the military assault rifle. This is the weapon which is killing at this very moment. It is symbolized by the Kolashnikov hand-held weapon which has the accuracy and range of old fashioned rifles combined with the capabilities of "rapid machine gun fire" and a muzzle velocity equal to or beyond that of World War II rifles. Twenty or more countries manufacture similar weapons and they are exported around the world. The assault rifle and the new generations of explosives provide a platoon with the firepower of a Napoleonic army. A British light machine gun developed for use from a helicopter is said to be capable of firing 6,000 rounds a minute. The relatively new Micro-Uzi resembles a large pistol and approximates the capabilities of the larger assault rifles in its muzzle velocity and destructive powers. Versions have been produced for this belt holster weapon which automatically fire 45, 9 mm and the very powerful 7.62 ammunition.

Those who would advance the cause of peace must read the strategies of the war makers. Several thousand years ago the literature of war began with the account by a Chinese theorist, who pointed out that wars are made and won by subtle maneuvers and by the efficient use of small units.

We physicians well understand the destructive power of high velocity small arms ammunition. The missile thus fired does not make a clean tunnel through the body. It transfers its kinetic energy to the victim in the direction of that tunnel and in waves perpendicular to its own pathway. Thus adjacent tissue far remote from the "bullet wound" is injured or destroyed by this kinetic energy. Remote organs are, in fact, blasted by the transferred kinetic energy. This phenomenon has been known since the end of the American Civil War and is called cavitation. To jog your memories I show you livers and other tissues far from the bullet track but still burst apart by that transferred kinetic energy. A 7.62 round fired from an Uzi demolishes a cement block by producing a huge cavity which surrounds the pathway of the bullet. The same weapon will penetrate 43 layers of the much vaunted protective cloth, known as Kevlar.

There are other lessons to be learned from the new technology known as the assault rifle. If massive destruction can be delivered by a small unit, we must anticipate refinements in the art of penetration of the enemy's static lines or the capability to covertly insinuate weaponry and its users into civilian areas. These small units distant from their bases will require a degree of medical self sufficiency and self reliance. We as civilian physicians and surgeons must know the capability of their weapons if we are to treat victims.

It has been suggested that the peace process would be advanced by a declared unwilling-ness on the part of physicians to treat the wounded. All of us in this room have taken the Hippocratic Oath. Whatever the situation in which someone is injured it would be indecent, indeed obscene, for us to turn our backs on suffering. It has been suggested that physicians in uniform are free to disobey their superiors and deny care to the wounded. The United States makes a civilized provision for non-combatant tasks for any conscientious objector but to covertly sabotage the medical care of other humans is as unethical as war itself.

Assault rifles are not the only technologically advanced weapons which threaten our generation and future generations. We now have explosives which, in small amounts, have many times the destructive capability of a stick of TNT. These explosives are relatively plastic and enormous destructive power may be hidden in a small truck such as the one used against the peace-keeping Marines in Lebanon, where one or two individuals killed over two hundred soldiers.

There are also nonnuclear chemical gases available as instruments of political and wartime mass destruction. The potential for chemical warfare is everywhere. The process which produces pesticides in underdeveloped countries for the battle against hunger can be diverted without notice – by the rest of the world – to the production of chemical gases derived from the intermediate products or byproducts of pesticides. Pesticide manufactur-ing is everywhere. The thousands of victims at Bhopal testify to the lethality of such chemicals and our inability to medically cope with such problems.

It is our duty as physicians to direct our attention to these weapons as well as to nuclear weapons.

I should also mention the nightmare of biological warfare. One need not have the sophisti-cated techniques of genetic engineering to produce large cultures of virulent organisms and their toxins. We have had reports of biological weapons used against political adversaries by the Bulgarian undercover agents operating in Great Britain. The chemobiological agent used can be derived from a plant which is commonly used by gardeners and landscape artists. We have had news reports of a major escape of biological "bullets" in the late 70's in the Soviet Union. Microbiological weapons are the most unthinkable of all unthinkable weapons and we must be prepared to oppose them with the same fervor with which we oppose nuclear weapons.

As I mentioned in an earlier discussion of disaster planning chaired by Dr. Safar, the peaceful atom of nuclear power is a genie in a bottle which threatens us now. Those who count missile launchers and bombers must also pay attention to disaster preparation at nuclear power plants. We grieve with our Soviet colleagues at the losses increased by what I and, I am sure, Dr. Safar, would regard as inadequate disaster preparation at Chernobyl.

Perhaps the most menacing weaponry, menacing because it is an immediate threat and more likely to be used, is the relatively high speed, ceramically armored, massively fire powered tank. It is inconceivable to me that we should put so much energy into countering nuclear weapons without concomitantly fighting for the reduction of menacing tanks. Massive tank forces stimulate the progress of nuclear weapons.

In summary, I must tell you that there is really no such thing as conventional war. There is a wide spectrum of weapons which threaten the human race. As citizens, ethics demand that we make an intelligent approach to the prevention of war. As physicians we must know all the weapons and their wounds and be prepared to heal humanity.

Enormous technological advances have been made in all areas of weaponry. The striking advance has been in the ability of a single soldier to cause enormous damage with hand held weapons and explosives. The distinction between nuclear war and conventional war is a distinction based on weapons and tends to distract physicians and others from the central issues of peace and war. There is a linkage between conventional weapons and nuclear weapons in that a vast increase in any conventional weapon, now technologically much improved, stimulates policy makers to fall back on the potential use of nuclear weapons. The role of the physician is clear. Whether in uniform or out of uniform we are the healers. Whatever political position we take we can take only one position toward the victim-patient and that is to heal with whatever resources we have at hand. It is incumbent on all physicians to learn all the etiologies of disease and all the characteristics of wounds that weapons cause so that we may best heal our patients.

Martin Silverstein

Discussion

Limited nuclear war.   There was general agreement that in the contingency of all out nuclear war a "nuclear winter" would occur. There is little or no role for physicians who survive other than the recovery of the human race. Dr. Silverstein felt that physicians should prepare themselves for this ultimate catastrophe, since whatever resiliency exists within the earth ecosystem will have to be nurtured by people who have given forethought to this event. The group felt strongly that as citizens of their respective countries they should oppose all movements toward war; as physicians their ethics and their oath would allow them no choice but to heal the wounded from traumatic events. Dr. Safar felt that physicians and the medical apparatus should not accept any number of nuclear (whether tactical or strategic) or major conventional war casualties. Dr. Silverstein felt that there was a strong feeling among the young physicians that they must prepare themselves for the treatment of any injury from any cause and that their ethics would forbid them from turning their backs on any injured people. The group generally believed that irregular partisans acting in a battle zone are entitled to the rights of uniformed soldiers under the Geneva Convention.

Single nuclear explosion   Dr. Safar recommended the study of single nuclear explosion scenarios originating from power plant explosions, terrorist attacks, or strategic surgical strikes. It was felt that the single nuclear explosion was a proper area for disaster medicine and that appropriate medical recommendations should be made to the organizers of the U.S. National Disaster Medical System as well as to similar organizations in other countries.

Biological and chemical weapons   The group felt that development of modes of casualty care and preparedness should be undertaken while at the same time physicians should press for international treaties outlawing such weapons. The physicians present felt that any such treaty arrangement should include verification by inspection.

Conventional weapons   The devastating effects of modern conventional hand weapons and weapons of mass destruction are not sufficiently appreciated by the public. A modern assault rifle firing thousands of rounds per minute can destroy organs distant from the missile path. A previously survivable shot through one lung now leads to exsanguination from torn heart, liver, spleen, etc. The destructive power of bombs and missiles carried by a few planes can destroy an entire city, without the use of nuclear warheads. It was felt that modern "conventional war" also has the potential to destroy the world. Therefore, the

IPPNW should add to its objectives the combatting of the roots of war in general and extend its political position to include opposition to all war whatever weapons are used.

Civilian casualties   What are the civilian casualty care potentials and obligations of military medicine in the event of a war? A joint recommendation is to press physicians and the nations in which they live to honor the Geneva Convention which calls for military and civilian medical services to treat combatants and civilians of all sides according to medical needs. We also recommended that the military consider increasingly combining military and civilian medical services, as has been achieved successfully in Israel. This would give military officers trauma experience in peacetime and have civilian medical services prepared to aid combatants and civilians hit by war as well as cross fertilize education.

Humanitarian vs. military objectives   Humanitarian objectives should be approached within the context of the Geneva Convention. Any dilemma arising from a superior officer's orders which require the physician to violate his Hippocratic Oath, his ethics, and the Geneva Convention should be resolved by the individual physician in favor of his ethical stance. Dr. Silverstein has taken the position that medical facilities be afforded to terrorists as well as their victims in an even handed way and this stand has met with favor with physicians in Ireland, England, France, Italy and the United States. The group agreed with this posture unconditionally.

Triage   Disaster medicine or catastrophe medicine was understood by most of the discussants to mean "war medicine" and "triage" was seen by them initially as an inflammatory word. After hearing disaster medicine defined as the mitigation of injury from natural, technological, industrial and conflict disasters, the group accepted the general concept somewhat reluctantly. Swiss and West German physicians understood their military medicine doctrine as identifying triage as a process by which combatants were optimally returned to combat. Dr. Silverstein described triage as the matching of medical needs to medical resources for the greatest good. One East German colleague presented a scheme for triage, essentially the same scheme as presented by Dr. Silverstein but with additional regulation by higher authority and committee.

Military behavior in international peace keeping   The group's recommendation was to draw attention to the potential good that physicians in UN peacekeeping forces can do, in collaboration with the International Committee of the Red Cross, in war zones such as Lebanon, Iraq-Iran, and Afghanistan.

Military forces and their role in peace time disasters   The preplanned roles of armed forces in general and military medicine in particular, in various countries, for helping in the event of a mass disaster such as major earthquakes were explored. The group recommendation is to make military and specifically military medicine a part of the U.S. National Disaster Medical Systems' and similar organizations' plans and implementation. This is necessary to achieve the maximal life saving potential of "disaster resuscitology". Only the military has the needed authority, communications, equipment and training and the needed airlift capability. These are not available to local or regional EMS systems.

Peacetime role of military medicine   The group discussed the peacetime role of military medicine. In addition to peace keeping duties and support of national disaster medical systems there was divided opinion as to the role of military training in providing discipline, education, and physical training.

Trauma and life support training   The majority of discussants initially felt that trauma life support training was military training. Dr. Silverstein described the American College of Surgeon's Advanced Trauma Life Support courses. It was evident that an understanding of trauma training was unclear among the discussants. At the end of the discussion they felt that they should not refuse to learn resuscitation and life support unconnected with nuclear war scenarios in the manner of the American College of Surgeon's Advanced Trauma Life Support system.

Chernobyl   A stimulating discussion ensued. It was agreed that much can be done to protect uninjured populations against fallout and something can be done to alleviate the effects of acute radiation even though even minor radiation can make tissue injuries much worse. In addition, the military should help in disaster preparedness for nuclear power plant accidents as well as for nonnuclear industrial accidents and for national mass disasters such as earthquakes and floods. The group felt that nuclear power plants should be better prepared for disasters than was the plant at Chernobyl and that information should have been more freely, rapidly, and accurately disseminated to other countries and the surrounding countryside by the local disaster managers.

War time psychiatry   Military psychiatry was discussed. The physicians' fear that military psychiatry is covertly designed to send soldiers back to the front, not to help restore devastated personalities.

Self mutilation   This item was discussed. In World War II it is estimated that over 10,000 German soldiers made themselves or were made ill or injured to avoid field service. Of course the fear of death is real and military psychiatry should be prepared to help in this area.

Resuscitation and trauma research   The group felt that the level of military sponsored research in resuscitation, critical care medicine and trauma medicine should be raised. There was concern among some of the discussants from Western Europe that military doctrine requires that combatants in need of resuscitation were not be treated. Silverstein said that while the basic process of triage (needs matched to resources) was adhered to in the U.S., and as far as he knew in all NATO nations, the precepts of Napoleon's military medical organization which required that healed soldiers be returned to combat should they be required are also followed.

Recommendations

Recommendations by the majority of participants in Discussion Session No. 18:

1. The IPPNW should include "disaster and military medicine" as topics in the plenary session of future congresses and also a discussion session on the same subjects.
2. The Geneva Convention must be defended – to treat the combatants of all sides and the civilians caught in the struggle equally, according to medical needs.

3. Military medicine triage should be based on sound medical principles and the long standing ethics of the medical profession maintained.

4. Triage is matching the appropriate levels of care with presenting needs and available resources; requires judgement based on experience; cannot be learned exclusively in mannequin courses; and is part of medical practice.

5. As many physicians as possible should learn resuscitation, including basic and advanced trauma life support. The group recommended the extension of the American College of Surgeons' Advanced Trauma Life Support training to colleagues throughout the world.

6. Not only nuclear war, but also modern "conventional war" represents destruction of our civilization. Moreover, increases in tanks, small arms and other forms of weaponry can escalate to nuclear war. The IPPNW should concern itself with the "roots of war" including violation of human rights, violence utilizing all weapons and explore how peace can be achieved by actions of the medical profession.

Tytti Solantaus, Finland

Psychological Effects of the Arms Race on Children

I am going to go through some of the research, which has been done on children and the threat of nuclear war during the past years. However, I will not give you a full review of the subject. So much good work has been done, and is being done, that it is impossible to cover the whole topic in a short lecture. This is quite a change, and an encouraging change, because only some years ago the task would have well been accomplished in half an hour.

I will concentrate on some aspects of the problem and discuss implications. For a speaker, a talk is always a chance to put forward one's own ideas to discuss them with others. Therefore a talk and the following discussion present a possibility for the speaker to develop ideas and thoughts further together with other people. I am especially keen on doing this with you, because it is not very often that one has a possibility to talk about this topic with other people who deeply share the interest and concern, and also are very informed about it.

Methodological Considerations

By far most of the work on the psychological effects on children of the threat of nuclear war has been done amongst adolescents. This is quite understandable, first, because of the importance of the period of adolescence in many developmental aspects, and second, because standard research techniques and methods, for example questionnaires, can be used among adolescents in a way not possible among smaller children. This has enabled an accumulation of studies in a very short time period. Although the lack of studies on small children is a drawback, the emphasis on adolescence has produced a fair amount of knowledge on one age period.

Some of the studies can be criticized because of selective samples or otherwise biased methods, but there are also studies which are foolproof in a traditional scientific sense. Nonetheless, they all contribute to the picture which is slowly emerging and to the hypotheses which wait to be tested.

Most of the studies have used questionnaires as a means of study. Questionnaires have, however, their limits in studying psychological processes. For instance, there is a limit on how much the subject can express himself or herself. This was poignantly expressed by a thirteen years old girl in Louis Borgenicht's study[1]. When she was asked if nuclear arms have had an impact on her thinking about future, she said: "I don't really want to think of it and sometimes I just run away from it. Just lots of sad things that cannot be expressed in this little square". (I wonder if she knows how widely quoted she has become!) Second, there is a lack of communication between the researcher and the subject, which is a major drawback. The issues cannot be clarified, and we do not, in fact, know if the researcher and the subject define concepts like anxiety or peace activity in the same way.

Nevertheless, we are dealing with a very new research area, and surveys do have a place in mapping out an unknown territory. However, it has to be remembered, that "the map is not the territory"[2].

Prevalence of Worry

One of the main objectives in the studies has been to assess the prevalence of worry and anxiety about nuclear war among adolescents. This has been important to counteract the arguments that adolescents in general are not interested in world affairs, and are not concerned about them. The studies have shown that this is not the case. They show that a sizable proportion of young people are worried, a smaller proportion express anxiety, but they also indicate that there are young people who do not think about the problem.

Two different methods have been used to assess the prevalence of the worry. There are studies which have used an open question about three primary worries: "When you think about your future, what three things are you most worried about?" Another set of studies has used a list of worries, from which the respondents can tick the items they feel most worried about. These two methods measure different aspects of the problem. The open question captures those worries which are spontaneously uppermost in the minds of the respondents. The worry schedule picks up those items which elicit most worry in the youngster, or resonate with him or her, when she or he is faced with the given options.

Open Question

In the Finnish study[3, 4] about 80% of 12- to 18-year-olds expressed a fear of war in the open question in spring 1983. The study was repeated among 11-, 13- and 15-year-olds in autumn of the same year, with about the same result[5]. The fear and worry about war was clearly the uppermost worry among Finnish young people. In a Canadian study[6] half of the sample expressed a worry about war, and it was, coupled with unemployment, the primary worry. The finding was quite different in the Goldenring and Doctor study[7] among Californian adolescents. Amongst them, only 12% referred to war as one of the three main worries. Austrian and English 11- to 15-year-olds fall in the middle range, as one third of them expressed a worry about war[5, 8, 9].

List of Worries

When presented with a list of worries, the number one worry among Swedish[10] and Soviet[11] youngsters was nuclear war. In Sweden 42% listed it as their greatest worry. Californian young people listed nuclear war third after parent dying and getting bad grades and 12% listed it as their main worry. All these studies were done in 1983/84.

Age and Sex Differences

There seems to be none or a very small sex difference in the general expression of worry[4,6,7,11], but there are also contradictory findings. In Holmborg and Bergström's study[10] girls were more worried than boys and also ticked "very worried" more often than boys (37 % vs 17 %). In the Finnish study[4] there was no sex difference in general worry, but a significant sex difference in relation to strong fear or anxiety. Girls expressed anxiety more than twice as often as boys (37 % vs 15 %).

The studies are consistent in finding a decline in general worry about war among both sexes. However, the age trend concerning strong fear and anxiety was different for boys and girls in the Finnish study. Among girls there was a slight, nonsignificant rise in anxiety, but among boys there was a drop. Boys expressed more anxiety at 12 than later[4].

Socio-economic Background

Only a few studies allow analysis of the socio-economic background. A British poll[12], the Bachman study in the States[13] and the Finnish survey[4] are all representative of the social structure of the respective countries and they did not find a correlation between social class and expression of worry. There has also been some discussion about the children of peace activist parents and their perception of the global situation. It would be very logical if they were more worried, maybe more anxious but also more optimistic about prevention. However, there is a minimal amount of data on this, and the findings are contradictory.

Cross National Comparison

The studies about the prevalence of worry about nuclear war indicate that worry about war constitutes one of the top worries among adolescents in these countries, but that there is considerable cultural variation. Young people in the Soviet Union and in the Nordic countries seem more worried about war than their agemates in the U.S.A. and parts of Western Europe. Canada seems to fall in between. There is a lot of additional data coming up about the national differences, and it would be interesting to hear about them during the discussion, especially if they contradict the findings this far.

We face one interesting problem when we try to explain the cross national differences. Traditional psychology and psychiatry explain worries and let alone fears on the basis of individual psychology or psychopathology. Children worries are often explained as projections from the problems arising from their developmental phase. However, if this were the case, we would not find such huge cross national differences. On the other hand, there is evidence in the van Hoorn and French study[14] that the reactions of young people and grownups are not very different. Opinion polls in Finland and Sweden also show that adults are as concerned as children; this is not a developmental projection. We are certainly dealing with a very real worry: the threat of nuclear war cannot be disputed.

Instead of turning to psychology, we have to turn to sociology to explain the cross national differences. The history, ongoing political processes, the ideology and the aims of the society have to be analysed in the respective countries to understand the differences in adolescents' worries about their future. This is a challenge to pediatricians, child psychiatrists, psychologists who do research in this area, because we are so accustomed to think that our disciplines are contextfree. It also takes an open mind, because strong stereotypes of other nations prevail as part of cold war and these studies are bound to shake them.

Likelihood, Survivability and Preventability of War

Roughly one half of young people in a British[12] and an American poll[16] and in the Goldenring and Doctor study[7] think nuclear war likely in their lifetime. Swedish youngsters[10] were more optimistic (26 %) and Soviet children in Chivian et al. sample even more so (12 %)[11].

Young people seem fairly realistic about the consequences of nuclear war. Well over half of the Soviet[11] (81 %) and Swedish youngsters[10] (68 %) think that nuclear war cannot be survived. The proportion was lower in the Goldenring and Doctor study[7] among Californian adolescents (42 %).

Young people's opinion about preventability of war vary from study to study (45 %[10], 65 %[7], 92 %[14] and 93 %[11]).

These findings are interesting, but at this point I would not like to make conclusions about cross national differences. There are several problems. First, the samples vary and they are not representative. Second, complex issues, like preventability of war, cannot be covered by only one or two questions. Furthermore, even seemingly straightforward questions can have different connotations in different cultural settings, and this cannot be controlled in a questionnaire study. The problem is even greater if the wordings differ from study to study.

The Swedish study[10] and two U.S. studies demonstrate these problems. Only 45 % of Swedish compared with 65 % of Californian young people thought nuclear war could be prevented. One is tempted to conclude that the Swedes are more pessimistic. However, only 26 % of the Swedish sample thought nuclear war was likely in their lifetime and the Swedes were in this question more optimistic than their Amercian counterparts (39 %). The impact of differences in sampling and the wording of the questions are demonstrated in two U.S. studies[7,14]. They report very different findings in optimism about prevention (65 % and 92 % resp.) among the same age group.

Anxiety about War and Mental Health

Maybe the most important question these studies were set to approach was whether anxiety about war has a deleterious impact on the psychological health of children. Quite a few hypotheses were put forward. Everything was argued from the threat of war having no impact at all to having a causal relationship to mental breakdowns, anxiety disorders and suicides. Although the basic question cannot be answered totally on the basis of available data, some important suggestions can be made.

First of all it is important to point out, that there are no major studies that have looked into the relationship between anxiety about war and psychological disorder. However, it is possible to approach the problem from different indirect angles. The studies do not support the hypothesis that worry or anxiety about war would have psychiatric sequelae.

Expression of general worry was related to better school achievement and better general adjustment in some studies[6,7]. In the Finnish study[4] we did not find that correlation, but aspects of coping and mastery, discussing the issue with others and sense of self efficacy in prevention, were related to better school achievement. Furthermore, expression of worry or anxiety was not related to psychosomatic symptoms or use of alcohol or tobacco[5]. In all of these studies worry and anxiety about war was related to positive outcome rather than anything negative. However, there is also evidence from Sommers and other's study[6] that in some young people the worry might be too stressful to bear, as 9 % and 16 % of the sample had sought counseling because of worries about nuclear war from a therapist or counselor at school.

Anxiety and Sense of Self Efficacy in Prevention of War

Two studies have looked into the intensity of fear or anxiety about war, the Finnish and the Canadian survey[16]. Their findings support each other. Because I am more familiar with the data from my own study, I will use it as an example. The data are based on a national sample of 1800 12- to 18-year-olds in Finland. For more details, see Solantaus and Rimpelä, 1986[17].

Over one third of girls and half of that of boys expressed strong fear or anxiety about war. Approximately 4% stated that they had experienced strong fear or anxiety more than three times during the preceeding month. Anxiety was positively related to discussions about war and peace with others. From this kind of data it is impossible to say whether discussions produced anxiety, or anxiety led to discussions. Most probably both mechanisms are in operation at the same time. The data also indicate that those who discussed war and peace with others were more often confident about their own contribution in prevention of war.

When we looked into the interplay of anxiety, discussions and sense of self efficacy in prevention, an interesting picture emerged. The data indicated that 1) anxiety was positively related to sense of self efficacy among those who discussed war and peace with others and 2) both very low and very high levels of anxiety were related to reduced sense of self efficacy.

The Role of Discussions

The next question comes naturally: What are the elements in discussions that make them so important in building confidence in prevention and especially in one's own efficacy? First, sharing an anxiety provoking issue with others gives one a feeling of not being alone with the problem and it also gives psychological support to face the anxiety and to get it into its right proportions. Second, the mere fact that discussions bring the adolescent into contact with others might be important as such because prevention of war can only be accomplished together with other people. Third, the adolescent might learn about the problem through discussing it with others and the role of knowledge in the development of sense of self efficacy in prevention has to be considered. The data do support a positive correlation. Those who did well in school and those whose teacher had talked about peace and war at school did feel more efficaceous in prevention of war.

The Role of Knowledge

Apart from this kind of general idea we have very little data on the role of knowledge. I would like to hypothesize that knowledge about peace and war issues can be divided into two categories: 1) knowledge about weapons, knowledge about consequences of nuclear war, that is, knowledge about different details related to the issue, and 2) knowledge about the societal processes which are behind armament, knowledge of how societies function, how the international community functions, how the interdependencies between nations work. These two sets of knowledge are profoundly and essentially different.

I would like to suggest that the two sets of knowledge function in different ways. Details about war, weapon systems, technical development, about the horrible consequences of nuclear war without knowledge about the social processes might lead in many youngsters – and why not in grown-ups? – to fatalistic views about the future and pessimism about the outcome. Indeed, Engeström[18] has found profound ignorance about social processes lurking behind a fatalistic outlook on life and the game-like perception of world politics cherished by many youngsters. Plain knowledge of details is more likely to only support one's existing ideology, no matter if it is peace or deterrence ideology. It does not necessarily force one to reconsider one's premises.

On the other hand, knowledge about social processes and the causes of the arms' race might have a different impact. This kind of knowledge which leads to understanding "what is this all about", is more likely to force one to consider peace as the only option for mankind, and also, by providing a structure, contributes to a more optimistic view of the future. If one can understand what has led to this situation, one can more easily also see a way out.

Development of Social Competence

Our study was, like most of the others, a cross-sectional one. We studied the young people at one point in their developmental continuum. We found that a group of them expressed strong fear or anxiety about war. We do not know, if another group had done the same earlier on, and still another group would do so in some later stage. Cross-sectional studies do not capture processes, and we are definitely dealing with a process. I would be ready to hypothesize that there are periods in a child's development when he or she becomes highly aware of social problems. At that point it is of great importance how adults deal with it. If the society and the close adults support that kind of concern in the young, if the problems treated with active responsibility, the young might take a step towards development of mastery of social problems by constructive social action. If the opposite happens and the young's concern is nullified, the development might head towards helplessness, fatalism, resignation from social responsibilities and maybe towards unconstructive rebellion. The studies have shown that those young people who make very little reference to war and report no worry or anxiety are the ones who are most often pessimistic about prevention[6, 7, 15].

This is a call for change in the adult community and underlines the importance of peace education. We know that war and peace are not often discussed with children and adolescents in the western society. Only about one third to two thirds of youngsters in the different studies report having discussed war and peace with their parents. (In the U.S.S.R. the case is different and war is often discussed between the generations[19]). Clearly, there is room for change.

The Role of Child Psychiatry

Before I finish, let me depart from my central theme and talk a little about child psychiatry in relation to the arms build up.

Prevalent theories of child development and mainstream psychiatric theories and practices always reflect the tendencies of the society of their time. This is very clearly seen in theories about the importance of the mother to the child's early development. In times of underemployment, the importance of outside stimuli is emphasized, and day care facilities are supported. Right now we are witnessing the reverse. High unemployment, and on the other hand, growing independance of women – a threat to the society – are two indicators of our time; and the emphasis is again on mothers.

If there is a tendency of mainstream developmental theories to support prevalent tendencies of the society, is child psychiatry any different? The main tendency in our society is the arms race. How does child psychiatry relate to the arms race?

The most important new trend in psychiatry during the past years has been the rise of family psychiatry. There has been a very welcome change in emphasis from the individual to the family. However, if one looks at the situation carefully enough, it becomes evident that there has not been much change. The individual has only been replaced by the family. Instead of taking the individual away from his lonely island to his family and the society, the family was moved there also. The social context of the family has not been established, let alone the global.

Importance of the family to child development is being pointed out repeatedly. Quite rightly so, but at the same time the child's and the family's links with the society are not acknowledged, let alone regarded as important to mental wellbeing. How social competence in larger social issues develops and how children cope with the threat of nuclear war or other global problems have not been of interest in mainstream child psychiatry.

The emphasis on fathers has drawn the fathers from the society to their families instead of giving both mothers and fathers a chance to participate in social activities. The way of life has become family centered without outside activities, and this is very much backed up by child psychiatry under the label of the "child's benefit". The fact that these closed families are not always very happy has not led to change in politics, but only to training of new therapists. Sometimes it takes an artist to make us understand what life is about. In Saint Exupéry's Little Prince the fox said something to the fact that "love is not looking each other into the eye, but looking out into the same direction".

Family centered ways of life with no social responsibility contribute to nuclear arms build up in several ways. First, by simply letting it happen. Secondly in an indirect way, because family way of life is very materialistic wealth-oriented. High living standards become a main priority in life. In order to keep up and raise the living standard other countries have to be exploited, and therefore kept in control. The causes for war become more and more abundant. In this circulus vitiosus, more and more weapons have to be built to keep the rising dissatisfaction in these countries in check. I think that recent happenings in the world situation clearly demonstrate this.

The image of health in medicine has been very individual. In child psychiatry it has meant a happy child in a happy family, and there has been no sphere in developmental child psychiatry dealing with the development of social competence in global problems. Our studies have shown that awareness of global problems and coping with them is a developmental issue, and mental health cannot be measured by lack of worry or anxiety.

There was an effort to legitimize these studies as part of traditional child psychiatry by showing that children are anxious. That kind of legitimization is not needed any more. For instance, when the research turns to smaller children, anxiety, showing that children are worried or anxious, does not need to be the main focus any more. These studies have to be done no matter whether children are worried or anxious or not. It is the development of social awareness and problem solving skills that are part of health rather than lack of disturbing feelings like anxiety.

Health education has consequently also centered around the individual. Health has been seen as one's own responsibility of one's own health and way of life. Eating healthy food, having enough exercise, not smoking and drinking have all been categorized as health behavior. Should not taking action towards the health of others also be part of health behavior, and hence, part of health education?[20] The ability to take responsibilty and social action in global and other social problems should be part of our definition of health.

BIBLIOGRAPHY

1. Borgenicht, L. (1985): Threat in the nuclear age: Children's responses to the nuclear arms debate. School Psychology International 6: 187–194.
2. Korzybski, A. Quoted in (1980): Bateson G. Mind and Nature, p. 37. Fontana Paperbacks, London.
3. Solantaus T., Rimpelä M., Taipale V. (1984): The threat of war in the minds of 12–18-year-olds in Finland. Lancet 8380: 784–785.
4. Solantaus T., Rimpelä M., Rahkonen O. (1985): Social epidemiology of the experience of the threat of war among Finnish young. Social Science and Medicine 21: 145–151.
5. Solantaus T. (1986): Hopes and worries of young people in three European countries. A WHO cross national study. Submitted for publication in Health Promotion.
6. Sommers F., Goldberg S., Levinson D., Ross C., LaCombe S. (1985): Children's mental health and the threat of nuclear war: A Canadian pilot study. In: Solantaus T., Chivian S., Vartanyan M., Chivian S., eds. Impact of the threat of war on children and adolescents. Proceedings of an international research symposium, Helsinki, Finland 1984. International Physicians for the Prevention of Nuclear War, Boston.
7. Goldenring J., Doctor R. (1985): California adolescents' concerns about the threat of nuclear war. In: Solantaus T., Chivian E., Vartanyan M., Chivian S., eds. Impact of the threat of war on children and adolescents. Proceedings of an international research symposium, Helsinki, Finland 1984. International Physicians for the Prevention of Nuclear War, Boston.
8. Barton E. (1985): Threat of war in the minds of children. Lancet 8422: 1: 226.
9. Gillies P., Elwood J. M., Hawtin P. (1985): Anxieties in adolescents about unemployment and war. British Medical Journal 291: 383–384.
10. Holmborg P. O., Bergström A. (1985): How Swedish children think and feel concerning the nuclear threat. In: Solantaus T., Chivian E., Vartanyan M., Chivian S., eds. Impact of the threat of war on children and adolescents. Proceedings of an international research symposium, Helsinki, Finland 1984. International Physicians for the Prevention of Nuclear War, Boston.
11. Chivian E. et al. (1985): Soviet children and the threat of nuclear war: A preliminary study. American Journal of Orthopsychiatry 55: 484–502.
12. Business Dicisions Ltd. Nuclear weapons study, a summary report. In Tizard B. (1984): Problematic aspects of nuclear education. Harvard Educational Review 54: 271–281.
13. Bachman J. G. (1985) in W. R. Beardslee: Children and adolescents and the threat of nuclear war: Implications of recent studies. Presented at Institute of Medicine, National Academy of Sciences. Conference on Medical Aspects of Nuclear War. September 22, 1985.
14. Van Hoorn J., French P. (1985): Facing the nuclear threat: a cross-age comparison. Presented at International Physicians for the Prevention of Nuclear War, Budapest, Hungary, June 1985.
15. Gallup, G. (1984) In W. R. Beardslee: Children and adolescents and the threat of nuclear war: Implications of recent studies. Presented at Institute of Medicine, National Academy of Sciences. Conference on Medical Aspects of Nuclear War. September 22, 1985.
16. Goldberg S. and others (1985). Thinking about the threat of nuclear war: Relevance to mental health. American Journal of Orthopsychiatry 55: 503–512.
17. Solantaus T., Rimpelä M. (1986) Mental health and nuclear war: A suitable case for treatment? International Journal of Mental Health. In press.
18. Engeström Y. (1985) Multiple levels of nuclear reality in the cognition, fantasy and activity of school-aged children. In: Solantaus T., Chivian E, Vartanyan M., Chivian S., eds. The Impact of the threat of nuclear war on children and adolescents. pp. 39–52. Proceedings of an international research symposium in Helsinki, Finland, June 1984. International Physicians for the Prevention of Nuclear War, Boston.
19. Andrejeva G. (1984) Peace education in the Soviet Union. Presented at the Fifth Congress of the International Physicians for the Prevention of Nuclear War, Helsinki, Finland, June 1984.
20. Rimpelä M. et al. (1986) The evolution of the juvenile health habit study. A paper presented in the Symposium of Health Behavior, Pitlochry, Scotland, February 1986.

284

SCIENTIFIC PROGRAMME

Alberto Malliani, Italy

Humanisation of Medicine; a Contribution to Peace

Time present and time past
Are both perhaps present in time future
And time future contained in time past.
T. S. Eliot, Four Quartets

However, much more is contained in time present than transpires from it: and it is only because of this that the future could be less frightening than anyone who dares to think could ever foresee. For man, living means always to be in a situation while projecting to modify it. Quality of life is defined not only by its actual condition, but also by the quality of the projects it is able to generate. The projects, a river which we should like to see flowing between the two opposing and necessary banks of realism and utopia. Realism intended as the articulated analysis of the already known and utopia as a window opening onto a still unexplored horizon.

The fact is, that realism has taken on the same tragic connotation as that of reality, both dominated by the omnipotence of a mechanism which is a purely productive creator of new needs, often absurd, and tireless inventor of objects, some to use, others never to use.

The unity of mankind seems to be a purely economical will. The planetary economy is described by an asymmetrical accumulation of wealth pumped by an industry which is ready to produce anything which can be sold. Unfortunately, for the first time on man's planet, objects, things, escaping every control, risk making history. The so-called realism, the pretension of keeping this volcanic magma under control, has become dangerous stupidity. This is why a project of the future, which could be capable of guaranteeing a future for human beings, will not escape so easily from some utopic components.

The concept of utopia is an historic concept and refers to projects of social transformation, the realisation of which we consider impossible. However, as Marcuse says about Utopia, you need to distinguish between a process in history such as the idea of a return to a supposed golden age and a project of transformation which appears utopian only because we do not know of any precedent historic realisation. Probably, it appeared utopian to many to end cannibalism and slavery. But, if the word stirs up a lot of perplexities let us talk, simply, about neo-humanism. Of a man who develops a real, very deep, happy culture of peace and who stops being gratified only by prevailing.

Many think that this is contrary to man's nature and for this reason such a project assumes an utopic aspect. In as much as "human nature" links us to the existing and therefore seems to exclude the essential changes necessary for choosing between peace and annihilation. On the other hand, Albert Einstein's "new manner of thinking" implies a change in human nature and this contains an utopian component.

There can only be a great respect for the pragmatism of IPPNW by which, alone, it has been possible to obtain so much success. I have personally obeyed such pragmatism like a faithful servant. But, one knows, everyone of us is his own history: whatever my devotion is, I cannot eradicate completely the roots of a culture from which I have grown. For this culture, the instruments of genocide are not a cause but a consequence. And, however much it is right not to take our eyes away from the armed hand and to give priority to try to stop it, still we should not forget the whole organism which is behind it.

From the moment in which I proposed the title of this discussion to the organizers of the Congress I was very explicit: I felt the need to explore a parallel space. I wanted to say that it was not my intention to be critical or interfere with the current which, in the circuit, managed to overcome, one after another, the resistances "in series": as there was no day in which the IPPNW was not reaching new goals. On the other hand no analysis, if it is true, should suffer by another different and parallel analysis.

I have reached the point which was the reason for this discussion. The doctors of the IPPNW accuse politicians and militarists for their blind paranoia, they censure scientists who collaborate with a technology of death, condemn industrialists who produce such instruments. Suppose that politicians, militarists, scientists and industrialists are, in reality, only products of a business which knows how to choose the right people at the right place . . . Who are the doctors in this society and what type of product do they represent? The response can only emerge by observing some of the faces of medicine we are familiar with.

What should the ultimate goal of medicine be? Perhaps, to guarantee a "good death": intended as a good natural death. One thing is certain: for this one good death others are necessary. Particularly in the hypothesis of a death without ghettos. And this goal should be worthwhile even for those who survive because no teaching, in as much as a message of life, could overcome the vision of a good death. But it is well known that current medicine does not worry much about good death. The majority of medical students finish their studies without ever having analyzed in depth the problem of death. A young doctor on the day he confronts, for the first time, the problem of the truth in front of a terminal illness and his relationship with a dying person, often discovers that our society has lost the culture of death. The problem seems to be considered unimportant, because it is not capable of interfering with the production: thus society benevolently permits the young doctor to grow, no one knows in which direction, assigning horizons of "personal conscience".

It is this medicine which has created for the dying person expressions like "there is nothing which can be done". In such moments, if medicine were solidarity, there would be much to do. But not in productive terms. Laboratory tests are of no use, expensive and miraculous drugs are no longer helpful: the circuit breaks. To conclude, death appears to be an unproductive event even if sandwiched by two highly productive realities.

No greater solidarity can be found in other aspects of medicine. To fight against tumours means to raise money, to claim precocious and clean operations and almost as a rule to turn one's back on the patient riddled with metastases who dies where he can, for the most part even without an adequate therapy against pain. Hospitals are famous for their efficiency, not for their solidarity. Especially if this solidarity involves negative economic decisions.

Analyzing the medical apparatus outside the business it represents is an irritating abstraction. If life is essentially made of needs projected towards the future, actual medicine has to be changed as much as the rest.

However, everybody has met some doctors who did not seem to be simple products. Everyone knows that the daily vision of bad death, the permanent experience of frailness, the deep emotion for human sufferings, all this renders some doctors different. As to the IPPNW, it is important, even fundamental, that all doctors touched by the awareness of a possible holocaust brought about by causes which offend man's wisdom, demonstrate immediately and in the simplest terms this awareness.

Personal behaviour and not only words, should characterize our organisation. In these days the cynicism seems to represent the fallout on the psyche of the "business über alles" and what is left of the great ideologies.

You can and must ask a doctor to be never touched by cynicism. But of medicine you must ask much more. Medicine should finally reflect on its own history behind the successes from which it has obtained far too much gratification. Medicine which spends fortunes for doubtful interventions, ready to spread wherever possible the need for drugs, but which has never tried to truly work in the schools to educate, to teach, to explain. For a doctor it is terrible to despise what he loves and to which he gives the best of his life. It is in this way that "désarroi" can turn into loss of identity.

Never has a movement of conscience made history. The river of history is flowing inexorably toward holocaust and the wind of conscience which blows in the opposite direction barely produces a few ripples on the surface of the water.

How can we make conscience win? Bacon said "to know is to can". Eliot said "make perfect your will". Probably, only the new generation may truly bloom with a "substantially new manner of thinking".

But if children have to be better than we are, we have to water them with essential knowledge and true examples. And we have to be better doctors.

If we truly want to do our best for peace it will not be enough to speak of peace: we must start a better medicine, based on solidarity. A medicine centered on man and not on profit. As a symbol, let us resume from ancient times the culture of a good death and let us honour the death of our patients.

By being doctors of peaceful medicine we shall at least gain the respect of our children for whom we can do so little.

By being peaceful doctors we shall at least open the door into the rose garden of human dignity.

The true revolution today is to organize a perfect planetary will of peace. Medicine can contribute to this revolution. In short, this is the problem: try to generate and germinate in the present the seeds of a vast, new and multiform project of life. Only if such a project reaches its critical mass, then, perhaps, for our children "there will be time" (Eliot), time to live, time to remember us.

Physicians support an Ecumenical Convocation for Peace

PHYSICIANS SUPPORT AN ECUMENICAL CONVOCATION FOR PEACE

Ulrich Gottstein, Federal Republic of Germany

Introduction

For the first time in the history of large medical congresses leading representatives of the Christian churches are meeting with physicians. This is also the first time that Christian physicians are voicing their desire for a dialogue with the churches, that physicians are calling on the Christian churches of the world to work together for the preservation of God's creation, yes, to work and to pray. This is also the first time in the history of the IPPNW that representatives of the world's Christian churches are speaking to us and are declaring their solidarity with us.

A few days ago we celebrated Pentecost, this important festival of the church that reminds us – through the Holy Ghost – of the nearness and the connection to God. The Acts of the Apostles teach us that the Lord's disciples suddenly began to talk to each other in many languages and dialects – and to the bewilderment and vexation of all the others – they could be understood.

Please do not let us regard Pentecost as a pious miracle but rather as a demand that finally brings together the Christian churches of the world to praise the Lord and to ask how Jesus Christ would speak and act in today's world that abounds with nuclear and other weapons intended for mass murder and mass destruction. We have met here at this medical congress and we talk in the different languages of more than 52 nations from the East and West, the North and South, but we feel united and have all pledged to strive for the same objective: to preserve the health and life of mankind and thereby God's whole creation.

In 1934 the young Rev. Dietrich Bonhoeffer, a member of the protestant "Confessing Church" who was later murdered by Hitler, called for a peace council of the churches, since he felt the threat of the great war. In 1985 at the last great meeting of Protestant Christians at the "Kirchentag" in Düsseldorf the nuclear physicist and philosopher Prof. C. F. von Weizsäcker had taken up Dietrich Bonhoeffer's demand again. We physicians want to thank him for his initiative.

Today I sincerely want to thank Prof. von Weizsäcker (Prof. von Weizsäcker acutely fell ill and was represented by Prof. Wolfgang Huber) for his willingness to speak to us and to present an analysis of our world with its dangers and explain the necessity of an ecumenical convocation for peace. Moreover, I cordially thank the representative of the American Catholic Bishops' Conference, the Rt. Rev. Bryan Hehir, the General Secretary of the Lutheran World Federation, Rev. Gunnar Staalsett, and the Soviet Bishop Sergei from Solnechogorsky, that they have travelled so far in order to consider and to pray together with us for the Christians' worldwide responsibility for the preservation of peace and the prevention of the use of nuclear and other weapons intended for mass murder and mass destruction. My thanks also go to many other representatives of the churches, e. g. Prof. Huber, President of last year's protestant "Kirchentag", Oberkirchenrat Dr. Barth as representative of Bishop Kruse, who is Ratsvorsitzender of the West German protestant churches and who sends us many wishes for God's blessing. I further welcome Rev. Volkmar Deile, past Secretary of "Aktion Sühnezeichen – Friedensdienste". General Secretary Emilio Castro from the World Council of Churches in Geneva and President Dr. Held from the Office for Foreign Relations of the Evangelical Church in Germany, and the Catholic Bishop Dr. Karl Braun, President of Pax Christi send us their best wishes. Also I thank many more representatives of the German Protestant and Catholic Churches who sit in the audience.

And last but not least let me thank you, dear colleagues, for coming and taking part in the discussions.

PHYSICIANS SUPPORT AN ECUMENICAL CONVOCATION FOR PEACE

Wolfgang Huber, Federal Republic of Germany

Toward a World Conference for Peace, Justice and Integrity of Creation

D ear ladies and gentlemen, first of all I want to present to you the compliments of Carl Friedrich von Weizsäcker, whom I phoned last night. He told me that he feels extremely sorry for not being able to travel for reasons of illness. It is of utmost importance to him that IPPNW has picked up the idea of a Peace Council in the way of arranging this special session, and this is indeed an exceptional event for which I want to express my gratitude. Last night I discussed the same issue at the yearly conference of one of the important Christian peace initiatives in this country, called "Christians for Disarmament". For this Christian initiative it was highly encouraging to hear that physicians committed to the prevention of a nuclear war are vigourously interested in the question of what the churches can efffectively do for peace and obviously want to contribute to find the answer. That is why it is my duty to convey greetings to you from the "Christians for Disarmament" as well as from the Presidium of the German "Evangelischer Kirchentag" which also assembled yesterday. And so I have already reached the first of four points to introduce this afternoon's issue. First, I want to say a few words about the origin of the idea discussed here, second I shall outline the present situation, third I will characterize some of the steps on the way to a Peace Council and fourth, I finally want to express a thought of hope.

The Origin of the Idea of a Peace Council

Dietrich Bonhoeffer, at that time a young German theologist engaged in the early ecumenical movement, addressed the ecumenical conference at Fanoe, Danmark, in August 1934 and called for a "Council of Peace" to proclaim the Peace of Christ in a mad world. In his view, so many people would have been relieved if the Church of Christ in the name of Christ would take the arms out of the hands of its sons, prohibiting war and proclaiming the Peace of Christ over a mad world. Bonhoeffer formulated this idea with such an intensity, because he was moved by a simple question which he articulated a few years earlier: "When will the Church of Christ find the right word at the right time?" He was from the beginning convinced that the issue of peace was the critical issue to prove whether the church was able to find just in time a word of joint responsibility. We all are aware that on the way to the Second World War the Church did not find this word, and we also know that we face the same question today with even more urgency. Therefore the delegates of the "Union of Evangelical Churches in the GDR" took up the impulse of Bonhoeffer when preparing the plenary assembly of the "Ecumenical Board of Churches" in Vancouver in 1983. The plenary assembly of the "Ecumenical Board of Churches" took up this impulse in the way that it was decided to start into the process of preparing a "World Conference for Peace, Justice, and the Integrity of Creation". Justice, peace, and the integrity of creation as well as the interdependence of these, are the issues Ecumenical Christianity is approaching in these years, because these are the central problems of life and survival at the present time. When 140,000 people assembled in Düsseldorf in June 1985 at the German "Evangelischer Kirchentag" under the heading "The Earth belongs to the Lord", they worried about how we can meet our responsibilty which results from the religious belief to the sovereignty of God over the earth. So the responsibility of the Church for justice, peace, and the integrity of creation was a central issue there. As a step towards answering that ecumenical impulse, the "Kirchentag" at Düsseldorf has formulated a proclamation initiated by Carl Friedrich von Weizsäcker, which I quote: "We ask the Churches of the world to appoint a Council of peace. Peace today is a prerequisite for the survival of humanity. It has not been attained. At an Ecumenical Council appointed for the sake of peace, the Christian Churches in joint responsibility must say a word, which humanity cannot ignore. Time is short. We ask Church leaders to do everything, so that a Peace Council assembles as soon as possible. We ask the parishes to strengthen the call for a Peace Council by their explicit support."

The present situation

The proclamation I just mentioned contains the sentence "Time is short". This sentence holds true in three ways. Time is short because the prevention of war in our world today is not secured. We are in a situation where the armament competition takes a new turn, and again it is aspired to secure peace by military and technological means, despite the fact we all know that peace cannot be secured by military technology but must be secured politically. Time is short also in the view of growing injustice in the relation between the industrialized nations and the Third-World countries, which means between the rich one-third and the poor two-thirds of mankind. Disparity is growing, injustice increases. If we on one hand are afraid of a nuclear war, we must say on the other hand that the war of hunger is already on its way and kills fourty to fifty million human beings each year. Not only in the view of the problem of war prevention, but also under the aspect of the problem of injustice we must say: time is short! The same is true in view of the destructive side effects of the human exploitation of nature. To some of us it became clear (again) after the experience of the last five weeks that the attempt of securing peace by sophisticated nuclear weapons and the attempt of a large-scale energy supply by nuclear power plants are just two different sides of the same coin, namely a handling of nature and human relations which is inhuman by not being natural.

In these three respects which are discussed by the ecumenical movement and by the Ecumenical Council of the Churches under the topics "justice", "peace", and "integrity of creation" it holds true: time is short. In all these respects the churches are confronted with the problem to find the right word at the right time. For all the three developments I described it holds true that they are incompatible with the principles of Christian belief and Christian ethics. The threat by mass destructive weapons and their use, the toleration of growing injustice in our world and the ongoing destruction of nature are factors incompatible with the confession of Christians to God, the Creator, the Reconciler, and the Redeemer of the world.

That is why the Churches are challenged not only by questions of practical ethics but also by problems pertaining to Christian belief and confession. Therefore it is justified to expect the Churches to search for the most universal, the most ecumenical, and the most responsible manner of unanimous speaking they can find, in order to dedicate themselves to peace and so to say a word which cannot be denied by other people of good intention. This is what we mean when we expect the Churches to proceed according to the historical model of a Peace Council, as long as we call the worldwide congregation of Christians we strive for a "Council".

Possible Steps Ahead of Us

During the last decades the world "Council" has been used in different situations. The Second Vatican Council was the exemplary and basic case of a council where bishops as representatives of the Catholic Church met to come to obligatory decisions. When Prior Rogé Schütz from Taizé called for a "Council of the Youth", the word "Council" was used for a process that comes from the basis of the parishes where renewal takes place. If we follow the idea of a Peace Council, we must look for the joint power of both, the process of renewal fortunately seen in many places including also the young generation within our Churches and beyond our Churches, and the process of taking over responsibility by those designated to represent and guide our Churches. In this way the event of a Peace Council assembly and the process of agreement on problems of endangered survival among parishes and peace initiatives belong together. To ensure that these two elements stay together, some have proposed to plan the process towards a worldwide Council of the Churches in three steps: A first step of *local* clarification and agreement within the groups working on the peace issue, namely parishes, peace initiatives, professional initiatives like IPPNW etc. A second step of clarifying specific *regional* problems in the different parts of the world, perhaps possible until 1988, to meet the challenges coming from outside, for example by a meeting of Church representatives from the nations being members of KSZE to discuss peace problems in the light of inquiries of Third-World countries. Finally the third step, which is more or less the hope that the world conference for peace, justice, and the integrity of creation scheduled for 1990 may have the true character of a Peace Council.

In summary then, I would like to present the following theses which might bring us on the way:

1. The Churches should advocate the abolition of war as an institution. With their special responsibilty for the image of man, the Churches must make clear that war is not a natural phenomenon, but a phenomenon of human history, that war is not a part of nature, but a product of human history which can be overcome by historical effort. The work for prevention of a nuclear war and for the abolishment of nuclear weapons should be understood as a step on the way to overcome war as an institution.
2. The Churches should on the basis of their understanding of "Shalom", of peace in the Jewish-Christian tradition, unequivocally emphasise: There is no peace without justice, but there is also no justice without peace.
3. Based on the tradition they represent, the Churches should make clear that there is no peace for mankind without reconciliation to nature.

Let me, at the end, formulate a word of hope. I am aware of the fact that for the Roman-Catholic Church the term "Council" has a strict canonical meaning and the same is true for the Orthodox Churches. My hope is that we reach consensus that we do not understand these different traditional definitions as an obstacle, but develop together a true ecumenical language for Christianity in an utmost uniform and responsible way. To my opinion, never before in history the Christian Churches faced a comparable challenge for practiced Ecumene than today. Their credibility will highly depend on the ability to express their responsibility for peace, justice, and the integrity of creation in a joint and liable manner.

PHYSICIANS SUPPORT AN ECUMENICAL CONVOCATION FOR PEACE

Sergei, Bishop of Solnechogorsky, U.S.S.R.

Peace Effort of the Russian Orthodox Church

D ear Brothers and Sisters, it is a great privilege for me to speak at this celebrated forum as an ecclesiastic from the U.S.S.R. I would like to convey greetings to you from the faithful and from Church leaders in the U.S.S.R. Let us take a look at the present spiritual life of my country. There are two points I would like to make here. It doesn't matter what confession is shared by this or that group of people in my country, they all try to keep the spiritual impulse alive they all share in the name of Christ. Secondly I would like to deal with the spiritual part of their life but also with peace-making. The Russian Orthodox Church has a long history of peace-making efforts and that history is rooted down, deep down in centuries and centuries of tradition. The Russian Orthodox Church conducting its peace-making efforts acts on the assumption that war is evil and evil has no place in life and evil is a sin. It is for this reason that our peace-making acitivities are viewed by the Russian Orthodox Church as an effort against sin. After nuclear weapons were used for the first time, the Russian Orthodox Church and other Soviet Confessions took a clear-cut position on this issue. They said "no" to nuclear arms, they said that nuclear arms should be banned and they said that nuclear arms should not exist on earth.

The Soviet believers held conferences, represented and attended by every religious group in our country. All those conferences were conducted against nuclear war. Those conferences were held in 1953, in 1969, a worldwide conference was held in 1973 and yet another world conference was held in 1982. And I would like to point out that the Soviet believers cooperate very actively with other peace organisations in the world against nuclear war and for peace. Those international organisations the Soviet believers cooperate with include the World Council of Churches, the European Conference of Churches and also secular organisations like the World Peace Council. Further we cooperate vigorously with the local Church organisations here in the Federal Republic of Germany and the national council of Churches here. We also cooperate with the Pax Christi International in the United States. Last year in Moscow round-table discussions were held within the framework of the 1982 world conference of religious leaders and attended by some religious figures and experts who talked about the topic "Space with no nuclear arms". It is very interesting to note that the experts from the United States of America, from the Soviet Union, West Germany and India were unanimously saying that nuclear disarmament was possible. It is for this reason that the Soviet believers have supported the appeal made by the Secretary General of the Soviet Communist Party, Michael Gorbachev, on January 15th, 1985, an appeal to eliminate nuclear weapons by the end of this century. Representatives from the Soviet Churches made a special appeal addressed to every other church organisation in the world concerning this topic.

I would like to conclude my very brief statement by expressing the hope that nuclear weapons shall be banned and war itself shall be banned. And I think we have grounds to believe that our wish will come true. When we started our peace-making activities there were people who said that the Soviet Church leaders and figures were involving themselves in politics. But now there are quite a few international Church organisations that are studying the problems of war and peace on the theological basis. And I think that this congress also gives me hope because this congress is attended not only by specialists, by physicians, professional people, but also by many other people of good will, who have gathered here to say "no" to nuclear war.

PHYSICIANS SUPPORT AN ECUMENICAL CONVOCATION FOR PEACE

Rt. Rev. Brian Hehir, U.S.A.

The Importance of the Ethical and Religious Aspect in the Nuclear Debate

I appreciate the opportunity to participate in this symposium. I have participated before, and members of the Bishops' conference of the United States have also participated in other IPPNW congresses. I should indicate at the beginning what I will be able to do this afternoon and what I will not be able to do. I am very interested in Prof. Huber's suggestion and Prof. von Weizsäcker's suggestion; I am in no position to comment on the position of the Catholic Church to the specific proposal that is offered; that would have to be done at a much higher level and by people who hold much higher positions than I do. What I will be able to do is to talk about the centrality of the moral religious factor in the nuclear debate. That will be the purpose of my remarks: "The centrality of the moral religious factor in the nuclear debate." We are now fourty years into the nuclear age and it gives us an opportunity to assess the meaning of the moment in which we live. We are fifteen years away from the third millenium. Midway through this century something happened in world affaires, that means that we face what the Catholic Bishops of the United States called a new moment in the nuclear age. It is the meaning of that new moment, the emergence of the nuclear age, that I wish to examine. I will speak to three themes about the new moment. First of all, the emergence of the moral factor in the public debate about nuclear policy; secondly, three themes about morality in the nuclear age; and thirdly, a word about the future of the nuclear debate.

I would submit that for much of the nuclear age we all, East and West, have been targets of the nuclear weapons. But there has not been for most of the nuclear age significant public popular involvement in the nuclear debate. There has been an intense technical debate for much of the nuclear age by people who are specialists, either military specialists, scientists or political figures. But one of the interesting features of the 1980's is the emergence of a serious significant popular engagement in the public debate about nuclear weapons. Obviously my experience is from the West and so I really only speak of that experience. It shows the emergence of a serious popular constituency concerned about the fate and future of the nuclear age. The American Catholic Bishops have become increasingly apprehensive about the fact that the normal process of politics is not in line with the dynamics and the demands of the nuclear arms race. Politics as usual is not adequate to catch hold of the nuclear arms race and to turn it around. Moreover, I think the physicians, certainly in the United States, are making a unique contribution to the popular debate. Physicians in our society hold an enormous moral authority. They normally are not regarded as people who enter political discussion, and the emergence of a significant number of physicians in the popular discussions has had a significant impact on the way the public sees the nuclear question. The religious organisations have not been silent on the question of war and peace. But there is a new urgency in the 1980's among religious communities cutting across Jewish and Christian lines about the reality of the new moment in the nuclear age. Just as people in the political order think that politics as usual is not sufficient to capture the dynamic of nuclear weapons, so the religious communities, which from their traditions have been able to discuss the question of war and peace for centuries, today understand that one must take the potential that is in the religious communities and deal with it much more urgently and dramatically regarding the question of war and peace in the nuclear age. Running through the popular debate is a serious, significant concern about the moral imperatives that living in the nuclear age force upon us. I submit that it is necessary at the outset to understand the significance of keeping alive this popular constituency concerned about nuclear war. If politics as usual is not adequate to the nuclear age then politics in an unusual fashion will only be brought about if there is serious sustained popular public engagement by people who are not professionally politicians, not professionally military people and not even professionally scientifically engaged in the question of the nuclear age. My first point therefore is to simply know one characteristic of the 1980's. Fourty years into the nuclear age people have focussed on the danger and the need to change our politics in a new way.

Secondly, as one looks at this popular debate about this new moment, I think it is necessary to say that we clearly are at a very crucial point as we look at the next fifteen years to the end of the century. If one traces the history of the nuclear age from 1945 until today it is clear that there appear certain critical moments when decisions are taken that set the direction for many years to come. The period of the late 1950's and early 1960's was such a time. Ideas were formed then that still guide the process of the nuclear age. The notions technically described as second strike deterrence, the understanding of the relationship of arms control and deterrence were formed and shaped in that period and today they still guide our thinking. I submit for a variety of reasons that I do not have the time to detail at this meeting that at the mid 1980's we are at another of these crucial turning points when people are thinking and rethinking the ideas by which the nuclear age is to be shaped. We should understand that this is not a normal period, this is a critical turning point. The ideas that will guide politically and strategically what happens to these weapons and how we think about war, politics and ethics in the nuclear age are set today in a fundamental way. So it is not just the emergence of a popular level of concern that is significant, it is also that the policy debate is at a critical turning point. Let me address three themes in that policy debate very briefly that will highlight, I think, what I mean by the turning point. The three themes are how we think first about war, politics and morality; how we think secondly about technology, strategy and morality; thirdly, how we think about economics, politics and morality. My purpose is simply to comment briefly on each of them.

The way we think about war, politics and morality in the nuclear age, I think, is the fundamental issue. The western world has thought about these questions since the beginning of the Christian aera. The discussion of the morality of warfare has been a fundamental theme in the Christian Church. It is reflected in the New Testament, it is given decisive direction by Saint Augustin in the fifth century and the discussion continues to this very day. When the American Catholic Bishops throughout Western Europe addressed the issue of the morality of warfare in the early 1980's they thought of themselves as standing in this tradition that reaches back to the New Testament. So it is not a new topic, the point is it is an old topic being discussed at a new moment. The absolute necessity in thinking about war, politics and morality in the nuclear age is to be clear about our starting point. It is to be clear about the utter uniqueness of nuclear weapons. It is to be clear about the fact that once we passed into the nuclear age it is necessary to rethink war, politics and morality.

The two people who taught the Western world to think about the relationship of war and politics and then war, politics and morality were in my judgement a 19th century Prussian general and a 5th century African Saint. The 19th century Prussian general Clausewitz said that war was the extension of politics by other means. He meant, I think, that war could be understood as a rational political endeavour, used to accomplish rational goals. Augustin in the 5th century said war under certain conditions was a morally justifiable activity. The uniqueness of the nuclear age is that the nuclear age challenges the conclusions of both, Clausewitz and Augustin. War today is not what war has been in the past. Nuclear war is neither politically rational nor morally justifiable. When he went to Hiroshima, John Paul II said: "In the past it was possible to destroy a town, a village, even a region – today, it is the whole planet that is under threat." I submit the Pope's statement is precisely the single idea by which the nuclear age should be evaluated. War is not what war has been. And he went on to say speaking to scientists that from now on it was only by a conscious choice that humanity could survive. Precisely, because war is not what war has been it is necessary to give a new direction to war and politics in the nuclear age. We must be utterly realistic about this: nuclear weapons will not go away easily. Sovereign states still govern the world, but we must manage a world of sovereign states that possess nuclear weapons in such a way that these weapons that continue to exist will never be used. Today political control over war, nuclear war specifically, is not simply a political necessity, it is a moral imperative. It is necessary to rethink war, politics and morality, for these weapons are utterly different than anything we have known before.

Secondly, we must think about technology, strategy and morality. We must do this because in the nuclear age technology is almost an independent force. The technological revolution in arms production goes through a new revolutionary cycle every five years. And so the question always arises whether politics guides technology or whether technology dominates politics. It is precisely in this way, again, that John Paul II thinks and talks about the nuclear question. He always puts it in the context of whether human beings will control their technology or whether they will be controlled by their technology. In the nuclear age we have the technology that will allow us to do almost anything. We can touch the beginning of life and we can threaten the end of all of it. We can shape the genetic future of the race and we can end human history. In the past the ability to touch the beginning of life and to threaten the end of all of it were functions that people believed belonged only to God. Today we possess the possibility to shape the beginnings of life and to threaten the end of all of it. In their Pastoral letter the American Bishops said of this time in human history: "We are the first generation since genesis to possess the capacity to do what we can do. The nuclear age teaches us to reread the book of genesis. For centuries people knew that they inherited a creation they did not create. They understood that they were stewards of that creation and that they were to pass it on to the next generation. We are the first generation since genesis to know that we inherit what we did not create, that we are entrusted with it but that we have the capacity not to pass it on." That reality reaffirms that war, politics and morality must be rethought from the beginning. Our technology must be controlled by us, not us by our technology. In an age in which we can do almost anything technologically the clear moral question is this: In a time in which we can do almost anything how do we decide what we ought to do? That is the fundamental question. If we do everything we can do technologically we are simply driven by our technology. If we take possession of our technology and give it direction, then we act in a human way. The second truth of the nuclear age is that we must control the technology of the age and not be controlled by it.

Thirdly, I turn to the relationship of economics, politics and morality. The fact of the matter is, that within our nations and much more dramatically on a global scale it is utterly clear that fundamental human needs are neglected. In our industrial countries of the East and West with more or less intensity poverty still exists in all too scandalous a fashion. But at the global level the disparity of living standards between the North of the globe and the rest of the globe is a moral and political scandal. In his "World Day of Peace Message" to the Church this year Johan Paul II said it was necessary to join the East-West-discussion and the North-South-discussion and that one could not absorbe the totality of the moral challenge of the age even in the face of the threat of nuclear war. That is one of the moral questions that we face and the other is the glaring poverty of the South, and neither East nor West have met that in any adequate moral way. It is clear that in very different political systems the struggle about the budget is the fundamental struggle in the political order. And if we have a defense spending budget, East and West, that goes uncontrolled, unconstrained, is allowed to grow without justification, then human needs will continue to be disregarded. Just as we must control our technology, so we also must be able to direct our economy in some realistic human sense. The unfulfilled human needs of the globe indict the powers of the East and the West for their military budgets that exist in our nations. The future of the nuclear debate over the next fifteen years seems to be utterly necessary to be understood not only in political terms or strategic terms but in normal terms. The questions we debate about touching the beginning of life, threatening the end of all of it and meeting the human needs of people who are brothers and sisters are not purely political questions. They are political questions with an utter irreducable moral dimension.

And so it is necessary that we discuss war, politics, technology and strategy, economics and politics in moral terms as well. And as we do that, it is necessary that the discussion be carried on in every sector of the society, among the specialists and among the public, among the scientists and among the monks and the priests and the ministers, among the teachers and among those who shape the direction of our society as its leaders. In my view there has been a change in the 80's, there is a new interest in the utter seriousness of the moment we face. But this is only the beginning, the last fifteen years of this century are a time in which the moral judgement on all of us will be tested by whether we control what we produce or whether we are controlled by it, by whether we give direction to our politics and our technology or whether it gives direction to us. John Paul II said the future of humanity depends upon making a conscious choice and directing policy by conscious choice. Our conscious choice will determine how we are judged politically and morally.

PHYSICIANS SUPPORT AN ECUMENICAL CONVOCATION FOR PEACE

Rev. Gunnar Staalsett, Lutheran World Federation

The Lutheran World Federation and the Ecumenical Peace Conference

B rothers and Sisters and Friends, I will hold you in no suspense, I will tell you that I am for a peace council and I do hope that the meeting here will contribute to strengthening that process towards a universal, ecumenical gathering of Christians to say a clear morally based "no" to nuclear war. When I had the honor to introduce the speakers at the Nobel Peace Prize ceremony in Oslo almost a year ago I underscored that the Nobel Peace Prize committee through years had interpreted and supported various aspects of peacework, such as elimination of hunger and poverty, aid to the millions of refugees, struggle against apartheid, promotion of justice and human rights. But last year, or that year when your organisation was honored, the committee said the most basic of all human rights, the right to live, for this and the coming generations is at stake, therefore let the prize this year concentrate the attention of the world on the need to mobilize all powers and all the creative resources of women and men of good will for the prevention of nuclear annihilation. That is why we are here today to unite resources of women and men, of young and old for the prevention of nuclear annihilation. We are here to affirm our "yes" to confidence building and cooperation, our "no" to confrontation and mutual destruction; we are here to say "yes" to a legitimate defence of the sovereignty of every nation but "no" to an arms race that fills the heavens and the earth with nuclear weapons, "yes" to defend freedom and justice, "no" to the destruction of this planet and the human race. My first meeting with one who received the Nobel Peace Prize was brought to my memory this morning listening to that very moving lecture in the plenary hall. As a student in my first year of theology at the university of Oslo I met Albert Schweitzer in 1954. This was the first time also that the students and the people of Oslo filled the streets in a torch-lit march to honor the laureate. At the rally in the city hall of Oslo after the formal Nobel ceremony one of my theology professors spoke in honor of Dr. Schweitzer. He spoke of him as a symbol of Christian and humanist values and his statement about Albert Schweitzer was the following: "If he is a humanist then I gladly would be a humanist." This reflected the debate of that time whether there is a common ground, a common set of values that makes it possible for Christian believers and humanists to join hands. I believe we have come a long way since then, up to this day, when the International Physicians for the Prevention of Nuclear War invite the Churches to cooperate in order to serve, to save the sacred creation and the gift of life.

I speak to you on behalf of one of the world communes of Churches, the Lutheran World Federation, an organisation with 104 member Churches around the world, from Iceland to Papua New Guinea, from Japan to El Salvador, in the U.S.A. and in the Soviet Union. Our member Churches count around 60,000,000 members. The federation was organised in 1947 out of the same experience that led to the organisation of the World Council of Churches. For more than a generation Christians around the world had been searching for a greater measure of unity. It was actually under the experience of the Second World War, with all its horror and destruction that the Churches finally were brought together. Their common dedication was then to serve the people who had suffered and to be part of the healing process in a humanity so violated, and to serve the building of the nations in the postwar world. Most of the Churches of the Lutheran World Federation are also members of the World Council of Churches and I have had the honor to serve on the Executive Committee of the World Council of Churches. The World Council of Churches and the Lutheran World Federation have been part of the peace movement from the beginning.

The question today is if we under the pressure of the ongoing struggle and the threat of nuclear annihilation find ourselves forced to go further on our way for peace as it has been suggested in the proposal by Dr. von Weizsäcker. Now, where are we in relation to the burning issues of our time? While I agree that your organisation concentrates on the *prevention* of nuclear war and I believe it is helpful and important for all that you do that, the Churches must have a broader agenda, namely peace, justice, freedom, human rights, the care of the endangered creation. This is not in opposition to the stands taken by you, rather you are the specialists, while we are the generalists, but we belong to the same healing ministry. Our concern is with the millions who are dying now in the South as a result of exploitation by the richer nations. Our concern is with all those who are suffering in whatever part of the world it is. In our latest statement from the Lutheran World Federation's Executive Committee, latest statement of peace, we spoke of the escalation of ideological confrontation accompanied by the proliferation of weapons for mass destruction, a proliferation which has propelled civilisation into the most dangerous period since the dawn of history. And we pointed out that the expenditure of vast financial resources for the production of armaments results directly in an extended exploitation of large segments of the world's population even to the denial of the basic necessities of life. And we went on to urge our member Churches around the world to take a clear stand against the further militarisation of outer space by urging all governments to abandon all forms of participation in such an enterprise. We urged our member Churches actively to oppose the proliferation of nuclear weapons including their further development, production and employment which implies in today's discussion that we are for a total test ban. And it was in this connection that we gave support to the idea of convening an ecumenical and global peace council that would consider the urgent problems of justice, of peace and care for the endangered creation. We have offered the good service of our organisation to be part of the process to help implement such a proposal. In my staff we have a theologian from the GDR who works on the theological analysis of the peace issues in our time. And we have appointed an assistant general secretary for international affairs and human rights, an American who will deal with the follow up of these decisions, so that we can see that we implement indeed a more active participation in peacework by the Churches around the world. The Churches are moving together, a consensus is emerging. Let me just give you two examples: The Reformed Church of Scotland last month reaffirmed its rejection of nuclear weapons by opposing their use for any reason and calling on the government of the United Kingdom to stop their further development, urging the government to withhold support from all escalations of the arms race including the U.S. star wars program. The United Methodists Church at a similar meeting of all its Bishops unanimously approved a statement of clear and unconditional "no" to nuclear war and to use any nuclear weapons. They also say that nuclear deterrence cannot receive the Churches' blessings.

It is in view of this emerging consensus that I am hopeful about a convocation of all Churches for peace. Such a convocation should be able to speak clearly and unanimously and provide an authoritative word on peace on behalf of the worldwide Christian community. It should be structured in such a way that the process leading up to the convocation should include Church members from the grassroots upwards. It should be developed in such a way that all the Churches can start within their own community, so that we do not get into the struggle between the various Churches, they want to do it this way, others want to do it that way. We want to see that all Churches can participate and from this participation there could be an emergence which leads to consensus. I believe that the council that von Weizsäcker has been proposing should aim to give a new moral teaching to the world which will maintain that nuclear war is no way to peace. When Reagan and Gorbachev agreed in Geneva that no nuclear war can be won, then the logic should force them to draw the conclusion that whatever makes a nuclear war possible must be done away with. The Churches can offer their moral support to a doctrine to supersede the old doctrine of "just war" which was referred to by the previous speaker.

But even if we would stick to this old doctrine of "just war", nuclear war would not be acceptable; just let me remind you of four criteria: In the doctrine of "just war" one said it is just if there is a reasonable hope of success. There is no hope of success in a nuclear war. The second criterion was that it should be possible to discriminate between those who were soldiers and those who were civilians. That is not possible in a nuclear war. They also formulated a criterion of proportionality. In the end the war must be doing more good than harm, that is not possible in a nuclear war. And fourthly, one of the criteria was that after the war there should be a restauration of the situation which prevailed before the war and that indeed is not possible after a nuclear war. We heard this morning about the so-called "terminal experiments" by Nazi doctors in the concentration camps, terminal experiments meaning that the death of the test person is part of the experiment. The world and humanity today are held hostage to such a terminal experiment with nuclear weapons. The only comfort for those who are responsible for the nuclear arms race must be that if a war breaks out there will be no one alive to judge them afterwards and no one to be judged.

But Christians believe that we are morally responsible not only to each other, not only to other human beings and to the creation, we are responsible to God. Christians believe that we do stand under the judgement of God, the Creator of Heaven and Earth. If we in our lack of wisdom will lead the world into such a situation that humanity, that this world is being destructed totally, we have a call to be carriors of hope, of future, be carriors of a sign of hope to the new generations. Let us give support to this idea of bringing men and women of good will together to speak that word about a world, in future a world in peace, because that is what is needed. We need to give this moral support to the politicians so that they are forced to find a new course for our generation and a future for the generations to come.

PHYSICIANS SUPPORT AN ECUMENICAL CONVOCATION FOR PEACE

Resolution of the Session

At this 6th World Congress of the "International Physicians for the Prevention of Nuclear War" (IPPNW) leading representatives of the world's Christian Churches – among them from the American Catholic Bishops' Conference, Rev. Bryan Hehir, the Soviet Bishop of the Russian-Orthodox Church, Sergei from Solnechogorsky and the Secretary General of the Lutheran World Federation Rev. Gunnar Staalsett – have met with us physicians from 52 nations. We have thought and talked about the Christian Churches' and the physicians' joint responsibility for life and health of mankind, for peace, justice and the preservation of God's creation with all its variety.

Never in the history of the world has the threat to mankind and nature loomed larger than it does today. Even if history abounds with horrible wars and atrocities, even if we had to mourn the death of millions of people and the destruction of the cities in many of the world's countries during the last World War the development of nuclear weapons has inaugurated a wholly new and different age. The survival of mankind is at stake.

In 1945 there existed three nuclear weapons, today more than 40,000 of them are deployed. This development was possible, because so many people no longer feel any responsibility to God and because they no longer fear the Lord's judgement.

We Christian physicians ask the world's Churches to gather in Christian love and faith for a large Peace Conference and to confess courageously to the people of the world and their governments that Christian faith is incompatible with the mass production, the deployment and the threat of using nuclear and other mass destructive weapons.

We physicians ask the world's Churches to listen to Jesus Christ and to answer the question how Jesus Christ would decide and speak today.

We physicians ask the Christian Churches of the world to remain credible for us by shunning political considerations and to speak up with courage.

We physicians ask the world's Churches for an unequivocal ethical statement.

For us Christians it is the highest task to obey God, the Creator of Heaven and Earth, and his son, Jesus Christ. And that means that we are obliged to do everything in our power to preserve this unique creation.

* * *

This resolution was unanimously accepted by the 300 participants of the session on 31. 5. 1986.

The Year Ahead

THE YEAR AHEAD

Evgueni Chazov, U.S.S.R.

Not Words But Real Deeds

Our 6th congress, which has become another contribution of physicians from over fifty countries of the world to the preservation of life on earth, is passing into history. We shall all keep in our memory the hospitality of our colleagues from the FRG, the kindness of the citizens of Cologne and the city's unique beauty, recalling the words of the great Heine:

> Rising high above the Rhine
> In the early morning dawn
> Stands the ancient sacred shrine
> The Great Cathedral of Cologne.

And, of course, we shall long recall our discussions, which were heated and often pointed but always characterized by good will and a desire to understand each other in order to contribute to the prevention of a nuclear catastrophe. We shall recall the atmosphere of trust which prevailed among us, physicians of different nationalities, people of various political and religious beliefs. This trust causes irritation among certain circles in the West that oppose the spirit of Geneva and East-West dialogue. Those circles would use any contrived pretext to try to sow mistrust among us and to create an atmosphere of suspicion and animosity and eventually destroy our movement – one of the most authoritative antiwar movements in the world. However, they have clearly underestimated the professional integrity and humanism of physicians, who cherish human life above everything else.

It is for the sake of life on earth that we live and work, to this we devote our energies and our knowledge, and no one will ever succeed in destroying our movement. This has been confirmed by the Cologne congress which has strengthened our prestige as well as trust among us. The trust which, unfortunately, is lacking among political leaders.

The congress took place in a complicated political situation. The U.S. government has failed to use the historic opportunity and ignored the Soviet moratorium on nuclear explosions. The contiuation of nuclear weapons tests, particularly for developing SDI systems, starts a new spiral of the nuclear arms race, which is especially dangerous since it extends into space. "The spirit of Geneva" is evaporating while the threat of nuclear war is growing. A war that would be even more tragic than we used to think.

Research conducted in the Soviet Committee of Physicians for the Prevention of Nuclear War by the group led by Leonid Ilyin indicates that laser systems deployed in space could also be used as an offensive weapon, since they are capable of starting fires in the cities. Accidents may happen to nuclear pumping systems for lasers deployed in space, which could lead to extensive radioactive contamination of the environment.

The loss of the Challenger, the tragedy at the Chernobyl nuclear power station and accidents at the Nevada nuclear test range once again confirm our repeated warning that even the most advanced technologies and the most sophisticated computers can fail. Given the continuous process of perfecting nuclear weapons and their increasingly extensive deployment – on land, under water and now in outer space – as well as the complexity of control systems, accidents involving nuclear weapons may lead to a global catastrophe.

We, the Soviet physicians, have had to deal with the consequences of the accident at the Chernobyl nuclear power station. Although it was not a nuclear explosion but rather an explosion of steam, strenuous efforts at a national level and the efforts of numerous medical personnel were required to eliminate the consequences. We are grateful to all scientists, physicians and medical personnel from many countries who, in the spirit of physicians' humane and noble calling, have offered their skills for the treatment of those affected by the accident. We are grateful to Professors Gale and Tarasaki and other medical workers who have worked hard together with Soviet physicians in treating patients suffering from radiation sickness.

The scale of the medical problem, with fifty-one persons seriously affected, cannot be compared to what might happen following the explosion of even the least powerful nuclear bomb. Nevertheless, major medical forces had to be mobilized. This fact provides another justification for our warning that medicine will be helpless in a nuclear war and civil defence measures will not be of significant value in saving mankind.

The situation in the world today is complex and dangerous. Many people are asking "What are we to do?" Can we, can the peoples of the world change the situation?

But is it not true that in our everyday work as physicians we face situations which threaten people's lives and sometimes seem hopeless? Do we give up? Do we turn away from the patient? On the contrary, the more complex the situation the harder we work. We gather our strength, skill and experience, seek help from our colleagues and do everything possible and sometimes even the impossible to save human life.

The Russian author Anton Chekhov, who was also a good physician, once wrote: "Being a physician is an act of courage, it requires self-assertion, a purity of soul and purity of thinking." Today this act of courage is performed in the name of life by people of pure thinking, people who hate nuclear weapons.

You have offered the world a medical prescription for the survival of humankind – the cessation of nuclear tests. You have spoken out against the nuclear arms race on earth and its extention to outer space. Instead of SDI, let us create the Medical Space Programme, which would serve the cause of preserving life on earth.

The Soviet Union and the United States, WHO and UNICEF, countries in the West and in the East, medical centres and universities around the world could use satellites to develop not a military system, but a system that would provide any physician in any country of the world the information or consultation necessary for saving human life. The international Cooperative Space Aid System has helped to save fivehundred lives in distress situations. The Medical Space Program could help to save thousands of lives.

What is most important is that this would be an example of what the nations of the world could do if they joined forces in the struggle against disease, hunger and illiteracy. This would be our best response to those who would like to sow hostility and hatred among us and continue the nuclear arms race in such an atmosphere. We cannot stand idly by. We have no right to remain silent.

For the sake of our patients' health, for the future of our children and grandchildren, we must demand from politicians and all political leaders not words, but real deeds to stop the nuclear arms race and totally eliminate nuclear weapons everywhere in our lifetime.

———————————

Bernard Lown, U.S.A.

The Urgency of Moral Outrage

I s it possible that this congress began a mere three days ago? In this brief time we have been educated, we have been stimulated, we have been challenged, but above all, there has been a deepening of old friendships and a forging of new ones. On Thursday I expressed admiration for the herculean efforts of our German colleagues. Now, the poverty of words prevents the articulation of the deepest feelings. I am in awe of this extraordinary achievement. I feel sorry for Dr. Chazov and his co-workers who have to reach the dizzying heights scaled by our German friends. If one group is to be singled out, it is the students, who have worked fourteen hours or more each day turning out documents and attending to necessary chores – our tribute to these unsung heroes and heroines!

Lessons of Chernobyl

We live in an age when intelligent people defer judgement to self-described experts, even on issues that concern their very survival. We have been conditioned to deny the evidence of our senses and ignore the incontrovertible. We have been assured by experts that nuclear war will not happen. But the elementary laws of probability tell us that an annual risk of nuclear war, even as low as one per cent, cumulates to a likelihood of fourty per cent when projected over the expected lifespan of today's young people. It is a statistical certainty that hair-trigger readiness cannot endure as a permanent condition. Ignoring the possibility of accident ascribes to man and his products a godliness that can never be achieved.

The world has been spared catastrophe, but our good fortune is fragile. Nuclear war is an accident waiting to happen. There is no dearth of warnings. Hiroshima and Nagasaki, Three Mile Island, Bhopal, Challenger, and Chernobyl are sharply etched vignettes of experience – lessons, so to speak – to educate us about the world's end. We shall be given no more precise warnings. We can only hope that the lessons will never be more concrete and tangible.

The Trap of Deterrence

As this audience knows, IPPNW has been calling for a cessation of all nuclear explosions. The Soviet Union has responded with a year-long moratorium. The United States has not reciprocated, a disappointment especially great for us as American physicians. Most informed commentators ascribe the U.S. govenrment's position to its desire to develop space weapons, which a test ban would retard. Few supporters of the plan speak of a total defense of the civilian population; the more pragmatic justify space weapons as necessary to strengthen deterrence. If we are to comprehend the threatened escalation in the nuclear arms race, we must examine its justification: the policy of deterrence. In essence, this policy is based on the supposition that nuclear weapons, by threatening unacceptable damage, restrain undesirable actions by an adversary. A number of illusions underlie this policy.

First is the illusion of numbers. If deterrence is the objective of military policy, what is the purpose in accumulating 50,000 strategic and tactical warheads, equivalent in the aggregate to more than four tons of dynamite for every man, woman, and child? Why such a blatant exercise in redundancy? A second illusion is the claim that nuclear weapons have conventional or political value. But all such claims rest on a hidden premise of limited nuclear war – "an event as likely as an explosion restricted to the top third of a keg of dynamite". (Muller J.E., Lown B., The Failure of Deterrence, Boston Globe, 1984). A third illusion is that deterrence has been a successful policy. It is commonly stated that the avoidance of war between the U.S.A. and the U.S.S.R. during the past fourty years is due to deterrence. This is an assertion not amenable to proof and lacking in persuasiveness. The two countries were not at war before the advent of nuclear weapons. They were, in fact, military allies. They do not dispute each other's borders; They do not engage in significant commercial rivalries. Fundamentally of course, the argument that deterrence has prevented catastrophe fails irredeemably when it fails just once. Any guarantee of peace with such a small margin of error is no guarantee at all.

An Immoral Policy

On the basis of this policy of deterrence, responsible governments are targeting entire nations. The front line has become everyone's home. Infants and the aged, the sick and the crippled are all targeted. The irreplaceable artifacts of human history, the creative and artistic achievements of the ages will not be spared incineration.

In the sorry recorded history of 5000 years of endless wars, some limits have been set on human savagery. Moral safeguards were raised to preclude the killing of unarmed civilians and health workers, the poisoning of drinking water, the incineration of open cities, and the spreading of infection. But nuclear barbarism threatens in one stroke all these painfully won but limited constraints. Total war – unprincipled in method, unlimited in violence, indiscriminate in its victims, and uncontrolled in its devastation – is now sanctioned military policy. Deterrence is a suspended sentence of mass murder to be executed at any moment. The idea of pointing nuclear missiles at entire nations is without precedent in moral depravity. We fought Hitler to rid the world of genocide. Have we defeated the enemy of humankind only to become infected with his immorality?

The Need for Moral Outrage

Information is not equivalent to knowledge, and possessing knowledge does not necessarily impart understanding. Nor does understanding consistently stimulate the appropriate activity to achieve change. The gap between cognition and involvement is frequently bridged by moral arousal.

We physicians, guardians of health and life, have an ethical categorical imperative to expose the bleak immorality of the policy of deterrence. We must not acquiesce to stockpiling weapons of mass extermination as the guarantors of national security. We must not permit the search for peace to proceed through overt flirtation with death. There are no conceivable circumstances which can justify the use of genocidal weapons. We need the moral courage to go further. We need to equate the possession of nuclear weapons with crimes against humanity. Would the building of thousands of gas chambers not be deemed repugnant to the laws of civilized society? It is appropriate, from this podium in Germany, to call for activation of a new war-crimes process, a new Nuremberg, to begin to examine the violation of international law implicit in the stockpiling of instruments of genocide.

Brooding over the nuclear threat for a quarter of a century now, I am led inexorably to the conviction that without exciting moral outrage among their intended victims, the dismantling of nuclear weapons will not succeed. Only unprecedented arousal of moral revulsion will provide the necessary spiritual energy.

Before departing for Cologne, I received a letter from a physician in which he requested that we remove his name, though he continues to support the principles of IPPNW. As a concentration camp survivor, he was revolted at holding the congress in Germany. These words released a surge of painful memories. My grandfather, uncle, aunt, and cousins, who were close to me, were burned alive by the Nazis. I regret that the physician who wrote to me was not here yesterday morning to listen to the impassioned words of conscience of Hanauske-Abel. After this emotionally draining talk, I met an Australian Jewish physician. He said: "I swore never to visit Germany. Now the circle is closed. For me, Germany has been redeemed by its IPPNW."

So, as we depart this congress, let us rekindle our indignation at the moral obscenity of the politics of nuclearism. Let us heed Hanauske-Abel as he amplifies the stilled words of courage and resolve of Sophie and her brother Hans Scholl and the other young members of the *Weiße Rose*. "What matters now is, not to allow oneself any rest until everybody is convinced of the utmost importance of the fight against this disorder."

In V-Day 1945, Norman Corwin delivered on Radio his poetic drama, "On a Note of Triumph". I quote the last stanza:

> Lord God of test-tube and blueprint
> Who joined molecules of dust and shook them till
> Their name was Adam,
> Who taught worms and stars how they could live together,
> Appear now among the parliaments of conquerors and
> Give Instruction to their schemes,
> Measure out new liberties so none shall suffer for his
> Father's color or the credo of his choice,
> Post proofs that brotherhood is not so wild a dream as
> Those who profit by postponing it pretend,
> Sit at the treaty table and convey the hopes of little
> Peoples through expected straits,
> And press into the final seal a sign that peace will
> Come for longer than posterities can see ahead,
> That man unto his fellow man shall be a friend forever.

Messages of Greeting

Javier Perez de Cuellar
Secretary General of the United Nations

It gives me great pleasure to send my warmest greetings to the Sixth Congress of the International Physicians for the Prevention of Nuclear War. I should like to express, once again, my appreciation of your commitment to the preservation of peace and life on earth which was so deservedly recognized by the award of the Nobel Peace Prize last year. Your Organization's role in stimulating a pointed awareness of the terrible consequences of nuclear war continues to be of great and growing importance.

It is known that a single nuclear exchange would be capable of dismantling within hours what it has taken centuries of civilization to build. The leaders of the two major nuclear Powers, the Soviet Union and the United States, have acknowledged on various occasions that "a nuclear war cannot be won and should never be fought". Yet the fact remains that there is still not a single agreement designed to stop and reverse the nuclear arms race. For the last four decades, the agglomeration of armaments has pursued its profligate course in both the nuclear and the conventional fields.

Past agreements on arms limitation and disarmament have introduced limits on some categories of weapons or have banned certain types of weapons. However, they have not been able to restrict the accumulation of nuclear warheads which at present number more than 50,000 with a total explosive capacity far greater than that of all ammunitions produced since the discovery of gunpowder. On-going negotiations, both bilateral and multilateral, within and outside the United Nations framework, have not yet produced tangible results, although recently various productive initiatives have been taken which retain their promise.

Security, of course, is the foremost concern of every state but the world must recognize that, in our age, security must not be sought, and indeed cannot be found, at increasingly higher levels of armed forces, weaponry and military expenditures. Only at lower, balanced and verifiable levels can it be sustained and assured. Such a recognition involves a reorientation of thinking and perceptions regarding security which is the duty of all those who are concerned with the survival and the health of the human race, especially the members of the healing profession, to promote. This is the most vital issue of our time and concern with it must be accentuated, rather than diminished, by the lack of concrete and substantial progress so far.

I extend you my best wishes for success in your endeavours.

Richard von Weizsäcker
President of the Federal Republic of Germany
Letter [Bonn, March 26, 1986] to the President of the 6th International Congress of the IPPNW

Dear Professor,

Thank you for your letter of March 10, 1986, in which you reiterated your invitation to me to give a welcoming address to the 6th World Congress of the IPPNW on 29.5. – 1.6.86.

I regret to have to inform you that I shall be on a state visit to Turkey at the time of your congress, and shall therefore be unable to accept your invitation.

I have been following with great interest the dedication with which you and your members are endeavouring to make the public aware, from a physician's point of view, of the terrible and uncontrollable consequences of a military conflict which escalates to a nuclear war. You are engaged in spreading your views worldwide, so that the nuclear threat to humanity may be banished. Your deep commitment will dictate the tone of the lectures given at your World Congress in our country. I hope that the congress will constitute a positive contribution to our common commitment to securing and maintaining peace in the world, by ridding ourselves of the causes of the threats to its survival, so that war may finally cease to be the means of solving political conflict.

With best wishes,

[signature]

Johannes Rau
Prime Minister of North Rhine-Westphalia, FRG

I welcome you to the opening of the 6th International Congress of IPPNW. The members of your organisation demonstrate through their activities that they understand the Hippocratic oath to mean the preservation of human life and the obligation to assume joint responsibility for the survival of humankind.

Your activities are anchored in the conviction that the responsibility for peace and for survival can no longer be left solely to political leaders as long as humankind has the capability to destroy itself.

Physicians from East and West, from North and South are collaborating within your organisation and proving to all of us that cooperation across borders is indeed possible. You are demonstrating to us the practical meaning of mutual security.

Your activities have made you troublesome to some politicians and some of your medical colleagues. You experienced this first hand at the awarding of the Nobel Peace Prize in 1985.

I would like to tell you that I consider your work encouraging and I offer you my recognition and respect. Today I would like to express my heart-felt agreement with the decision of the Nobel Peace Prize Committee.

Factual medical knowledge underlies your position, which is that you as physicians would be ineffective in assisting the victims of a war fought by modern means.

You warn against the illusion of a limited nuclear conflict and the waste of resources used in the production of newer, more dangerous and more expensive weapon systems. This is a very important contribution that supports the politics of peace in all countries of the world.

Last year at your international congress you unanimously demanded a stop to nuclear testing. I support this demand. A nuclear test ban is also a test of the seriousness and willingness to stop the nuclear arms.

This is an important first step in preventing nuclear weapons development and thus further increasing the already existing dangers. Fundamental disarmament measures must subsequently follow. I do not see any further obstacles for a nuclear test ban now that the Soviets have declared a unilateral moratorium.

Both nuclear superpowers must ultimately give a sign to stop the madness of the continuing development of nuclear weapons. This applies equally, and particularly, to the development of space weapons, which are being incorporated into the arms race.

We need bread for people, not new weapons in space. We have enough unsolved problems here on earth that warrant greater research and development efforts, that more credibly warrant the unimaginable millions being spent.

Your congress is dedicated to Olof Palme, the unforgettable peace politician and instigator of the concept of mutual security that we Social Democrats represent.

In 1984 Palme observed: "All probable calculations of the aftermath in the event of a nuclear war, of the immediate and unprecedented horrors, the far-reaching ecological and biological damage, which would result, unequivocally lead to the conclusion that no one is capable of winning a nuclear war and that we are all risking our destruction." [from a November 1984 greeting to the IPPNW section of the FRG]

This is true. Because we all risk our destruction, as Palme said, for this reason alone governments and people cannot leave peace in the hands of the superpowers.

That is why the disarmament initiative of the six prime ministers of four continents, of which Palme was a committed member, was so necessary. Olof Palme's legacy has become an obligation to me.

Everyone wanting peace and disarmament must become active and must be prepared to take on responsibility.

For us Germans that means that we must do our utmost to see that nuclear missiles and weapons disappear from both German states.

Therefore, I welcome the Palme Commission proposal to create a nuclear-free zone in Europe along the border of the military alliances. It could help to ease the tensions at this most dangerous point on the continent and open up other ways to achieve a mutual security and comprehensive disarmament.

It is my deepest conviction that we have no other choice than to prevent a war. War must not be used as the last resort for it is an unacceptable and irresponsible tool of politics.

Please allow me to remark on an issue that I know affects the physicians of the FRG: so-called disaster medicine.

The accident in Chernobyl has made it clear to everyone in Europe: the nuclear threat knows no boundaries; to counter this mutual threat we must have mutual security.

I am in favor of civil defense protection in the event of a disaster. It is indisputably necessary to provide our citizens with optimal medical care in technological or natural catastrophes.But I am a rigorous opponent of any mixing of civil defense medicine and military defense medicine. It cannot be the task of politics to let physicians contribute to the illusion that war is a catastrophe as any other. Instead we must make the unprecedented horrors of a nuclear war impossible and not mislead people into believing that they could control the unthinkable, the horrors of a nuclear war with health care plans for disasters.

The will of the people must be represented in their governments if they want to attain the goal of securing peace through disarmament and making the unthinkable impossible. Your contribution is to work to enable people all over the world to gain an insight into the necessity of this goal.

I wish you and the 6th International Congress of IPPNW continued success.

Ronald Reagan
President of the United States of America

The International Physicians for the Prevention of Nuclear War has once again assembled in pursuit of an important goal – reducing the risk of nuclear war. It is a goal that I and every American gladly share, for each of us seeks a safer, more stable world, one without nuclear weapons and free from the fear of nuclear war.

Pursuit of this goal cannot be one of public rhetoric; it must be one of concrete action. For this reason, I have set as my highest priority the achievement of deep, equitable, and verifiable reductions in the nuclear arsenals of the U.S. and the U.S.S.R. I have sought to build on my agreement with General Secretary Gorbachev last November to accelerate the negotiations, especially in areas of common ground.

In Geneva and other negotiating fora, we have serious proposals on the table. In START we have proposed a fifty per cent reduction in strategic nuclear weapons, appropriately applied. We have also proposed a realistic schedule for the global elimination of U.S. and Soviet longer-range INF missiles. In the defense and space talks, we have proposed an "open laboratories" initiative designed to build confidence on both sides that the respective research for strategic defense being carried out by the Soviet Union and the United States is not offensive in nature. At the Stockholm conference on confidence- and security-building measures and disarmament in Europe, we and our allies have proposed specific steps to build confidence and reduce risks. Building trust based on openness and honesty is essential for the safety of the world as the recent tragic events in Chernobyl underline.

At the conference on disarmament, we have put forth a comprehensive, verifiable ban on chemical weapons. At the MBFR talks in Vienna, we and our allies have recently made a new proposal on the reduction of conventional forces in Europe. We have also offered a number of initiatives to provide for effective verification of existing nuclear testing limitations contained in the threshold test ban treaty, satisfaction of which will enable us to move forward on ratification of these two treaties.

I earnestly hope that these initiatives can become the first of many concrete steps to reduce arsenals and risks of war, build confidence and trust, and lead ultimately to a world free of nuclear weapons. Regrettably, the Soviet Union has thus failed to respond positively at the negotiating table to these proposals. We are also greatly concerned by Soviet failure to comply with major arms control agreements, agreements we have complied with scrupulously, or to join us in a framework of truly mutual restraint.

Reducing risks, building confidence, and achieving deep reductions of nuclear arsenals is a long and arduous task, requiring dedication, patience, and hard work at the negotiating table. We know this, but we are ready to negotiate. I ask the Soviet Union to join us in practical measures that move us even closer to the goal of a safer, more stable world, built on increased confidence and trust, and free from the risks of war.

Evgueni Chazov on Behalf of Michael Gorbachev
General Secretary of the Communist Party of the Soviet Union

The academician Evgueni Chazov has conveyed to the participants in the 6th congress of International Physicians for the Prevention of Nuclear War greetings from Michael Gorbachev, General Secretary of the CPSU Central Committee. Michael Gorbachev points out that by providing authoritative data on the medical and biological consequences of nuclear war physicians increase public awareness of the need to vigorously oppose those who, in today's nuclear and space age, think in terms of outdated military doctrines and refuse to see the catastrophic threat looming today over every family and person. The noble efforts of physicians seeking to save people from the specter of the "last epidemic" – nuclear war – have won their movement universal respect.

Michael Gorbachev wishes the delegates attending the congress success in their work for the benefit of all.

Agostino Cardinal Casaroli, Secretary of State of the Vatican, on Behalf of Pope John Paul II
Telegram [May 28, 1986] to Bernard Cardinal Law, Archbishop of Boston

His Holiness Pope John Paul II has learned of the 6th World Congress of the International Physicians for the Prevention of Nuclear War and he asks you to convey to all participants his best wishes and the assurance of his pastoral interest.

The promotion of peace and justice in a nuclear age requires efforts not only to prevent the use of nuclear weapons but also to strengthen the bonds of trust and fraternal collaboration.

With the hope that the congress will further these goals his Holiness invokes upon all taking part God's gifts of peace and joy.

[Signed: His Eminence Cardinal Casaroli / Secretary of State / The Vatican]

Decisions of the
IPPNW
International Council

A Message from the IPPNW to the Six Leaders of the Five Continent Peace Initiative

Gentlemen: We write to you on the occassion of our Sixth World Congress, a gathering dedicated to the late Olof Palme. As you made clear in your joint statement of March 3rd, commitment to concerted action for peace and disarmament "is our duty and our least tribute" to his memory.

We commend you for your persistent and eloquent campaign on behalf of the world's future. In particular, we applaud your promotion of a ban on nuclear explosions as a practical and substantial measure to reverse the momentum of the arms race. A mutual Soviet-American test moratorium – which you have advocated in your joint messages to President Reagan and General Secretary Gorbachev – has been the single arms control measure which the IPPNW has emphasized for the past year. We urge you to continue your calls for the negotiation of a comprehensive test ban treaty and to reiterate your offer to help verify any halt in nuclear testing.

As physicians, we know that medicine would have little to offer the victims of nuclear weapons. As the tragedies of Chernobyl and the space shuttle Challenger should remind us, the human and mechanical systems which restrain those weapons are ultimately unreliable. The world cannot rest easy while a nuclear Sword of Damocles hangs over its head. Your leadership in alerting people everywhere to these truths deserves the gratitude of all. Your continued efforts are needed by all.

Please know of the support of this federation for your program. Nothing would better serve the memory of Olof Palme than the realization of his dreams. We pledge our best efforts to that end.

Respectfully yours,

Members of the International Council
International Physicians for the Prevention of Nuclear War

Cologne, Federal Republic of Germany
27 May 1986

An Appeal to the President of the United States and the General Secretary of the Communist Party of the Soviet Union

Dear Mr. President / Dear Mr. General Secretary:

Physicians take an ancient oath to safeguard life and health. This sacred commitment compels us to join with colleagues of differing political convictions, religious persuasions and cultural backgrounds to alert humanity to the growing nuclear peril. In the six years of our existence, IPPNW has educated millions to the basic truths of the atomic age:

Nuclear bombs are not weapons, but instruments of genocide:

– To possess them does not signify military strength;
– To accumulate them does not guarantee superiority;
– To use them will inflict genocide on victims and suicide on aggressors;
– Medicine will have nothing to offer the millions afflicted and traumatized by a nuclear war, not even relief of pain before their agonizing death;
– There will be no place to hide in a nuclear war: darkness and cold will enshroud the Earth.

Knowledge of these stark facts has not slowed the accumulation of overkill.

Throughout the world, increasing insecurity is being purchased at an even greater cost. Scarce resources are diverted to burgeoning military stockpiles as social and health needs remain unfulfilled. Hunger is everywhere, and every day more than 40,000 children perish for want of food, inexpensive immunization and safe drinking water.

Physicians do not despair when confronting a difficult illness. We prefer to light a candle rather than decry the darkness. We have proposed a prescription – a cessation of all nuclear testing – to begin a journey away from the brink. A moratorium on nuclear explosions will impede the driving force behind the arms race: the development of ever more sophisticated, more accurate, more miniaturized, more destabilizing, less verifiable first-strike weapons. Such a test halt need not await improved relations between your two countries; advances in seismology have removed the need for trust in monitoring verifiable compliance.

Our worldwide campaign on behalf of this medical prescription has borne fruit. The cessation of nuclear explosions by the Soviet Union, begun on Hiroshima Day 1985, represents an historic peace initiative. Support has been demonstrated by resolutions in both houses of the United States Congress urging the executive to pursue test ban negotiations. Another positive development is the energetic promotion of a test ban by the six heads of state comprising the Five Continent Peace Initiative who have offered their services to monitor compliance.

The United Nations General Assembly has voted overwhelmingly in favor of expanding the Partial Test Ban treaty of 1963 into a comprehensive treaty banning all detonations.

A stop to all nuclear explosions would build confidence between your two governments. It is an easily understood measure supported worldwide by ordinary people who comprehend that in the nuclear age provision for a common security through disarmament and the elimination of nuclear weapons is the only guarantee for peace and survival.

We therefore urge the following steps:

- That the United States join the Soviet Union in a mutual moratorium on all nuclear explosions;
- That the mutual moratorium remain in effect until the successful negotiation of a comprehensive test ban treaty; and
- That the negotiations for a test ban begin immediately and be pursued expeditiously.

Your governments, representing the world's two most powerful states, bear a special responsibility to all humanity to ban nuclear testing as the first step leading to the elimination of nuclear weapons from the arsenals of nations.

To provide concrete expression of your commitment to future generations and to protect the health of generations today, especially the children, we also call upon you to take the following steps:

- Guarantee the resources for immunizing all the world's children by the year 1990, the goal of the World Health Organization and the United Nations Children's Fund;
- Appropriate part of the monies saved by disarmament for public health programs on behalf of children in developing nations;
- Exclude the development of space weaponry and instead contribute to a health communication program to make available the advantages of medicine to all humankind.

These measures are within the reach of your two countries. In this International Year of Peace, you can demonstrate that science and its handmaiden technology have but one objective: to improve the quality of life on earth, not threaten its extinction. The tragedies of Chernobyl and the space shuttle Challenger remind us of the fragility of all human and mechanical systems, including those controlling the weapons which endanger life itself.

Humanity has been given new warnings that, as Albert Einstein once said, "We shall require a substantially new manner of thinking if mankind is to survive."

We physicians hold fast to the dream that reason will prevail. We ask that you seize the moment to set in motion deeds consistent with your stated quest for peace.

Respectfully yours,

Members of the International Council
International Physicians for the Prevention of Nuclear War

Cologne, Federal Republic of Germany
27 May 1986

IPPNW is a non-partisan federation of medical groups in 49 nations.
The organization was awarded the 1985 Peace Nobel Prize.

A Medical Prescription of the International Physicians for the Prevention of Nuclear War

The nuclear arms race threatens the health and the very existence of every human being on our planet. Because medicine can offer no meaningful response to the horrors of nuclear war, physicians worldwide have acknowledged their professional responsibility to work for the prevention of this final epidemic.

When faced with a life-threatening disease, a physician's responsibility does not end with diagnosis. It demands a prescription for interrupting the disease process itself. On July 1st, 1985, the International Physicians for the Prevention of Nuclear War adopted a Medical Prescription for interrupting the greatest threat to human health. It urged

AN IMMEDIATE MORATORIUM ON ALL NUCLEAR EXPLOSIONS

AS THE FIRST, ESSENTIAL STEP

TO REVERSE THE NUCLEAR ARMS RACE.

IPPNW reaffirms this medical prescription for the coming year, and calls upon the governments of the United States and all other nuclear powers to join the U.S.S.R. in a test moratorium that would remain in effect until the successful negotiation and signing of a comprehensive test ban treaty.

The benefits of this physicians' prescription for the prevention of nuclear war are evident:

1.

A nuclear explosion ban is a clear focal point for rallying world public opinion behind a single, important, readily achievable arms control proposal, thus sidestepping the paralyzing complexity of most other proposals.

2.

A nuclear explosion ban is verifiable. Both the United States and the Soviet Union have agreed to on-site inspections. Even without them, however, modern seismic techniques can distinguish earthquakes from underground explosions as small as one kiloton. Trust in this matter is no longer an issue.

3.

A nuclear explosion ban will impede the development of new generations of nuclear war-heads, including those designed to power space-based systems, those capable of acting as first-strike weapons, and those that are so small and mobile that future arms control verification might be rendered impossible.

4.

Leading scientists, East and West, have stated that test detonations are not necessary to ensure the reliability of nuclear arsenals. In fact, few nuclear test explosions have ever been conducted for this purpose.

5.

A nuclear explosion ban would not decrease the security of any country, but would increase the security of all.

6.

A nuclear explosion ban would strengthen the Non-Proliferation Treaty, which seeks "to achieve the discontinuance of all test explosions for all time and to continue negotiations to this end ..."

7.

A nuclear explosion ban will create both psychological momentum and a political climate in which additional disarmament achievements will be possible.

8.

A proposed nuclear explosion ban provides a litmus test for distinguishing those political leaders who are committed to ending the nuclear arms race from those who tolerate its continuation.

For all these reasons, International Physicians for the Prevention of Nuclear War has adopted a moratorium on all nuclear explosions as its Medical Prescription for the coming year.

* * *

Passed by the unanimous vote of the International Council of International Physicians for the Prevention of Nuclear War (IPPNW), 27 May 1986.

Index of Authors

Abrams, Herbert L., MD Professor of Radiology
  Member in Residence, Center for International Security and Arms Control
  Stanford University, 320 Galvez Street, Stanford, Cal. 94305, USA
Andrews, John T., MD
  400 New Street, Gardenvale, Vic 3185, Australia
Atkov, Oleg Y., MD
  Soviet Cosmonaut, National Cardiology Research Center
  Cherepskovskaya Ul. 15, Moscow 121500, USSR

Bach, Wilfrid, Professor Dr.
  Director, Forschungsstelle für Angewandte Klimatologie und Umweltstudien
  Westfälische Wilhelms-Universität Münster, Robert-Koch-Str. 26. D-4400 Münster, FRG
Barnaby, Frank, Professor
  Former Director, Stockholm, International Peace Research Institute SIPRI
  Brandreth, Station Road, Chiebolton, Stockbridge, Hants, SO20 6AW, GB
Bonhoeffer, Karl, Professor Dr. med.
  Director, Institute of Anaesthesiology, Cologne University
  Joseph-Stelzmann-Str. 9, D-5000 Cologne 41, FRG
Brown, Graham, MD
  The Walter and Eliza Hall Institute of Medical Research
  Royal Melbourne Hospital, Vic 3050, Australia

Chazov, Evgueni I., Academician MD
  Director-General, National Cardiological Research Center
  Cherepskovskaya Ul. 15, Moscow 121500, USSR

Dienstbier, Zdenek, Professor Dr.
  Director, Institute of Biophysics and Nuclear Medicine
  Charles University, Ovochy Trh. 5, CS-11000 Prague 1, CSSR
Dürr, Hans-Peter, Professor Dr.
  Director, Werner-Heisenberg-Institute for Physics
  MPI for Physics and Astrophysics, Föhringer Ring 6, D-8000 Munich 40, FRG

Eisenberg, Leon, MD, Professor of Psychiatry
  Department of Social Medicine and Health Policy, Harvard Medical School
  25 Shattuk Street, Boston, Ma. 02115, USA

Falin, Valentin
  SPPNW Solyanka Kl. 14, 109801 Moscow, USSR
Foege, William F., MD
  Task Force for Child Survival
  1989 N. Williamsburg Drive, Decatur, Ga. 30333, USA

Galbraith, John Kenneth, Professor Ph. D.
  Paul M. Warburg Professor of Economics, Emeritus;
  207 Littauer Center, Harvard University, Ma. 02138, USA

Thorsson, Inga
  Under-secretary of State
  Ministry for Foreign Affairs, Box 16121, S-10323 Stockholm 16, Sweden
Trapeznikov, Nikolai, MD
  Deputy Director, National Oncological Scientific Center
  USSR Academy of Medical Sciences, Solyanka Ul. 14, 109801 Moscow, USSR

Vittachi, Tarzie
  UNICEF, 866 UN Plaza, 48th 1st Street, New York, NY 10017, USA

Waldenström, Urban, MD
  Fragesroevaegen 25 c, S-79153 Falun, Sweden